The metallic elements

The Metallic Elements

R.V. Parish

Senior Lecturer in Chemistry
University of Manchester Institute of Science and Technology

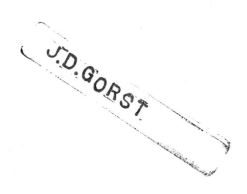

Longman

London and New York

Longman Group Limited London

Associated companies, branches and representatives
throughout the world

Published in the United States of America
by Longman Inc., New York

First published 1977

Library of Congress Cataloging in Publication Data

Parish, Richard Vernon, 1934–
   The metallic elements.

   Bibliography: p.
   Includes index.
   1. Metals.   I. Title.
QD171.P33   546.3   76-54330
ISBN 0-582-44278-8

Set in Linotron Times
and printed in Great Britain by
J. W. Arrowsmith Ltd., England

This volume is dedicated to the late
Professor Sir Ronald S. Nyholm, F.R.S.,
(29.1.17 – 4.12.71)
whose energetic approach to inorganic chemistry
was the inspiration of many

Contents

Preface

This book is an attempt to bring together descriptive inorganic chemistry and its theoretical rationalisation. Several excellent texts already exist which cover one aspect or the other but none does both in a satisfying manner. I have also tried to avoid the pedagogic pitfall of presenting the theory first, followed by a selection of facts. Science does not work in this way, and students should be encouraged to think in a scientific fashion. In the main, therefore, the factual material precedes the rationalisations. In order to limit the factual material to manageable dimensions, I have made no attempt at a comprehensive coverage, choosing rather to examine the three most basic systems for each set of metals, viz. the halides, oxides, and aqueous chemistry. This restriction is not particularly severe, since it allows an appreciation of the ranges of oxidation states and types of bonding without burdening the text with exotic or unrepresentative material. Further study of particular elements or types of compound should follow a basic, elementary treatment of the Periodic Table as a whole. By omitting the non-metals a relatively uniform treatment of three-quarters of the known elements can be made, to which a study of the remainder could easily be added.

The rationalisation of inorganic chemistry is best achieved in thermodynamic terms, and I must acknowledge the pioneering efforts of Dasent and Johnson, whose treatments have proved invaluable. It is also a pleasure to thank my colleagues Frank Bowden and John Dwyer for their helpful criticisms of parts of the manuscript and the editor, Alan Sharpe, for his unfailing assistance.

R.V.P.

Acknowledgements

We are grateful to the following for permission to reproduce copyright material:

The American Chemical Society for a table by O. Johnson from *Inorganic Chemistry* Vol. 12, 1973. Reprinted by permission of The American Chemical Society; the author and Cambridge University Press for a table by Dr. V. Heine in *The Physics of Metals* 1969; The Chemical Society for table by D. A. Johnson from *Journal of the Chemical Society* 1969, 1974; International Union of Crystallography for an appendix from *Acta Crystallographica* 1970, **B26**, 1046 and *Acta Crystallographica* 1969, **B25**, 925; United States Department of Commerce for data from *National Bureau of Standards Circular* 500 and *Technical Note* 270; Academic Press Inc. and respective authors for a table by T. C. Waddington from *Advances in Inorganic Chemistry and Radiochemistry* Vol. 1, 1959, and two tables by J. D. Dunitz & L. E. Orgel from *Advances in Inorganic Chemistry and Radiochemistry* Vol. 2, 1960; John Wiley & Sons Inc. for a table from *Mechanisms of Inorganic Reactions* by F. Basolo and R. G. Pearson 2nd Ed., 1967.

Introductory bibliography

1.   Specific references are given at the end of each chapter, but some general books require frequent citation. These are conveniently referred to by the abbreviations shown below, which will be followed by a list of chapter numbers, e.g. **HJ**, 29, 34 – chapters 29 and 34 of Heslop and Jones.

BENT – J. C. Bailar, H. J. Eméleus, R. S. Nyholm and A. F. Trotman-Dickinson (Eds.), *Comprehensive Inorganic Chemistry*, Pergamon Press, 1973. An extremely comprehensive treatment in five volumes, giving detailed coverage of the occurrence and chemistry of all the elements and also some special topics. An excellent reference text.

CW – F. A. Cotton and G. Wilkinson, *Advanced Inorganic Chemistry*, 3rd edn, Wiley, 1972. A thorough, comprehensive text giving much factual information about all elements and some theoretical background in atomic structure and bonding, but very little linking of the facts to the theory. Strong on coordination chemistry and ligand-field theory.

D – W. E. Dasent, *Inorganic Energetics*, Penguin, 1970. Good, readable presentation of the application of thermodynamics to ionic, covalent and aqueous inorganic systems. Data clearly presented with some useful tabulations. Knowledge of factual chemistry assumed.

ES – H. J. Eméleus and A. G. Sharpe, *Modern Aspects of Inorganic Chemistry*, 4th edn, (previously Eméleus and Anderson), Routledge and Kegan Paul, 1973. Well-written introductory treatment of selected areas of inorganic chemistry.

H – J. E. Huheey, *Inorganic Chemistry*, Harper and Row, 1972. A well-written, thoughtful text, often raising points ignored by other authors, but an uneven and incomplete selection of topics.

HJ – R. B. Heslop and K. Jones, *Inorganic Chemistry*, Elsevier, 1976. (Formerly Heslop and Robinson, 3rd edn., 1967). Readable account of factual chemistry, with valuable introductory chapters on background theoretical aspects.

J – D. A. Johnson, *Some Thermodynamic Aspects of Inorganic Chemistry*, Cambridge University Press, 1968. An excellent treatment of ionic, covalent and aqueous inorganic systems in terms of energetics. Contains much useful data. Knowledge of factual chemistry is assumed.

MM – K. M. Mackay and R. A. Mackay, *Introduction to Modern Inorganic Chemistry*, 2nd edn, International Textbook Co., 1972. Readable text giving some of the theoretical basis of inorganic systems and a fairly simple survey of factual chemistry.

PW – G. S. Phillips and R. J. P. Williams, *Inorganic Chemistry*, (2 volumes), Oxford University Press, 1965. Systematises and rationalises much inorganic chemistry but assumes a knowledge of factual chemistry. Not an easy book for the elementary student.

W – A. F. Wells, *Structural Inorganic Chemistry*, 4th edn, Oxford University Press, 1975. Comprehensive review of structures of solid inorganic compounds with useful and readable introductory chapters.

2.   Other generally useful texts covering wide areas: H. F. Mark, J. J. McKetta and D. F. Othmer, *Encyclopaedia of Chemical Technology*, 2nd edn, Wiley Interscience, 1963–71. Detailed accounts of many technologically important materials and processes.

D. M. Samuel, '*Industrial Inorganic Chemistry*', *Royal Institute of Chemistry Monographs for Teachers*, No. 10, 2nd edn, The Chemical Society, 1970. Brief but useful survey of the manufacture and uses of many elements and their compounds.

3.   The following older comprehensive treatments contain much useful information:

L. Gmelin, *Handbuch der anorganische Chemie*, Springer-Verlag, 1924 onwards. A series of volumes with updating supplements appearing frequently.

J. W. Mellor, *Comprehensive Treatise on Inorganic and Theoretical Chemistry*, Longman, 1922–37 and supplementary volumes (1958 onwards).

P. Pascal, *Nouveau Traité de Chimie Minérale*, Masson, 1956 onwards.

H. Remy, *Treatise on Inorganic Chemistry*, Elsevier, 1956.

N. V. Sidgwick, *Chemical Elements and Their Compounds*, Oxford University Press, 1950.

4.   Some articles in primary or review journals will be cited. These are distinguished by using the following italicised abbreviations of the name of the journal:

Acc. Chem. Res., Accounts of Chemical Research.   *Adv. Inorg. Chem. Radiochem.*, Advances in Inorganic Chemistry and Radiochemistry.   *Coord. Chem. Rev.*, Coordination Chemistry Reviews.   *Educ. Chem.*, Education in Chemistry.   *Inorg. Chem.*, Inorganic Chemistry.   *J. Chem. Educ.*, Journal of Chemical Education.   *J. Chem. Soc.*, Journal of the Chemical Society.   *J. Inorg. Nucl. Chem.*, Journal of Inorganic and Nuclear Chemistry.   *Prog. Inorg. Chem.*, Progress in Inorganic Chemistry.   *Quart. Rev.*, Quarterly Reviews (The Chemical Society).   *Rev. Pure Appl. Chem.*, Reviews of Pure and Applied Chemistry.

Chapter 1
Introduction

Inorganic chemistry is the study of the structures, properties, reactivities and compounds of all the elements, excluding only the catenated compounds of carbon. Over one hundred elements are known, so that the subject is vast; it is, of course, still expanding in its own right, but it also blends imperceptibly into other disciplines such as metallurgy, biochemistry, and mineralogy, as well as being linked to other branches of chemistry through coordination chemistry and organometallic chemistry. The aim of this book is to provide a general basis of systematic inorganic chemistry onto which the other subjects can be grafted. Attempts will be made, wherever possible, to give intelligible explanations and rationalisations of the observed behaviour and, for these purposes, I believe that it is important to follow a basically scientific procedure. That is, following the 'Scientific Method', to examine the factual material first, then to look for common features and patterns in the 'data', and only then to try to explain the patterns in terms of some sort of theoretical framework. It is, of course, not possible to explain everything; the data are not always complete and there are often anomalies which are still beyond comprehension. Nevertheless, it should be possible to build up a general, logical picture and to understand some of the individual breaks in the patterns.

To provide a survey of the systematic chemistry of all the elements would be an enormous task, beyond the capacity of both reader and writer, and restrictions and simplifications are necessary to give a manageable body of material. Two limitations are therefore imposed. Firstly, only the metallic elements are considered; this eliminates only 23 elements but has the advantage that those remaining have many common characteristics, one of the most important being that much of their chemistry can be discussed in terms of simple, ionic behaviour. Secondly, no attempt is made to give a comprehensive coverage of all the types of compound formed by each metal but, by treating the same sets of systems for each group of metals (the halides, the oxides, and the aqueous chemistry), it is hoped that the similarities and differences will become apparent. The chemistry shown can then be related to the positions of the elements in the Periodic Table.

The basis of the rationalisations used will be energy. It has been said that organic and inorganic compounds differ in that the former owe their existence to kinetic effects while the latter are better understood in terms of thermodynamics. It is certainly true that all organic compounds are thermodynamically unstable in air; on the basis of energetics they would be expected to oxidise spontaneously to carbon dioxide and water, e.g.

$$C_2H_5OH + 3O_2 \rightarrow 2CO_2 + 3H_2O$$

Fortunately, this reaction does not proceed at room temperature in the absence of a catalyst, ethanol is kinetically stable (at least until after consumption!). However, in the majority of cases, simple inorganic reactions give the products expected on thermodynamic grounds, e.g. zinc dissolves in hydrochloric acid. Occasionally the anticipated reaction seems not to occur, for instance aluminium would be expected to react with air or water with the evolution of much energy, but is normally unaffected by both of these reagents. In this case, the predicted oxidation does occur but the product adheres very closely to the metal surface, protecting it from further reaction. In the main, it seems reasonable to seek thermodynamic rationales for the observed behaviour of inorganic systems. Fortunately, no more than a very elementary knowledge of thermodynamics is required; a brief introduction is given below and further guidance is available from the texts listed at the end of this chapter.

It is assumed that the reader will have a basic knowledge of the structure of the atom, the radial and angular distributions of s-, p-, and d-electrons, and the structure of the Periodic Table. References to these topics will also be found in the Bibliography.

Since the metallic elements have many characteristics in common, much of their chemistry can be discussed within closely related frameworks. In order to avoid much repetition, it is useful to introduce some concepts and definitions before proceeding to the detailed chemistry. The remainder of this chapter is devoted to such topics.

1.1   Metals

The first and most basic requirement is to define the **metallic elements**. Many elements are immediately recognisable as metals by characteristic physical properties, metallic lustre, conduction of heat and electricity, etc. Most of them also form simple salts, chlorides, sulphates, carbonates, etc., in which the metal is cationic. On any of these bases, the elements of the s-, d-, and f-blocks of the Periodic Table (Fig. 1.1) are undoubtedly metallic. The elements of the p-block

Fig. 1.1   The quantum-blocks of the Periodic Table

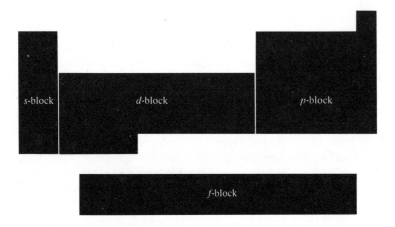

are less easy to characterise, since this block contains elements of all types, ranging from the unequivocally metallic, like aluminium, to the equally recognisable non-metals such as oxygen, sulphur and the halogens, and even the 'noble' gases (their 'nobility' having been challenged in recent years, they will henceforth be called the 'rare' gases). Useful working criteria of metallic behaviour are the formation of cationic species in aqueous solution or the solubility of an oxide in acids (this is not the tautology it may seem, see Chapter 8). On this basis, the p-block metals are aluminium to thallium in Group III, germanium to lead (Group IV), antimony and bismuth (Group V). As might be expected, the borderline elements (germanium, antimony, bismuth) also have some of the characteristics of non-metals, and are often classified as semi-metals or metalloids.

Table 1.1 Electron affinities and dissociation energies

A	$E_A/kJ\ mol^{-1}$	$D(A_2)/kJ\ mol^{-1}$	A_2
Li	−60	105	Li—Li
Be	+241	0	Be⦂ ⦂Be
B	−83	289	⦂B ⇈ B⦂†
C	−122	630	⦂C=C⦂
N	0	946	⦂N≡N⦂
O	−142	493	↑ ↑ † ⦂O=O⦂ ↑ ↓
F	−322	158	⦂F̈—F̈⦂
Ne	+29	0	⦂N̈e⦂ ⦂N̈e⦂

† The electron configurations of the B_2 and O_2 molecules cannot be expressed simply in valence-bond terms. In each case the molecule contains two unpaired electrons which occupy a degenerate pair of molecular orbitals. In B_2 these orbitals are bonding, giving a bond order of one (two half-bonds). In O_2 the unpaired electrons are antibonding; together with the three bonding electron pairs this gives an overall bond order of two.

1.2 Ionic and covalent bonds

Two extreme types of bonding can be envisaged, ionic and covalent, and examples of each will be found in the chemistry of most metals. It is therefore useful to revise the factors which lead to the formation of each type of bond.

The electronic configuration of an atom is determined by the balance between electron–nuclear attraction and electron–electron repulsion and exchange effects. Since electrons are in continuous motion and, on average in a free atom, are distributed uniformly about the nucleus, the nuclear charge is not completely shielded in any one direction. Thus, although the net charge on the atom is zero, an external electron approaching the atom experiences an attractive potential which is often large enough for the electron to be captured and bound, forming an anion, with release of energy. The enthalpy of the process

$$A(g)+e^- \rightarrow A^-(g)$$

is known as the *electron affinity* of the atom A, designated E_A; values for the elements of the second Period are given in Table 1.1. Most atoms have negative values, representing an effective positive charge at the periphery of the atom, which increases with increasing nuclear charge. Positive values are found for a few atoms which have filled or half-filled sub-shells, when the attraction is offset by unfavourable exchange and electron–electron repulsion effects.

When two atoms are brought together, the effective positive charge of each polarises the electrons of the other, particularly the relatively weakly-bound outer electrons (the valence electrons), so that electron density becomes concentrated in the region between the two nuclei. The valence electrons of each atom are now attracted by both nuclei and a stable diatomic molecule may result. This situation is often more formally described in terms of overlap of orbitals and the formation of bonding molecular orbitals giving σ- or π-bonds, but the basic binding force of the **covalent chemical bond** is the electrostatic interaction of the bonding electrons with the nuclei between which they are located. [It also appears necessary, for the formation of a stable molecule, for the valence electrons on one atom to pair spins with those of the other; if this is not possible, exchange and correlation effects keep the electrons apart and away from the internuclear region, leading to repulsion, as in Ne_2.]†

When the two atoms of a diatomic molecule are the same, the electron density is distributed equally between them and the bond is *homopolar* (Fig. 1.2a). If the two atoms are not identical, the more electronegative‡ will attract the bonding electrons more strongly. The overall electron distribution will now be asymmetric with greater electron density, and hence a fractional negative charge, on this atom. (Fig. 1.2b). The greater the electronegativity difference between the atoms, the more uneven is the charge distribution and an extreme case can be envisaged in which an electron has been transferred effectively entirely from one atom to the other, forming a wholly **electrostatic**, or **ionic bond**.

Fig. 1.2   Electron distributions in (*a*) homopolar covalent bond (*b*) heteropolar covalent bond with partial ionic character (*c*) ionic bond

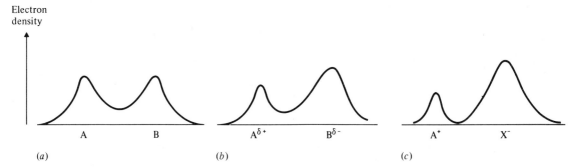

On this basis it should be possible to describe any bond in terms of its ionic or covalent character. High covalent character is found in bonds between very similar atoms and becomes 100 per cent in homonuclear molecules. High ionic character is favoured by large differences in electronegativity of the atoms, and low charges and/or large radii of the ions. The last two factors affect the electric potential gradient between the ions. The higher the charges and the smaller their separation, the greater the field to which the electrons are subjected, the more the cation will polarise the anion, and the greater the covalent character of the bond. Determination of the distribution of electron densities in ionic solids clearly shows these polarisation effects (Fig. 1.3). If the bonding were 100 per cent ionic, there would be a point between the ions at which the electron density became zero, as is observed for instance in sodium chloride. In lithium fluoride, with a much smaller internuclear separation, the minimum electron density is $1\cdot9 \times 10^5$ e pm^{-3} ($0\cdot19$ e Å^{-3}), and the ions are clearly distorted from the expected spherical shapes.

The metallic elements have low electronegativity, are relatively easily ionised and, in their common compounds, are coupled with non-metallic elements of high electronegativity. It is frequently a good approximation to consider such compounds as being essentially ionic, with the metal forming discrete cations and the non-metal discrete anions. This *ionic model* is a very convenient basis for the discussion of the properties of these compounds, and is widely used throughout the rest of this book. It is important to realise, however, that it is only a conceptual

---

† This is obviously a very incomplete description of the formation of a covalent bond; some other factors are considered in section 1.5.2. below.

‡ Electronegativity has been defined (by Pauling) as the capacity of an atom in a molecule to attract electrons to itself. It is thus not the same as electron affinity, which refers to isolated atoms. One definition (due to Mulliken) takes the average of the electron affinity and ionisation energy (see section 1.5.1) as a measure of electronegativity. In any one Period, electronegativity increases with increasing nuclear charge.

Fig. 1.3   Electron distribution in lithium fluoride. Note the distortion of the electron cloud of the cation towards the anion and the non-zero electron density between the ions (after J. Krug, H. Witte and E. Wölfel, *Z. Phys. Chem.* (Frankfurt), **4**, 36 (1955))

model which approximates to the actual state of affairs. As the charges increase and the ions become more polarising (or more polarisable) the bonding will show progressively more covalent character and departures from ionic behaviour are to be expected. The limitations of the ionic model are discussed further in section 1.4 below.

1.3   Stability and thermodynamics

'Stability' is a term which is often used rather loosely and is open to a variety of interpretations. Properly defined, of course, it is unambiguous, and suitable definition or qualification should always be given.

As mentioned earlier, there are two broad types of stability, kinetic and thermodynamic. A compound may often be unreactive under conditions in which thermodynamic considerations would indicate that reaction should occur. Chemical reactions involve the rearrangement of bonds, electrons, and atoms from a configuration of relatively low energy to another of lower energy, but the system must pass through intermediate configurations of higher energy. Thus, even though the reaction would evolve considerable energy, if there is insufficient thermal energy available for the system to surmount the energy barrier (the activation energy) no reaction will occur. Such **kinetic stability** is quite common; for instance, a mixture of carbon monoxide and air should react exothermically to form carbon dioxide, but such mixtures are indefinitely stable at room temperature unless energy is supplied in the form of a flame or a spark.

On the other hand, there may be no reaction possible, under the prevailing conditions, which would lead to a lowering in energy of the system. Such a system has **thermodynamic stability**, and it is this type of stability or reactivity which is the main concern of this book. It should be noted, however, that both types of stability have been defined in terms of a system rather than of a compound. While it sometimes happens that a compound is unstable to spontaneous decomposition, as nitrogen tri-iodide dissociates explosively to nitrogen and iodine, it is more common for a compound to react with another element or compound to form new substances. It is then not possible to define what has happened to the energy of any one component, it is the energy of the system as a whole which is lowered by reaction. It is therefore necessary to specify the composition of the mixture which may react or the type of reaction, e.g. aerial oxidation, disproportionation, reaction with acid. Thus, tin(IV) chloride, $SnCl_4$, is in some senses a stable compound, in that it will not dissociate into tin(II) chloride and chlorine or tin and chlorine, nor will it react with oxygen. It is, however, very reactive towards water, and fumes vigorously even in moist air. Thus, tin(IV) chloride is

> stable with respect to dissociation
> stable to atmospheric oxidation
> unstable to hydrolysis.

The second of these is a kinetic effect, and this reaction will proceed at higher temperatures.

In defining the energetics of reactions, three important thermodynamic quantities must be considered, **enthalpy** (H), **free energy** (G), and **entropy** (S). For any system, it is the changes in these quantities, ΔH, ΔG, ΔS, which determine the direction and extent of the reactions which are possible. These are related by the well known expression

$$\Delta G = \Delta H - T\Delta S$$

The enthalpy is simply the heat which is liberated when the reaction is carried out at constant pressure. If the pressure is one atmosphere and the temperature 298 K (standard conditions) the standard enthalpy change is obtained, ΔH_{298}^0. A reaction which results in the liberation of heat has, by convention, a negative value for ΔH; such *exothermic* reactions result in a loss of energy by the system, and a gain by the surroundings. Reactions for which $\Delta H > 0$ are said to be *endothermic*. To a good approximation, enthalpy changes are independent of temperature.

The extent of reaction is governed by the free energy change, ΔG, which is related to the equilibrium constant by the second important relationship

$$\Delta G = -RT \ln K$$

[R is the gas constant, $8 \cdot 31$ J K^{-1} mol^{-1}, and the equilibrium constant, K, is given by the product of the concentrations (strictly the activities) of the products divided by that of the reactants, the concentrations referring to those prevailing when equilibrium has been reached

$$K = \frac{\Pi a_{products}}{\Pi a_{reactants}}]$$

At 298 K, $\Delta G/(kJ \ mol^{-1}) = -5 \cdot 703 \log K$ so that, for a reaction to go essentially to completion $(K > 100)$, ΔG need be only about -12 kJ mol^{-1}, a very modest value.

Unfortunately, free energies are not easy to measure, whereas enthalpy data may be obtained more readily (e.g. by direct calorimetric measurement of the heat liberated). It is often necessary, therefore, to base discussions on enthalpy data alone, and to use qualitative estimates of entropy. Entropy is more difficult to discuss simply, but it is related to the amount of freedom which a system has. The greater the number of ways in which a system can achieve the same energy, the greater the entropy. For a molecule there are contributions to the entropy from its vibrational, rotational and translational motion, so that gases generally have much higher entropies than liquids, which have greater values than solids, for which the entropies are generally very small. This leads to the commonly used assumption that a reaction in which the number of molecules increases has a positive entropy change $(\Delta S > 0)$ of magnitude related to the size of the increase; entropy changes are particularly important in reactions involving the appearance or disappearance of molecules (or atoms) from the gas phase. As a (very) rough guide, ΔS is about 150 J K^{-1} mol^{-1} for every simple gaseous molecule formed (complex molecules can give much higher values).

A reaction of great importance, energetically, is that in which a compound is formed from its elements,

$$M + \frac{n}{2}X_2 \rightarrow MX_n$$

If this formation reaction is performed under standard conditions the elements are in standard states and have, by definition, zero enthalpy. The heat evolved is then entirely that associated with the formation of the compound, the standard enthalpy of formation, designated ΔH_f^0. Similarly, the free energy and entropy changes are ΔG_f^0 and ΔS_f^0. In the majority of cases the product is a solid and the non-metal reactant is gaseous, so that ΔS_f^0 is negative and ΔG_f^0 is less negative than ΔH_f^0. For any other reaction, the overall enthalpy change is given by the difference between the sums of the enthalpies of formation of the products and reactants, and similarly for the free energy and entropy changes:

$$\Delta H^0 = \sum_{\text{products}} \Delta H_f^0 - \sum_{\text{reactants}} \Delta H_f^0$$

1.4 The ionic model

The basic postulate of the ionic model is that ionic solids may be treated as arrays of hard, elastic, spherical cations and anions, packed together so that adjacent ions are touching. The energetics and structures of many solids are conveniently described in these terms, since the energies are governed primarily by electrostatic interactions and the structures by geometric constraints, both of which can be readily calculated.

1.4.1 Structures of ionic crystals

The structures of ionic crystals can be understood in terms of the packing together of spherical ions so that each ion is in contact with the maximum number of ions of opposite charge, maximising the electrostatic attraction, with ions of like charge as far apart as possible, minimising the repulsion energy. This usually results in highly symmetrical lattices. Since the anions are generally larger than the cations, structures are normally described in terms of the arrangement of the anions, with the cations fitting into appropriate holes in this framework.

The maximisation of electrostatic interactions suggests that the ions should be packed as closely as possible. This is a characteristic of ionic and metallic structures in which the bonding is non-directional; covalent structures usually have relatively open lattices and low coordination numbers. There are two ways in which spherical atoms or ions can be packed together with maximum filling of space. Consider first a two-dimensional layer. When all ions are touching each is surrounded hexagonally by six others (Fig. 1.4). The ions in this layer define a series of equilateral triangles of which there are two types having apices pointing in opposite directions, $\triangle$ and $\triangledown$. Each set of triangles forms exactly the same pattern as the ions, so that if a second layer of ions is fitted over the first these ions will all lie over triangles of the same type. The first layer may be designated the A-layer and its triangles $\triangle_A$ and $\triangledown_A$. Suppose the second layer, B, is fitted over the $\triangle_A$ sites. This layer itself defines arrays of triangular sites, $\triangle_B$ and $\triangledown_B$, into which the next layer of ions may be fitted (Fig. 1.5). It will be seen that each $\triangle_B$ lies over a $\triangledown_A$ and each $\triangledown_B$ over an A ion. If, as successive layers are added, the $\triangle$ and $\triangledown$ sites are used alternately, the even layers will lie exactly over each other and the odd layers will lie over each other but staggered with respect to the even layers (Fig. 1.6). This may be described as an ABABAB . . . sequence, and defines an **hexagonal close-packed** (hcp) array. The hexagonal symmetry is obvious from the structure of the layers.

Fig. 1.4   Close-packed layer of ions

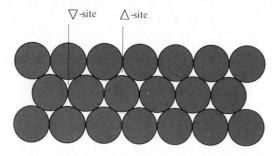

Fig. 1.5   A and B layers superposed

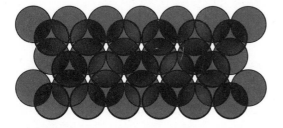

Fig. 1.6   Section through hcp lattice

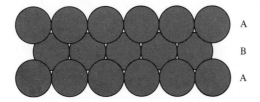

An alternative stacking is possible if successive layers all cover sites of the same type, i.e. B over $\triangle_A$, C over $\triangle_B$, and so on. The ions of the C-layer are now positioned over $\triangledown_A$ sites, but the next layer will lie exactly over the A-layer and the sequence begins again. This is an ABCABC arrangement, known as **face-centred cubic** packing (fcc) or **cubic close packing** (ccp). These names arise because this array actually has cubic symmetry which can be seen by viewing from a different angle (Fig. 1.7). These are the two simplest close-packed structures, but other regular sequences can be envisaged and are sometimes found.

The majority of elemental metals adopt one of the close-packed structures, but an array of ions all of the same charge would clearly be unstable unless cations were introduced to give some electrostatic binding. The cations are accommodated in the spaces between the anion layers. With the arrangements described above, there are only two distinct sites available. The B-layer ions lie over a $\triangle_A$ site, creating a space surrounded tetrahedrally by four ions, a *tetrahedral hole*, whereas the $\triangledown_A$ sites are covered by $\triangle_B$, forming a six-coordinate *octahedral hole*. Each anion in any one layer contributes to six octahedral sites, e.g. a B-ion in an hcp array is adjacent to three $\triangledown_A$ sites in each of the A-layers above and below it. Since each octahedral site is shared between six anions, there is on average one octahedral site per anion. The tetrahedral sites are less easy to count, but each B-ion is adjacent to six $\triangle_A$ sites in the neighbouring layers and also has a $\triangle_A$ site immediately above and below it, so that every anion is associated with eight tetrahedral sites. Each tetrahedral

Fig. 1.7 Views of the fcc lattice. The surface of the upper portion of section (*a*) slopes away from the viewer at 54.5°. The black ions outline one face of the cube unit. Section (*b*) is perpendicular to (*a*) through X—X (see Fig. 1.9 for a different view)

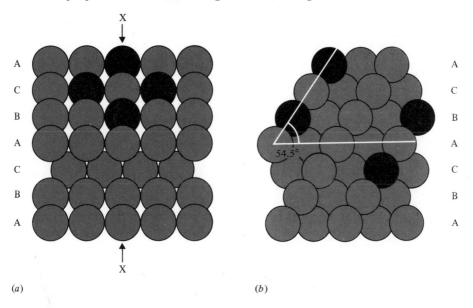

(*a*)   (*b*)

site is shared between four anions, so that there are on average two tetrahedral sites per ion. The same ratios are obtained for fcc lattices, and the two types of site are illustrated in Fig. 1.8.

Fig. 1.8 Tetrahedral and octahedral sites in an fcc lattice. There is one octahedral site at the centre of each cube edge and one at the centre of the cube, and one tetrahedral site at the centre of each octant. (In this and subsequent Figs. the ions are shown much reduced in size, for clarity)

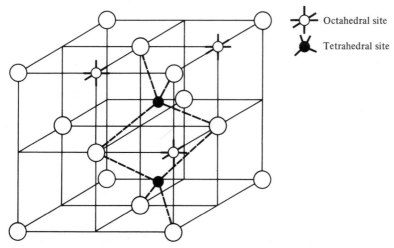

○ Octahedral site

● Tetrahedral site

A large number of ionic crystal lattices can be described in terms of fitting the appropriate number of cations, according to the stoicheiometry, into octahedral or tetrahedral sites in the two close-packed arrays of anions. Usually all the cations occupy the same type of site. The structures

Table 1.2   Structures formed by filling various proportions of cation sites in fcc and hcp anion lattices

Fraction of sites occupied	Stoich-eiometry	Prototype compounds	
		fcc	hcp
Octahedral sites			
all	MX	NaCl (rock-salt)	NiAs
2/3	M_2Y_3		α-Al_2O_3 (corundum)
1/2	MX_2	$CdCl_2$	CdI_2
1/3	MX_3	$CrCl_3$	BiI_3
1/6	MX_6		α-WCl_6
Tetrahedral sites			
all	M_2Y	anti-CaF_2 (anti-fluorite)	
3/4	M_3Y_2	anti-C–M_2O_3	
1/2	MX	ZnS (zinc blende)	ZnS (wurtzite)
1/3	M_2Y_3	γ-Ga_2S_3	β-Ga_2S_3
1/4	MX_2	α-$ZnCl_2$	β-$ZnCl_2$
1/6	MX_3		Al_2Br_6
1/8	MX_4	SnI_4	

Notes

a) X is uninegative, Y dinegative

b) anti signifies that the cations and anions have been interchanged, i.e. in Li_2O (anti-fluorite structure) the Li^+ ions occupy the F^- sites of the CaF_2 lattice

c) The CaF_2 and C–M_2O_3 structures are more usually described in terms of simple cubic arrays of anions with cations in the body-centre positions (see text).

formed are summarised in Table 1.2 and some of the more common lattices are illustrated in Fig. 1.9. When the available sites are not all occupied, the ions are usually arranged in a regular way (but see Ch. 10). In the fcc layer-lattices ($CdCl_2$- and $CrCl_3$-structures) only one-half or one-third of the cation sites are occupied. The octahedral sites form layers between the ABCABC layers of anions and alternate layers of cation sites are completely empty with the other layers being completely or two-thirds full. Thus, if the AB sites are occupied, the BC sites are empty, and so on. These structures therefore consist of sandwich layers, anion–cation–anion, anion–cation–anion, and materials with these lattices give characteristically flake-like crystals.

Which structure is adopted by any particular compound depends on the relative sizes of the ions (tetrahedral holes are smaller than octahedral sites) and on the degree of covalency. These factors are discussed below, but it is noticeable that for mono-, di-, and tri-valent metals, tetrahedral cation sites are preferred by the *p*-block metals and by sulphides and selenides, and hcp anion arrangements seem to be favoured by larger, more polarizable anions.

Some structures are based on the less compact simple cubic packing of anions or atoms, which leaves an eight-coordinate site at the centre of each cube. If these sites are filled by atoms of the same type, the **body-centred cubic** (bcc) lattice results. This is formed of two interpenetrating simple cubic sub-lattices. When these sub-lattices are composed of different ions, the CsCl-structure is obtained. If half the cation sites are vacant, the CaF_2-structure is formed which, as seen above and in Fig. 1.9, can also be described in terms of an fcc array of cations with anions in all the tetrahedral sites. In the C–M_2O_3-structure, adopted by the $4f$-metal oxides, one-quarter of the anions in a CaF_2-type lattice are systematically missing.

One other structure is sufficiently common to be worth describing here, viz. that of rutile (TiO_2). This structure is based on an hcp array of O^{2-} ions with Ti^{4+} ions in half of the octahedral holes. The structure is distorted, apparently by repulsion between like ions, particularly the

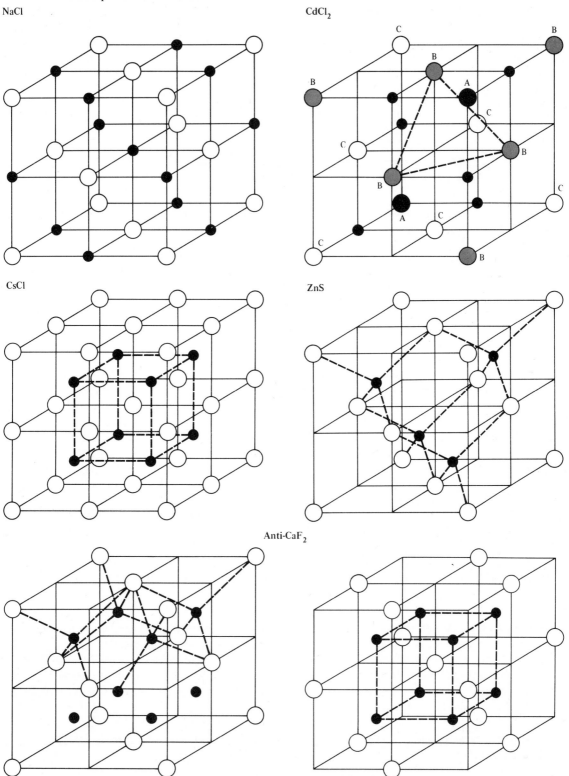

Fig.1.9 Common structures based on fcc and bcc anion lattices. Two views of the anti-CaF$_2$-lattice are given to show the relation to the bcc CsCl-lattice. In CdCl$_2$, the close-packed ABCA planes are indicated

highly-charged cations. The result is that the cations remain stacked in columns throughout the lattice but the hexagonal layers of anions become buckled (Fig. 1.10).

Fig. 1.10   The TiO$_2$-structure. The dashed lines indicate the (distorted) hexagonal layers

● = Ti^{4+} + = vacant Ti^{4+} site   ○ = O^{2-}

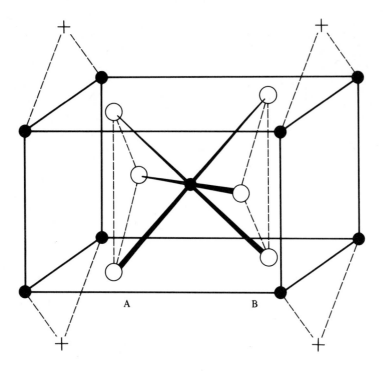

1.4.2   Lattice energies

The formation of one pair of ions from separated neutral atoms is always an endothermic process. Even in the most favourable case, that of caesium and fluorine, more energy is required to ionise the caesium atom than is gained in forming the fluoride ion:

$$Cs(g) \rightarrow Cs^+(g) + e^- \qquad \Delta H^0 = +376 \text{ kJ mol}^{-1}$$

$$F(g) + e^- \rightarrow F^-(g) \qquad \Delta H^0 = -333 \text{ kJ mol}^{-1}$$

Hence $Cs(g) + F(g) \rightarrow Cs^+(g) + F^-(g) \qquad \Delta H^0 = +43 \text{ kJ mol}^{-1}$

However, this calculation ignores the potential energy due to the electrostatic attraction between the ions, which is $-e^2/4\pi\varepsilon_0 r$. [e is the magnitude of the electronic charge, $1 \cdot 602 \times 10^{-19}$ C; ε_0 is the permittivity of space, $8 \cdot 854 \times 10^{-12}$ F m^{-1}; r is the internuclear separation.] When the ions are 303 pm apart, as in the crystal, the electrostatic energy is -459 kJ mol^{-1}, so that the true energy of the ion-pair, relative to the separated atoms, is -416 kJ mol^{-1}.† In forming a solid lattice, the

---

† Other interactions which are ignored are closed-shell repulsions (positive enthalpy change), London, or polarisation effects (negative), and zero-point energy (positive), which probably raise the energy of the system by about 30 kJ mol^{-1}.

electrostatic energy is even greater, since the ions are packed together in a cubic array in which every cation is surrounded by six anions and vice versa. The energy of the crystal relative to the infinitely separated gaseous ions is -744 kJ mol^{-1}. This energy could be taken as a measure of the strength of binding of the crystal lattice. The **lattice energy**, U, is normally defined by the reverse process, i.e. the lattice energy of a crystal MX is the enthalpy of the process

$$MX(s) \rightarrow M^+(g) + X^-(g) \qquad \Delta H^0 = U$$

Lattice energies are therefore always positive. Strictly, the definition should refer to the dissociation at absolute zero, and values for other temperatures should take account of the specific heat of the solid and the gaseous products; these corrections are small, typically 10–15 kJ mol^{-1}, and they are usually ignored.

There is no way in which the lattice energy can be directly measured; all 'experimental' values quoted here or elsewhere have been derived from some type of energy cycle. There are, however, several ways in which values may be estimated.

The major component of the energy is the net electrostatic, or Coulomb, energy, U_C. If the ions are treated as point charges and their separation and geometrical arrangement are known, this energy is readily, if tediously, calculated. For CsF, which has the same crystal structure as NaCl, each cation is immediately surrounded by six anions so that the internuclear separation is 303 pm, but there are also twelve cations at a distance of $303\sqrt{2}$ pm, eight anions at $303\sqrt{3}$ pm, six more cations at $303\sqrt{4}$ pm, and so on throughout the lattice. If these interactions are summed over the whole lattice it can be shown that, for any crystal with this arrangement of ions, the general expression for the electrostatic part of the energy is

$$U_C = -\frac{1 \cdot 74756 N_A Z_+ Z_- \, e^2}{4\pi\varepsilon_0 r}$$

[N_A is the Avagadro constant, $6 \cdot 02 \times 10^{23}$ mol^{-1}, Z_+ and Z_- are the charges on the cation and anion respectively ($+1$ and -1 for CsF)]. The numerical term in this expression, $1 \cdot 74756$, is the summation of the geometrical terms, $1 - 12/\sqrt{2} + 8/\sqrt{3} - 6/\sqrt{4} + \ldots$, and is known as the *Madelung constant*, often given the symbol A. A Madelung constant can be evaluated for any crystal lattice of known geometry; some common examples are given in Table 1.3. Three values are quoted. The first corresponds to the general formula given above, and is determined only by the

Table 1.3   Madelung constants for common crystal structures

Crystal type	A	A'	M/(10^5 pm kJ mol^{-1})
sodium chloride (NaCl)	1·74756	1·74756	2·4217
caesium chloride (CsCl)	1·76267	1·76267	2·4487
zinc blende (ZnS)	1·63806	1·63806	2·2755
wurtzite (ZnS)	1·64132	1·64132	2·2801
fluorite (CaF$_2$)	2·551939	5·03878	3·4999
rutile (TiO$_2$)	2·408	4·816	3·345
cadmium iodide (CdI$_2$)	2·355	4·71	6·54†
corundum (Al$_2$O$_3$)	4·1719	25·0312	5·7956†

† precise value depends on the ratio c/a for the unit cell
A refers to the relationship $U_C = -A N_A Z_+ Z_- \, e^2/(4\pi\varepsilon_0 r)$
A' refers to the relationship $U_C = +A' N_A Z_\pm^2 \, e^2/(4\pi\varepsilon_0 r)$
M refers to the relationship $U_C = -M Z_+ Z_-/(r/\text{pm})$
(for further discussion of Madelung constants, see D. Quane, *J. Chem. Educ.*, **47**, 396 (1970))

geometry; it is independent of the charges, Z_+ and Z_-, and the internuclear separation. It is more usual, although more confusing, to use values, A', which incorporate the ionic charges:

$$U_C = \frac{A'N_A Z_\pm^2 e^2}{4\pi\varepsilon_0 r}$$

In this expression, $Z_\pm$ is the highest common factor of Z_+ and Z_-, e.g. 1 for NaCl, CaF_2, CdI_2, Al_2O_3, 2 for ZnS, TiO_2 or MgO. The quantity M, quoted in the final column of Table 1.3, contains all the constant factors

$$U_C = -\frac{MZ_+Z_-}{r}$$

Note that, in contrast to A and A', M is not dimensionless.

The Coulomb energy must be balanced by a repulsive interaction which increases rapidly as the internuclear separation decreases and the electron clouds of the ions interpenetrate, otherwise the lattice would collapse to a point. Following Born and Landé, it is generally assumed that the energy of this interaction, U_B, is inversely proportional to some power of the internuclear distance, so that the total lattice energy is given by the sum of U_C and U_B

$$U = U_C + U_B = -\frac{AN_A Z_+Z_- e^2}{4\pi\varepsilon_0 r} + \frac{B}{r^n}$$

where B is a constant to be evaluated. The equilibrium internuclear distance, r_0, must correspond to the minimum energy of the system, i.e. dU/dr should be zero for this distance, thus enabling B to be evaluated. Hence

$$U = -\frac{AN_A Z_+Z_- e^2}{4\pi\varepsilon_0 r_0}\left(1 - \frac{1}{n}\right)$$

The value of n depends on the particular ions concerned, and can be determined from compressibility data (the resistance to compression of a crystal is a measure of the repulsions between the ions). The values shown in Table 1.4 are average values for ions of different types. In crystals containing ions of different n-value, the average is used. The repulsion energy is thus typically about 10 per cent of the Coulomb energy.

The repulsion energy is sometimes expressed differently, being considered to be proportional to $\exp(-r/\rho)$. This form is suggested by the exponential falling-off of electron density at large distances from the nucleus in closed-shell atoms and ions. The constant ρ is found from compressibility measurements to have an average value of 34·5 pm, so that the (Born–Mayer) expression for lattice energy is

$$U = -\frac{AN_A Z_+Z_- e^2}{4\pi\varepsilon_0 r_0}\left(1 - \frac{\rho}{r_0}\right)$$

Table 1.4   n-values for the Born–Landé lattice-energy expression

Ion configuration	n
$1s^2$ (He-type)	5
$1s^2 2s^2 2p^6$ (Ne-type)	7
$[Ne]3d^{10}$ (Cu^+-type), $[Ne]3d^{10}4s^24p^6$ (Ar-type)	9
$[Ar]4d^{10}$ (Ag^+-type), $[Ar]4d^{10}5s^25p^6$ (Kr-type)	10
$[Kr]5d^{10}$ (Au^+-type), $[Kr]5d^{10}6s^26p^6$ (Xe-type)	12

In addition to these terms, corrections should be applied for the zero-point energy (*ca.* +5 kJ mol^{-1}, negligible) and for dispersion forces (also known as London or van der Waals' forces). The latter are relatively small (30–40 kJ mol^{-1}) for small ions, but increase rapidly with increasing size and increasing polarisability of the ions. In these cases there are likely to be substantial contributions to the binding energy of the crystal from covalency effects, and lattice energy values calculated on the ionic model would not be expected to be very accurate; the difficulty of assessing the magnitude of the dispersion forces is therefore not serious.

To use these semi-theoretical expressions for lattice energy, both the crystal structure and the internuclear distance must be known, which is not always possible. Average values of ionic radii are available (see below), from which quite good estimates of the internuclear separation may be made, and the stoicheiometry and relative sizes of the ions will often suggest a probable lattice type. Nevertheless, it is often useful to employ an approximate expression derived by Kapustinskii, which is applicable to all ionic crystals. Kapustinskii noted that the ratio A/v, where v is the number of ions per formula unit, is roughly independent of the crystal type, but increases slightly as the coordination number of the ions increases. Since the internuclear distance also increases with coordination number, the ratio $A/(vr_0)$ is less sensitive still to crystal type. It is therefore possible to treat all crystals as if they had the same crystal structure, using an appropriate average Madelung constant and ionic radii. Kapustinskii chose the NaCl-lattice as standard, for which $v = 2$, so that the expression for U became

$$U = -\left(\frac{1 \cdot 74756}{2}\right)v \cdot \frac{N_A Z_+ Z_- e^2}{4\pi\varepsilon_0 r_0} \cdot R$$

where R is the repulsion term. If all the constants are gathered together, this becomes

$$\frac{U}{kJ\,mol^{-1}} = -\frac{(1 \cdot 214 \times 10^5)v Z_+ Z_-}{(r_0/pm)}R$$

1.4.3 Ionic radii

Lattice energies can be calculated from a knowledge of the internuclear separations of the ions, which may be derived from X-ray studies. The ionic model suggests that it should be possible to divide the internuclear distance into contributions from the individual ions, i.e. to assign **ionic radii** which should be the same for all crystals containing that ion. This idea is supported by the observation that, for a series of compounds such as the alkali–metal halides, differences in internuclear separation between corresponding salts are sensibly constant. For instance, the data of Table 1.5 suggest that an Rb$^+$ ion is about 14 pm larger in radius than a K$^+$ ion, and the radii of halide ions show similar roughly constant differences. Similarly, in compounds containing large

Table 1.5 Internuclear separations and ionic radii (pm)

X	d_{K-X}	$(r_{Rb} - r_K)$	d_{Rb-X}
F	267	(15)	282
$(r_{Cl} - r_F)$	(48)		(47)
Cl	315	(14)	329
$(r_{Br} - r_{Cl})$	(15)		(14)
Br	330	(13)	343
$(r_I - r_{Br})$	(23)		(24)
I	353	(14)	367

anions the internuclear separation is independent of the cation, as shown by the isostructural magnesium and manganese chalcogenides (Table 1.6). For the oxides the values for the two metals are different, whereas for the sulphides and selenides they are the same, suggesting that in the last two cases the distance is governed by the separation of adjacent anions rather than by anion–cation contact. If this were so, the anion radius would be given by the internuclear separation divided by $\sqrt{2}$ (from the geometry of the NaCl-lattice). Once a value has been established for the radius of one ion, values for other ions are readily obtained. If this method is not adopted, the apportioning of the internuclear distance between the ions is a considerable problem; recourse to some theoretical model is necessary, and various methods have been employed.

Table 1.6   Internuclear separations in MgY and MnY (pm)

Y \ M	Mg	Mn
O	210	224
S	260	259
Se	273	273

In terms of the accuracy with which internuclear distances are reproduced, the best set of radii available are those due to Shannon and Prewitt, who analysed data for over 1000 oxides and fluorides. They derived values of 140 pm and 133 pm for the radii of O^{2-} and F^- respectively, and assumed linear relationships between the volume of the unit cell of the crystal and the volume of the cation. Their values are listed in Appendix F, and those for the alkali metals are compared with values derived by other authors in Table 1.7. It is found empirically that the radius of an ion depends on its coordination number, increasing with increasing coordination.

Table 1.7   Ionic radii (pm) estimated by various workers

	Shannon–Prewitt	Pauling	Goldschmidt	Johnson[†]
Li^+	74	60	78	92
Na^+	102	95	98	118
K^+	138	133	133	145
Rb^+	149	148	149	156
Cs^+	170	169	165	168

† A. O. Johnson, *Inorg. Chem.*, **12**, 780 (1973)

Ionic radii are of direct use in calculating lattice energies, but it is also possible to discuss the broad features of the structures of ionic solids on this basis. Electrostatic considerations suggest that the coordination numbers of the ions should be as large as possible, consistent with the stoicheiometry and the relative sizes of the ions. Each ion must be in contact with as many ions of opposite charge as possible, but this number is governed by the relative radii of the ions; it is the **radius-ratio**, r_+/r_-, which is critical. Consider an octahedrally coordinated cation as in, say, the NaCl-lattice. The minimum radius which the cation may have and still be in contact with all the anions may be calculated readily from the geometry of the system, which demands that the sum of the ionic radii be $\sqrt{2}$ times the anion radius (see Fig. 1.11)

$$r_+ + r_- = \sqrt{2}r_-$$

Fig. 1.11   The geometry of anion–cation coordination. (*a*) octahedral, (*b*) cubic, (*c*) tetrahedral

(*a*)   (*b*)   (*c*)

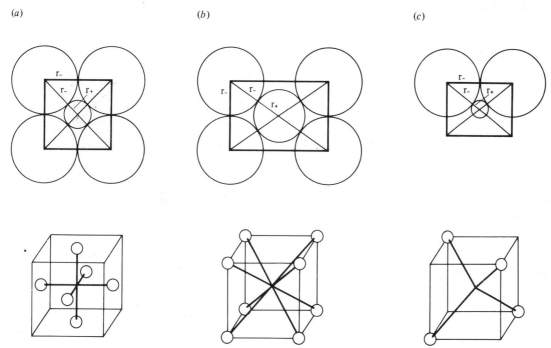

Hence the minimum radius-ratio which is likely for this structure is 0·414. As the ratio increases from this value, the anions move apart and eventually a point will be reached at which it is possible to introduce extra anions and to increase the coordination number of the cation. The survey of structure types showed that the next most common coordination number is eight (seven-coordination is rare, presumably because it does not allow the formation of symmetrical, closely packed structures). The minimum radius-ratio for cubic coordination can be calculated from the fact that the main diagonal of a cube is $\sqrt{3}$ times the length of the edge,

$$r_+ + r_- = \sqrt{3}r_-$$

$$r_+/r_- = 0·732$$

If the radius-ratio is smaller than 0·414, a cation on an octahedral site cannot maintain contact with all the anions. Some examples of such structures are known in which the cation appears to be displaced to one side of the octahedron, maintaining contact with three anions. These materials often have interesting and useful dielectric properties (ferroelectricity) since the application of a suitably large electric field can make the cation 'jump' from one side of the octahedral hole to the other. A substance in which this occurs is barium titanate, $BaTiO_3$, in which the small Ti^{4+} ion can be 'rattled', and this compound is used in radio aerials and computer flip-flop (memory) systems.

In the majority of cases, reduction in the radius ratio leads to a reduction in the coordination number to four. A tetrahedral site may be defined in terms of a cube whose face-diagonal is the sum of the anion radii. Hence,

$$r_+ + r_- = \sqrt{3}r_-/\sqrt{2},$$

$$r_+/r_- = 0·225$$

For compounds of stoicheiometry MX, geometric constraints thus suggest that the zinc-blende structure should be found if the radius-ratio lies between 0·225 and 0·414, the rock-salt structure for 0·414 to 0·732, and the caesium-chloride structure for values greater than 0·732. For these prototype crystal structures the actual ratios of the radii of the ions are: ZnS, 0·408; NaCl, 0·563; CsCl, 0·939. In general, quite good agreement is obtained between observed and expected structures, although several exceptions are known (see below and Ch. 2).

1.4.4   Validity of the ionic model

The ionic model has very clear conceptual advantages. It is easy to describe crystal structures in terms of close-packed arrangements of hard spheres, and calculations of lattice energies (and hence of enthalpies of formation and of reaction) can readily be made. Extensive use is made of the model, particularly in discussions of the energetics of inorganic compounds, apparently with considerable success. Nevertheless, such a simple model should not be accepted without a critical appraisal of its validity.

Firstly, it should be asked what the evidence is for the existence of ions. Most ionic substances have high melting points and other physical properties suggestive of strong binding. The melting points increase with decreasing inter-nuclear separations (Fig. 1.12), and with increasing charge on the ions. The molten salts usually have good electrical conductivity and the solids are often soluble in water or other polar solvents, to give conducting solutions, and in both cases it is easily shown that the conductivity is due to both cations and anions. While all these observations are consistent with the presence of ions in the solid, none of them proves their presence.

Fig. 1.12   Melting points of alkali–metal halides *vs* internuclear separations

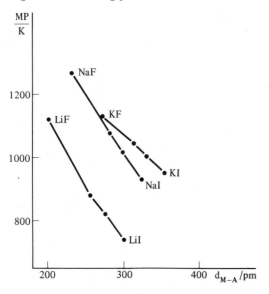

Calculations of lattice energy based on the electrostatic treatments given above show very good agreement with 'experimental' values obtained from enthalpies of formation using the Born–Haber cycle (see below), especially when 'extended' calculations are employed which allow for van der Waals' attractions, etc. These values, together with those from the Born–Mayer and Kapustinskii treatments are shown in Table 1.8 for the alkali halides. The agreement between calculation and experiment is usually excellent, but again this does not substantiate the model. The

Table 1.8 Lattice energies (kJ mol^{-1}) for alkali–metal halides

	Born–Haber cycle	'extended' calculation	Born–Mayer calculation	Kapustinskii calculation
LiF	1009·2	1019·2	1018	952·7
LiCl	829·3	837·6	813·1	803·7
LiBr	788·7	792·9	772·5	792·9
LiI	733·9	736·8	716·5	713·0
NaF	903·7	901·2	885·5	884·9
NaCl	769·0	771·5	757·3	752·7
NaBr	736·0	738·5	720·7	734·3
NaI	688·3	687·4	671·5	673·6
KF	801·2	805·4	744·9	788·7
KCl	697·9	702·5	689·9	680·7
KBr	672.4	674·9	658·9	674·9
KI	631·8	637·6	617·4	614·2
RbF	768·2	765·8	760·7	760·2
RbCl	677·8	677·8	662·4	661·9
RbBr	649·4	653·1	635·0	626·3
RbI	613·0	619·2	596·4	589·9

Values in the first three columns are converted from those quoted by T. C. Waddington, *Advances in Inorganic Chemistry and Radiochemistry*, **1**, 157 (1959).

agreement could be, and to some extent is, fortuitous as will be shown below. It is perfectly conceivable that other models could give similar or better agreement.

Equally, many structures are compatible with the radius–ratio rules, but there are several significant exceptions. Even among the alkali halides, often considered to be 'model' ionic compounds, exceptions can be found. For instance, the rubidium halides would be expected to have the CsCl-structure and the lithium halides the zinc-blende structure, whereas all have the NaCl-structure. These observations suggest that other factors may favour the rock-salt structure.

The best evidence for ions comes from the study of electron density distributions in crystals. The electron densities fall to very low values between the ions, and the total electron densities correspond to those expected for the ions; for example, in KBr the electron density is effectively zero 157 pm from the potassium nucleus and 173 pm from the bromine nucleus, and the integrated electron densities correspond to 35·8 ($\pm 0 \cdot 4$) electrons associated with the potassium position and 18·4 ($\pm 0 \cdot 2$) with the bromine position, compared to 36 and 18 for K^+ and Br^-. Similar results have been found for other systems.

The observant reader will have noted that the distances quoted above for the minimum electron density in KBr do not correspond to any of the ionic radii given earlier. The potassium ion is larger and the bromide ion is smaller than the conventional assignments of radii would suggest. Similar differences between derived and 'observed' radii are found for other crystals, the deviations always being in the same directions (Table 1.9). These changes suggest covalency: the addition of electron density to a cation would be expected to increase its radius, and loss of electrons from an anion would decrease the radius. In some cases, the electron density does not fall to zero between the ions. Figure 1.13 shows the electron density along the internuclear axes for NaCl, LiF, and CaF$_2$; although in NaCl the density falls effectively to zero, the minima in LiF and CaF$_2$ are $1 \cdot 9 \times 10^5$ and $2 \cdot 3 \times 10^5$ e pm^{-3} respectively. Despite these indications of covalent character, the electron counts show the numbers of electrons expected for ions. It is clear, however, that radius-ratios based on these radii bear no relation to the simple geometric considerations used above.

Table 1.9   Radii corresponding to electron density minima in ionic compounds

	r₊/pm	r₋/pm
LiF	92	109
NaCl	118	164
KCl	145	170
KBr	157	173
CaF₂	126	110
CuCl	110	125
CuBr	110	136
MgO	102	109
NiO	94	115

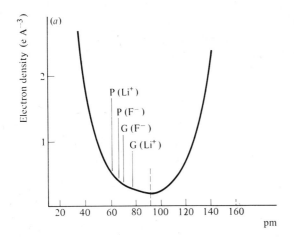

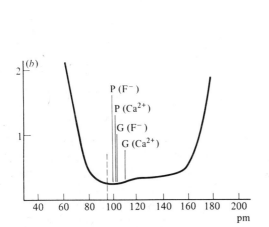

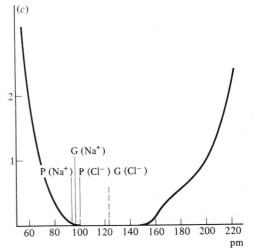

Fig. 1.13   Electron density distributions in (*a*) LiF, (*b*) CaF₂, and (*c*) NaCl. Distances are in pm from the cation nucleus. The minima and the positions corresponding to the Pauling (P) and Goldschmidt (G) radii of the ions are marked. (Drawn from the data of (*a*) J. Krug, H. Witte and E. Wölfel, *Z. Phys. Chem.* (Frankfurt), **4**, 36 (1955); (*b*) A. Weiss, H. Witte and E. Wölfel, *ibid*, **10**, 98 (1957); (*c*) H. Witte and E. Wölfel, *ibid*, **3**, 296 (1955))

A more disturbing feature is that the radii derived from these measurements differ from one compound to another. The cation radii are sensibly constant, but those of the anions vary widely, e.g. the radius of the chloride ion appears to be 187 pm in CsCl, 164 pm in NaCl, but only 125 pm in CuCl. The radius of the anion decreases with increasing polarisability and increasing polarising power of the cation; the oxide and sulphide ions, for instance, show greater variation than halide ions. Such trends are not entirely unexpected. From the wave-nature of the electron it is unlikely that an ion would have a definite radius. Some polarisation of the electron clouds is to be expected, especially of the anion by the cation, and this effect would become more marked the greater the formal charge on the cation. Such redistribution of electron density amounts to the inclusion of some covalent character in the bonding, which must become more pronounced the greater the formal charges on the ions. It seems unlikely that any atom bears an actual charge much greater than unity.

The effects of covalency are discernible in the crystal structures adopted by various types of compound. The two ZnS-structures, involving tetrahedral coordination, are adopted only by polarisable metals and non-metals, notably the sulphides, selenides and tellurides of the early *p*-block metals. Many di- and tri-halides have layer structures in which it is clearly more favourable to concentrate the bonding, which must be partially covalent, within the layers leaving adjacent layers of anions with no cations between them. On a purely electrostatic basis the cations would be expected to be distributed uniformly throughout the lattice. It even seems possible that the rubidium halides might adopt the NaCl-structure against the radius-ratio predictions, in order to achieve a measure of covalency. In the NaCl-structure the *p*-orbitals on each ion are directed exactly towards those of each of the six neighbours.

A discussion of crystal structures based on derived ionic radii is thus seen to be somewhat unreliable [cf. Adams for further treatment of this point]. Such radii are of use in obtaining values for internuclear separations but cannot be taken in any way as indicating the actual sizes of the ions.

Nevertheless, despite this inadequacy, the ionic model appears to give good estimates of lattice energies, and is widely assumed to be reliable for this purpose. Presumably, there is a fortunate cancelling of errors. If the actual bonding between the ions involved substantial covalency, the bond energy would be greater than that calculated on a purely ionic basis even if the observed internuclear distance were used, because the covalency arises from the build-up of electron density between the nuclei, closer to the nuclei than in the purely ionic situation. The ionic model thus underestimates the binding energy of the lattice in this respect. On the other hand, the ionic model takes the full formal charge to be associated with each ion, thus overestimating the electrostatic energy. Also the ionic lattice-energy calculation assumes that the ions are point-charges and makes no allowance for the shielding of one ion by others, again overestimating the electrostatic contribution. It appears that these features are self-compensating, and lattice energies calculated on the ionic model may be taken as reasonable estimates of the binding energies of solid halides, oxides, etc.

1.5   Energy cycles

Hess' Law states that the energy released or absorbed by a process is independent of the way in which the process occurs; the energy change is determined by the initial and final states only. In the present context the important processes are chemical reactions, particularly those in which compounds are formed from the elements, or dissociate or disproportionate to give other compounds. It is often convenient to analyse the energetics of such reactions in terms of hypothetical reaction paths which involve individual steps which can be related to fundamental properties of the elements. The most familiar treatment is the formation of an ionic compound considered in terms of the Born–Haber cycle, but similar energy cycles may be used for the formation of covalent compounds and hydrated ions, and the interconversions of compounds.

Fig. 1.14   Born–Haber cycle for formation of MX_n

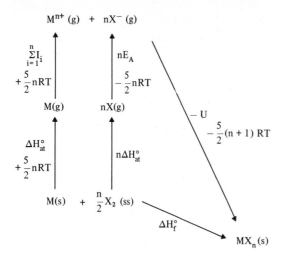

1.5.1   The Born–Haber cycle

The formation of an ionic compound from its elements may be considered in terms of the energy cycle shown in Fig. 1.14, first used by Born and Haber. Usually only enthalpy terms are considered. The steps involved are:

(1) The **enthalpy of atomisation** of the metal, ΔH_{at} (sometimes called the enthalpy of sublimation) – the energy required to convert the solid metal into separate gaseous atoms

$$M(s) \rightarrow M(g) \qquad \Delta H = \Delta H_{at}$$

(2) The **ionisation energy**, $\sum_i I_i$ – the energy required to remove electrons from the gaseous metal atoms. These values can be determined from emission spectra (e.g. in an electric arc) of metallic vapours, and are usually quoted for individual steps, i.e. I_1 refers to the removal of one electron from the neutral atom, I_2 to the removal of an electron from the mono-positive ion, and so on

$$M(g) \rightarrow M^+(g) + e^- \qquad \Delta H = I_1$$
$$M^{n+}(g) \rightarrow M^{(n+1)+} + e^- \qquad \Delta H = I_n$$

(3) The enthalpy of atomisation of the non-metal, $\Delta H_{at}(X_2)$ – in the case of fluorine, chlorine and oxygen, which are gaseous at normal temperatures, the enthalpy of atomisation is simply one-half of the **dissociation enthalpy**, $D(X_2)$, of the diatomic molecules. In other cases the non-metal is a liquid or solid in the standard state and the appropriate enthalpy of vaporization must be included.

$$\tfrac{1}{2}X_2(ss) \rightarrow X(g) \qquad \Delta H = \Delta H_{at}(X_2) = D(X_2) + \Delta H_{vap}$$

[(ss) signifies standard state].

(4) The **electron affinity** of the non-metal, E_A – the enthalpy change for the combination of a gaseous non-metal atom with an electron

$$X(g) + e^- \rightarrow X^-(g) \qquad \Delta H = E_A$$

For the major non-metallic elements, one electron is taken up exothermically, but the addition of a second electron is always endothermic, e.g.

$$O(g) + e^- \rightarrow O^-(g) \qquad \Delta H = -142 \text{ kJ mol}^{-1}$$

$$O^-(g) + e^- \rightarrow O^{2-}(g) \qquad \Delta H = +844 \text{ kJ mol}^{-1}$$

It is usually convenient to combine the enthalpy of atomisation and the electron affinity into one term which, of course, represents the enthalpy of formation of the anion

$$\tfrac{1}{2}X_2(ss) + e^- \rightarrow X^-(g) \quad \Delta H = \Delta H_f(X^-) = \Delta H_{at} + E_A$$

(5) The **lattice energy**, U – the enthalpy of combination of the gaseous ions into the solid lattice

$$M^{n+}(g) + nX^-(g) \rightarrow MX_n(s) \qquad \Delta H = -U$$

In cases where gaseous species are produced or removed, an additional term of $\tfrac{5}{2}RT$ per mole should be included to take account of the fact that quantities such as ionisation energies are strictly changes in internal energy measured at absolute zero, whereas the energy cycle requires the enthalpy changes at 298 K. To assess their contribution accurately would require a knowledge of the heat capacity at constant pressure of each of the species concerned. For example, for ionisation

$$M(g) \rightarrow M^+(g) + e^-(g)$$

$$\Delta H^0_{298} = \Delta U_0 + \int_0^{298} [C_p(M^+) + C_p(e^-) - C_p(M)] \, dT$$

[ΔU_0 is the change in internal energy of the system.]

To a good approximation it may be assumed that the gaseous species behave as ideal monatomic gases with a heat capacity of $\tfrac{5}{2}R$ at all temperatures above absolute zero. Hence

$$\Delta H^0_{298} = \Delta U_0 + \int_0^{298} \left[\tfrac{5}{2}R \right] dT = U_0 + \tfrac{5}{2}R \times 298$$

These terms are largely self-cancelling around the energy cycle, but in any case at 298 K, $\tfrac{5}{2}RT$ amounts to only 6·18 kJ mol^{-1}, which may reasonably be ignored.

The sum of steps around the cycle in one direction must be equal to that in the other direction, so that

$$\Delta H^0_f(MX_n) = \Delta H^0_{at} + \sum_{i=1}^n I_i + n\Delta H^0_f(X^-) - U$$

It thus becomes possible to analyse trends in, say, enthalpies of formation of a series of compounds in terms of the various factors which contribute. In comparing, for instance, the various dihalides of one metal, the terms which change from one compound to another are $\Delta H^0_f(X^-)$ and U, while in contrasting one metal with another ΔH_{at}, I, and U must be considered. In such cases it is often possible to use the known value of ΔH^0_f and the other parameters to calculate the lattice energy, but where this cannot be done an estimate of U may be made and a value for ΔH^0_f obtained. Such comparisons are a powerful way of analysing trends in behaviour of inorganic compounds, and will be much employed in later chapters.

1.5.2   Covalent compounds

The Born–Haber cycle refers only to the formation of ionic compounds. Many compounds are plainly not ionic, even to a first approximation. Tin(IV) iodide, for instance, behaves as a molecular, covalent compound like the other tin tetrahalides. Although the SnI_4 lattice *could* be described as an fcc array of I$^-$ ions with Sn^{4+} cations occupying tetrahedral holes, such a description would be rather unrealistic in view of the high polarisability of the large iodide ion. It is possible to calculate the lattice energy using the ionic model, and hence to obtain a value for the enthalpy of formation. If this is done (Table 1.10), SnI_4 appears to be strongly endothermic, a result which clearly indicates the unreliability of this approach.

Table 1.10 The enthalpy of formation of SnI_4 (kJ mol^{-1})

$\Delta H_{at}(Sn)$	$\sum_{i=1}^{4} I_i$	$4\Delta H_f(I^-)$	$-U_{Kap.}$	$\Delta H_f(SnI_4)$
301	8989	-780	-7420	$+1090$

It would be preferable in cases such as these to use an energy cycle appropriate to covalent compounds (Fig. 1.15), i.e. to consider as the exothermic term a **bond energy**, E_{M-X}, representing the dissociation of a molecule into neutral atoms

$$MX_n(g) \rightarrow M(g) + nX(g) \qquad \Delta H = nE_{M-X}$$

Fig. 1.15 Energy cycle for formation of a
covalent compound, MX_n

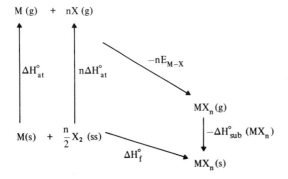

This definition is analogous to that of lattice energy, except that it refers to gaseous MX_n. Bond energies defined in this way are sometimes called thermochemical bond energies or bond energy terms, and they can obviously be derived when the enthalpy of formation is known. Unfortunately, there is no way of calculating such bond energies. A quantity more amenable to theoretical treatment, in principle at least, is the **intrinsic bond energy**, which is the energy required simply to disrupt the bonds without allowing the product species to relax to new equilibrium electronic configurations. This configuration cannot be observed directly. For instance, the ground-state configuration of a tin atom is $[Kr]5s^2 5p^2$. To form tin tetraiodide, four unpaired electrons are required to pair with the single valence electrons of four iodine atoms, so that the tin atom must be promoted to an excited state with configuration $[Kr]5s^1 5p^3$. States such as these are usually spectroscopically observable and their energies can be obtained. However, this is not the state in which the tin atom would be immediately after the breaking of four tin-iodine bonds in SnI_4. In the excited sp^3-tin atom the spins of the four electrons will be correlated (coupled with each other) but this feature is lost in the formation of a molecule. The state in which the tin atom combines with the iodine atoms is one in which the spins of the valence electrons are completely randomised, sometimes called the *valence state*. Since the valence state can never be observed, its energy can only be estimated. In principle the intrinsic bond energy could be calculated by suitable molecular-orbital methods, but such estimates are still very approximate.

Many attempts have been made to derive sets of bond energies which may be used to estimate the total bond energy of a complex molecule. This treatment embodies the assumption of additivity, i.e. that the bond energy derived from one molecule is applicable to another molecule and that the energy of a bond between two atoms is independent of the other atoms bound to each. These assumptions being somewhat unrealistic, this treatment is rather approximate, although it is reasonably successful for closely-related series of molecules such as hydrocarbons.

In general, then, the covalent model is much less useful in analysing data than the ionic model. It should be emphasized that this is not because it provides a less real description of chemical systems; indeed, as has been pointed out earlier, all bonds possess some covalent character, and molecular-orbital methods can, in principle, describe bonds of any degree of covalency or ionicity. The difficulty with the covalent model is simply lack of data and the complexity and inaccuracy of quantum mechanical calculations.

1.6   Oxidation-state diagrams

A useful way of displaying the relative stabilities of a series of compounds of one metal is to plot the free energies (or enthalpies) of formation against the oxidation state. To enable comparisons to be made readily, the value per mole of metal is taken. The resulting **oxidation-state diagram** shows clearly and graphically the inter-relations between the various compounds.

Three basic patterns of behaviour can be recognized; these are illustrated in Fig. 1.16a–c, which may be taken to refer to a metal, M, and a halogen, X. Figure 1.16a shows a hypothetical but common pattern, two compounds MX and MX_2 with negative enthalpies of formation, the second being more negative than the first. Both compounds are thus stable to *dissociation* into the elements since the dissociation reaction, being the reverse of the formation reaction, is necessarily endothermic. The origin of the diagram represents the enthalpy of the elemental metal since, by definition, this is its standard state with zero enthalpy. On addition of the halogen to the metal the enthalpy of the system is lowered with exothermic formation of MX and then MX_2. If sufficient halogen is available, MX_2 should be formed, since this process releases most energy. With a deficiency of halogen, say one half-mole, there would seem to be two possibilities: either half the metal would react to form MX_2, or all of the metal would react to give MX. The enthalpy of a mixture of one half-mole of metal and one half-mole of MX_2 would be represented on the diagram by the mid-point of the line joining the origin (M) and the point for MX_2, i.e. point A. The enthalpy of this mixture is clearly higher than that of one mole of MX, and the mixture would be expected to react exothermically with formation of MX:

$$\tfrac{1}{2}M + \tfrac{1}{2}MX_2 \;\rightarrow\; MX \qquad \Delta H^0 = \Delta H_f^0(MX) - \tfrac{1}{2}[\Delta H_f^0(MX_2) + \Delta H_f^0(M)] < 0$$

Thus, if the supply of halogen is limited, the lower halide is formed. This also means that the lower halide can be obtained by reducing the higher halide with elemental metal. Put another way, MX is stable to *disproportionation*† into $M + MX_2$. When the oxidation-state diagram is a concave-upwards curve, all the compounds are stable to disproportionation and all should be obtainable under appropriate conditions.

---

† The terms dissociation and disproportionation are often confused in student usage, but should be carefully distinguished. Dissociation refers to the loss of one component, usually the non-metal, and formation of a compound of the metal in a lower oxidation state

$$MX_n \;\rightarrow\; MX_{n-1} + \tfrac{1}{2}X_2, \qquad MX_n \;\rightarrow\; MX_{n/2} + \frac{n}{4}X_2, \text{ etc.}$$

while in disproportionation two new oxidation states are formed, one higher and one lower than the original, i.e. the available non-metal is redistributed between the products, but none is lost as the free element

$$MX_n \;\rightarrow\; \tfrac{1}{2}MX_{n+1} + \tfrac{1}{2}MX_{n-1}, \qquad MX_n \;\rightarrow\; \tfrac{1}{2}MX_{2n} + \tfrac{1}{2}M, \text{ etc.}$$

Fig. 1.16   Typical oxidation-state diagrams for MX and MX_2. The point A represents the enthalpy of the mixture $\frac{1}{2}M + \frac{1}{2}MX_2$. (*a*) MX and MX_2 stable to dissociation and disproportionation, (*b*) MX unstable to disproportionation, (*c*) MX_2 unstable to dissociation

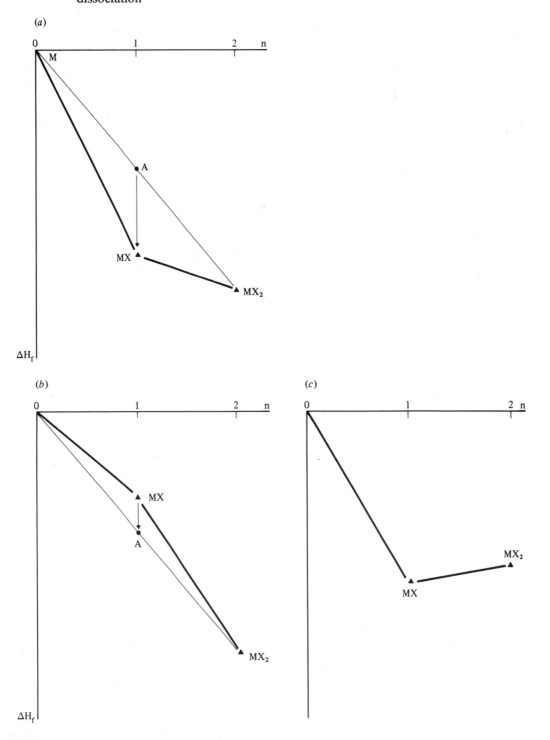

If a compound is unstable to disproportionation, the curve would be convex-upwards, as in Fig. 1.16b. The point for MX now lies above that for $\frac{1}{2}M+\frac{1}{2}MX_2$, so that the disproportionation reaction is exothermic

$$MX \rightarrow \tfrac{1}{2}M+\tfrac{1}{2}MX_2 \qquad \Delta H^0_{disp} = \tfrac{1}{2}\Delta H^0_f(MX_2)-\Delta H^0_f(MX)<0$$

If ΔH_{disp} is sufficiently negative it may not be possible to prepare MX at all. In some cases compounds which are unstable to disproportionation can be obtained because they are kinetically stable; they usually disproportionate on heating.

The third pattern of behaviour is shown in Fig. 1.16c. Here, MX_2 is stable with respect to dissociation into the elements but is unstable to loss of some halogen and formation of MX, i.e. the reaction

$$MX_2 \rightarrow MX+\tfrac{1}{2}X_2 \qquad \Delta H^0_{diss}<0$$

is exothermic. Now it is MX_2 which either cannot be made or, if it can, owes its existence to kinetic effects.

Frequently these three types of behaviour appear in combination, and many examples of each type will be found in the following chapters.

To obtain a reliable picture, free energies, rather than enthalpies, should be plotted on the oxidation-state diagram. Free energies of formation are less negative than the corresponding enthalpies, and increase with increasing temperature, owing to the entropy term

$$\Delta G_f = \Delta H_f - T\Delta S_f \qquad \Delta S_f<0$$

Consider a series of compounds MX, MX_2, MX_3, etc. which at one temperature are all stable to disproportionation and dissociation (Fig. 1.17a). In the formation reactions

$$M+\frac{n}{2}X_2 \rightarrow MX_n$$

Fig. 1.17   Oxidation-state diagrams for two temperatures. In (*b*), corresponding to the higher temperature, MX_3 is unstable to dissociation

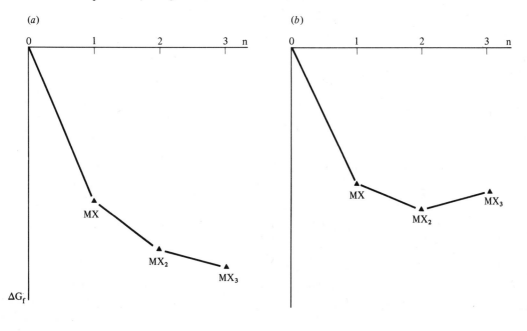

the entropy change, ΔS_f, is negative and arises mainly from the removal of the (usually gaseous) halogen or non-metal. As the temperature is raised ΔG_f becomes less negative and this effect becomes more pronounced as n becomes larger. Thus, as the temperature is raised all compounds become less stable, but the effect is greatest for highest oxidation states. The oxidation state diagram becomes shallower and more curved and may, if the temperature is raised enough, begin to curve upwards. At this stage (Fig. 1.17b) the final compound of the series has become unstable relative to the penultimate one. Compounds involving high oxidation states are therefore less thermally stable than lower compounds, and a useful route to the lower compounds is often to prepare the highest compound using an excess of non-metal and then to heat the product.

1.7 Aqueous systems – E^0-values

Much chemistry is performed in aqueous solution, and it would be convenient to display the relative stabilities of the various cationic and anionic species on an oxidation-state diagram similar to that used for halides or oxides. This, however, is not directly possible, since data would be required for formation reactions which cannot be observed directly, such as

$$M(s) \rightarrow M^{n+}(aq) + ne^-(aq)$$

This reaction is only a *half-reaction* and can be studied only when coupled with another half-reaction which consumes the electrons, e.g.

$$\frac{n}{2}X_2(ss) + ne^-(aq) \rightarrow nX^-(aq)$$

so that the composite reaction is

$$M(s) + \frac{n}{2}X_2(ss) \rightarrow M^{n+}(aq) + nX^-(aq)$$

The enthalpy of such a reaction could be measured, but there is no way of dividing the resulting value between the two half-reactions.

In many cases the coupled half-reactions can be studied in an electrochemical cell, when the e.m.f. of the cell is related directly to the free energy of the reaction. Consider the reaction

$$Fe + Cu^{2+}(aq) \rightarrow Cu + Fe^{2+}(aq)$$

familiar to every schoolboy who has dipped a penknife into copper sulphate solution. The two half-reactions concerned here are

$$Fe \rightarrow Fe^{2+}(aq) + 2e^-(aq)$$

$$Cu^{2+}(aq) + 2e^-(aq) \rightarrow Cu$$

These reactions may be studied in a cell consisting of a copper electrode immersed in a solution of a copper(II) salt and an iron electrode in an iron(II) solution. The two solutions must be in electrical contact but not allowed to mix appreciably; this can be achieved by use of a porous porcelain separator or a conducting bridge made from an ionised salt such as potassium nitrate in a gelatinous matrix like agar. Such a cell may be represented schematically by the diagram

$$Fe|FeSO_4(aq)\|CuSO_4(aq)|Cu$$

In this cell, provided the Cu^{2+} concentration is not very much less than that of Fe^{2+}, the iron electrode becomes negatively charged as Fe^{2+} ions pass into solution, leaving electrons on the electrode. At the copper electrode the reverse process occurs, Cu^{2+} ions are discharged making this electrode positive. When the electrodes are connected, electrons flow from iron to copper through the external circuit and the reaction proceeds. The e.m.f., E, of the cell is related to the free energy of the reaction by

$$\Delta G = -nFE$$

where n is the number of electrons involved in the reaction (in this case two) and F is the Faraday constant ($9 \cdot 648 \times 10^4$ C mol^{-1}; note that 1 volt = 1 J C^{-1}, so that ΔG is obtained in J mol^{-1} when E is in volts). Under standard conditions, i.e. the solutions are at unit activity, the e.m.f. of the cell is the *standard e.m.f.*, E⁰, in this case 0·78 V, so that the corresponding standard free energy is $\Delta G^0 = -150$ kJ mol^{-1}.

A series of half-reactions could be compared by coupling each of them with the same half-reaction and measuring the e.m.f. of the resulting cells. Absolute values are assigned using the half-reaction involving hydrogen as an arbitrary standard

$$\tfrac{1}{2}H_2(g) \;\rightarrow\; H^+(aq) + e^-(aq) \qquad E^0 = 0$$

The standard hydrogen electrode is obtained by passing gaseous hydrogen at one atmosphere pressure over a platinum electrode immersed in an acidic solution in which the activity of the hydrogen ion is unity. The **standard redox potential**, E⁰, of a half-reaction is then defined as the e.m.f. of the cell in which the left-hand half-cell is the standard hydrogen electrode and the right-hand half-cell is that corresponding to the desired half-reaction. For instance, for the Fe^{2+}/Fe couple the cell would be

Pt, H_2 (1 atm)$|H^+(aq)$ (a = 1)$\|Fe^{2+}(aq)$ (a = 1)$|Fe$

the e.m.f. of which is $-0\cdot44$ V (i.e. the right-hand electrode, iron, is negatively charged). Thus, for the half-reaction

$$Fe^{2+}(aq) + 2e^-(aq) \;\rightarrow\; Fe$$

$$E^0 = -0\cdot44 \text{ V} \quad \text{and} \quad \Delta G^0/F = +0\cdot88 \text{ V}, \qquad \Delta G^0 = +84\cdot9 \text{ kJ mol}^{-1}.$$

Note the signs show that the reaction as written is unfavourable. The spontaneous reaction is

$$Fe + 2H^+(aq) \;\rightarrow\; Fe^{2+}(aq) + H_2$$

for which $E^0 = +0\cdot44$ V   and $\Delta G^0 = -84\cdot9$ kJ mol^{-1}.

In defining the *red*ox potentials, the half-reactions are written as *red*uctions and the oxidised and reduced forms are indicated as postcripts to E⁰, e.g. either $E^0(Fe^{2+}/Fe) = -0\cdot44$ V or E^0, $Fe^{2+}/Fe = -0\cdot44$ V.

An energy cycle for the formation of the hydrated cation from the elemental metal can be constructed (Fig. 1.18), which involves the atomisation and ionisation enthalpies together with that of conversion of the gaseous cation to the hydrated form. This latter, the **enthalpy of hydration**, ΔH_{hydr}, corresponds to dissolving the gaseous cation in an infinite quantity of water

$$M^{n+}(g) + \infty H_2O \;\rightarrow\; M^{n+}(aq) \qquad \Delta H = \Delta H_{hydr}$$

To relate these quantities to E⁰-values would require estimates of the entropies (to allow conversion to free energies) and the inclusion of the appropriate values for the hydrogenic species (see Ch. 2, p. 44).

Standard redox potentials for very many half-reactions have been measured, and values are tabulated in Appendix B. Since these values are related to the free energies of the half-reactions, they may be used to construct oxidation-state diagrams. The free energy of each species is plotted as $-nFE^0(M^{n+}/M)$ or, more usually as the volt-equivalent, $\Delta G^0/F = -nE^0(M^{n+}/M)$. Thus, (Fig. 1.19) the point for Fe^{2+} is plotted as $(2, -0.88\text{ V})$. In many tables not all possible $E^0(M^{n+}/M)$-values are given, e.g. $E^0(Fe^{3+}/Fe)$ is not usually quoted. However, the value of $E^0(Fe^{3+}/Fe^{2+})$ will be found, which can be used to fix the position of Fe^{3+} on the oxidation-state diagram. The half-reaction is

$$Fe^{3+}(aq) + e^- \rightarrow Fe^{2+}(aq) \qquad E^0 = +0.77\text{ V},$$

i.e. since $n = 1$, $\Delta G^0/F$ for the oxidation of Fe^{2+} to Fe^{3+} is 0.77 V, and the Fe^{3+} point must lie 0.77 V higher than for Fe^{2+}, at $(3, -0.11\text{ V})$. Hence $E^0(Fe^{3+}/Fe)$ may be calculated to be -0.037 V.

Fig. 1.18   Energy cycle for formation of hydrated metal ion

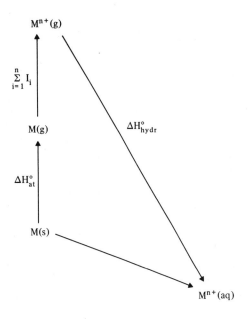

Oxidation-state diagrams constructed in this way (sometimes called *Ebsworth diagrams*) may be interpreted in the same way as other diagrams provided it is remembered that the zero of energy is not absolute but refers to the H^+/H_2 couple. Thus the iron diagram shows that both Fe^{2+} and Fe^{3+} are stable relative to iron metal, and Fe^{2+} is the more stable and would be expected to be formed in preference to Fe^{3+}. The conditions under which this applies, however, are those of oxidation by H^+, reaction with acid

$$Fe + 2H^+(aq) \rightarrow Fe^{2+}(aq) + H_2$$

Species for which $\Delta G^0/F$ is positive are not now inherently unstable, but are merely better oxidants than the proton. In general, species which lie at the top of a line on the oxidation-state diagram with positive slope are oxidants and those at the top of lines of negative slope are reductants; in both cases reaction will proceed until the minimum of the curve is reached. Note that the slope of the line joining two points is the standard redox potential for that couple.

The data given above refer to standard acid conditions (pH = 0). It is also possible to obtain values in alkaline solution, although many species are then hydroxides or hydrated basic oxides.

Fig. 1.19   Oxidation-state diagram for Fe in acid solution, (*a*) in the absence and (*b*) presence of oxygen

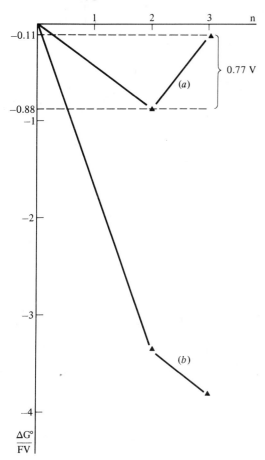

Two different conventions are used in quoting redox potential values for alkaline solution. Under standard alkaline conditions ($a_{OH^-} = 1$, pH $= 14$), the half-reaction involving hydrogen is

$$H_2O + e^-(aq) \rightarrow OH^-(aq) + \tfrac{1}{2}H_2$$

for which, by definition, $E^0_{OH} = 0$, and many tables of values refer to this scale. It is more convenient for present purposes to have all redox data referred to the same basis, i.e. to the reaction $H^+(aq) + e^-(aq) \rightarrow \tfrac{1}{2}H_2$. These two reactions differ by the ionisation of water

$$H_2O \rightleftharpoons H^+(aq) + OH^-(aq)$$

for which the free energy corresponds to $E^0 = -0.83$ V. That is, on the H^+/H_2-scale the standard alkaline half-reaction has $E^0 = -0.83$ V. E^0_{OH}-values can therefore be corrected to H^+/H_2-scale by the relation

$$E^0_b = E^0_{OH} + 0.83 \text{ V}$$

where E^0_b refers to basic conditions but is measured on the same scale as for acid conditions. All values quoted in later chapters for basic solution are E^0_b-values.

In precisely similar manner, redox-potential values may be referred to any selected half-reaction. Since most aqueous chemistry is performed in the presence of air, which may result in further oxidation, it is often helpful to refer E^0-values and the oxidation-state diagram to the half-reaction

$$\tfrac{1}{2}O_2 + 2H^+(aq) + 2e^-(aq) \rightarrow H_2O$$

for which $E^0 = +1\cdot23$ V.† In the case of the iron species illustrated above, the reactions of interest would now be

$$Fe + \tfrac{1}{2}O_2 + 2H^+(aq) \rightarrow Fe^{2+}(aq) + H_2O$$

and $\quad Fe + \tfrac{3}{4}O_2 + 3H^+(aq) \rightarrow Fe^{3+}(aq) + \tfrac{3}{2}H_2O$

or $\quad Fe^{2+}(aq) + \tfrac{1}{4}O_2 + H^+ \rightarrow Fe^{3+}(aq) + \tfrac{1}{2}H_2O$

For these three reactions, E_O^0-values may be defined as follows:

$$E_O^0(Fe/Fe^{2+}) = E^0(Fe, O_2/Fe^{2+}, H_2O) = -E^0(Fe^{2+}/Fe) + E^0(O_2/H_2O) = +1\cdot67 \text{ V}$$

$$E_O^0(Fe/Fe^{3+}) = E^0(Fe, O_2/Fe^{3+}, H_2O) = -E^0(Fe^{3+}/Fe) + E^0(O_2/H_2O) = +1\cdot27 \text{ V}$$

$$E_O^0(Fe^{2+}/Fe^{3+}) = E^0(Fe^{2+}, O_2/Fe^{3+}, H_2O) = -E^0(Fe^{3+}/Fe^{2+}) + E^0(O_2/H_2O) = +0\cdot46 \text{ V}$$

On the oxidation state diagram the points for Fe^{2+} and Fe^{3+} would now lie at $(2, -3\cdot34$ V) and $(3, -3\cdot81$ V) respectively (Fig. 1.19).‡ In the presence of oxygen, therefore, reaction of elemental iron with acid should not stop at iron(II) but proceed further to give iron(III); this accords with experience.

E_{bO}^0-values can be calculated precisely analogously to refer to basic solutions in the presence of oxygen.

Bibliography

Atomic structure and the Periodic Table
H, 1; **HJ**, 3; **MM**, 2; **PW**, 2.
A. K. Barnard, *Theoretical Basis of Inorganic Chemistry*, McGraw-Hill, 1965.
E. Cartmell and G. W. A. Fowles, *Valency and Molecular Structure*, 3rd edn, Butterworth, 1966.

---

† Note that E^0-values do not depend on the number of electrons involved, they effectively represent the free energy change per mole of electrons.
‡ The student will probably find the computation easier to perform accurately by working with free energies directly, carefully balancing the numbers of electrons:

$$Fe \rightarrow Fe^{3+}(aq) + 3e^-(aq) \quad \Delta G^0/F = -0\cdot11 \text{ V}$$
$$\tfrac{3}{4}O_2 + 3H^+(aq) + 3e^-(aq) \rightarrow \tfrac{3}{2}H_2O \quad \Delta G^0/F = -3\cdot69 \text{ V}$$
$$\overline{Fe + \tfrac{3}{4}O_2 + 3H^+(aq) \rightarrow Fe^{3+}(aq) + \tfrac{3}{2}H_2O \quad \Delta G^0/F = -3\cdot80 \text{ V}}$$

N. N. Greenwood, *'Principles of Atomic Orbitals'*, *Royal Institute of Chemistry Monographs for Teachers, No. 8*, The Chemical Society, 1964.

H. J. Eméleus and J. S. Anderson, *Modern Inorganic Chemistry*, 3rd edn, Routledge and Kegan Paul, 1960, Chapter 1.

Thermodynamics and energy cycles

D, 1 – 2; **J**, 1.

E. A. Guggenheim, *'Elements of Chemical Thermodynamics'*, *Royal Institute of Chemistry Monographs for Teachers, No. 12*, The Chemical Society, 1960.

J. R. W. Warn, *Concise Chemical Thermodynamics*, Van Nostrand, 1969.

J. Waser, *Basic Chemical Thermodynamics*, Benjamin, 1966.

P. A. H. Wyatt, *Energy and Entropy in Chemistry*, Macmillan, 1967.

The ionic model

CW, 2; **D**, 3; **ES**, 3; **H**, 3; **HJ**, 4; **J**, 2; **MM**, 4; **DW**, 5; **W**, 4, 6.

D. M. Adams, *Inorganic Solids*, Wiley, 1974. Chapters 1–5 are an excellent treatment of crystal structures, showing the relations between apparently different structures. A critique of the ionic model.

N. N. Greenwood, *Ionic Crystals, Lattice Defects and Non-Stoichiometry*, Butterworths, 1968. Chapters 1–3 are a readable, detailed account of ionic structures and bonding.

Oxidation-state diagrams and E^o-values.

D, 5; **ES**, 5; **H**, 7; **HJ**, 8; **J**, 4; **MM**, 7; **PW**, 9.

E. A. V. Ebsworth, *Educ. Chem.*, **1**, 123 (1964). Short article on construction and use of oxidation-state diagrams from E^0-values.

W. M. Latimer, *Oxidation Potentials*, Prentice-Hall, 1952. Comprehensive survey of data available up to 1952.

A. G. Sharpe, *'Principles of Oxidation and Reduction'*, *Royal Institute of Chemistry Monographs for Teachers, No. 2*, The Chemical Society, 2nd edn., 1973. An excellent, simply written monograph.

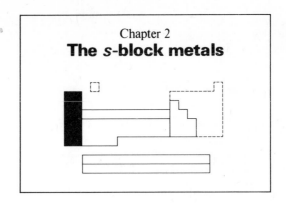

Chapter 2
The *s*-block metals

The chemistry of the *s*-block metals is the simplest of any group of elements in the Periodic Table, because each element displays only one oxidation state: +1 for the alkali metals (lithium to caesium), and +2 for beryllium, magnesium and the alkaline earth metals.† A great deal of their chemistry is explicable in terms of simple ionic bonding and the number of covalent compounds is small, lithium, magnesium and, particularly, beryllium providing the most examples. These metals are also of great economic importance, especially sodium and magnesium, but also potassium and calcium, since they are relatively abundant and, more importantly, occur in concentrated deposits. Magnesium is now an important structural metal and the other metals are used mainly as their salts, which have convenient solubilities, while the cations are chemically inert and do not interfere in the reactions of the anions. The metals sodium, potassium, magnesium and calcium are also of considerable biochemical importance.

2.1 Occurrence, isolation, and uses

The abundances, major ores, and principal compounds of the *s*-block metals are shown in Table 2.1.

By far the most important metal, economically, of this block is sodium. Practically all chemical processes, and therefore the large majority of all consumable goods, depend on sodium salts at some stage of their manufacture. The sodium salts themselves are all derived from the carbonate or hydroxide which in turn are obtained from common salt, large deposits of which occur all over the world. Sodium carbonate is manufactured on a vast scale, chiefly by the Solvay (ammonia-soda) process, in which salt solution is treated with ammonia and carbon dioxide to precipitate sodium bicarbonate (the major sodium salt with a conveniently low solubility–this solubility is appreciably less in the presence of ammonium chloride). The carbon dioxide required is partly obtained by heating the bicarbonate (giving the final product, sodium carbonate) and partly by heating limestone. The resulting calcium oxide is used, after slaking, to recover the ammonia. The essential reactions are:

$$2NaCl + 2CO_2 + 2NH_3 + 2H_2O \rightarrow 2NaHCO_3 + 2NH_4Cl$$

$$2NaHCO_3 \rightarrow Na_2CO_3 + CO_2 + H_2O$$
$$CaCO_3 \rightarrow CaO + CO_2$$
$$CaO + H_2O \rightarrow Ca(OH)_2$$
$$2NH_4Cl + Ca(OH)_2 \rightarrow 2NH_3 + CaCl_2 + 2H_2O$$

---

† Historically, beryllium and magnesium were not classed as alkaline earth metals, a convention which is maintained here.

Table 2.1

Element	Abundance (%)†	Principal Ore	Location	Major Commercial Product
Li	0·006 (0·001)	Spodumene, $LiAlSi_2O_6$	Americas, USSR, Spain, Africa	Li_2CO_3 $LiOH.H_2O$ Li
Na	2·83 (1·06)	Rock salt, NaCl Trona, Na_2CO_3	Widely distrib. Wyoming, USA	Na_2CO_3 NaOH
K	2·40 (0·04)	Sylvinite, (Na, K)Cl Carnallite, $KCl.MgCl_2.6H_2O$	Canada USSR Germany	KCl, K_2SO_4 KNO_3, K_2CO_3 KOH
Rb	0·012 (0·00001)	Lepidolite, $KLi_2Al_2Si_3O_{10}(OH, F)$	Rhodesia	Rb
Cs	0·001 (0·0002)	Pollucite, $Cs_2Al_2Si_4O_{12}$	Sweden, Americas, Africa	Cs
Be	>0·001	Beryl, $Be_3Al_2Si_6O_{18}$	Africa. S. America	$Be(OH)_2$ Be
Mg	1·93 (0·127)	Sea-water Dolomite, $MgCa(CO_3)_2$	USA, USSR Norway	Mg MgO $MgCO_3$
Ca	3·39	Limestone, $CaCO_3$ Dolomite, $MgCa(CO_3)_2$ Gypsum, $CaSO_4$	Widely distrib. Widely distrib. Widely distrib.	$CaCO_3$ $CaCl_2$ $CaSO_4$
Sr	0·02	Celestite, $SrSO_4$ Strontianite, $SrCO_3$	UK	$Sr(NO_3)_2$
Ba	0·04	Barytes, $BaSO_4$ Witherite, $BaCO_3$	Americas Africa	$BaSO_4$ $BaCO_3$ BaO

† Figures in brackets are abundances in sea-water.

Thus, everything is recycled except the starting materials, sodium chloride and calcium carbonate, and the products, sodium carbonate and calcium chloride. The last of these is one of the major sources of calcium compounds.

Sodium hydroxide is now produced almost entirely as a by-product in the manufacture of chlorine by electrolysis of salt solution. The demand for chlorine has risen so dramatically that the supply of caustic soda is often more than can be consumed, so that the lime-soda process (the double decomposition of slaked lime and sodium carbonate) is hardly ever used. Two types of electrolytic cell are employed. In one a steel cathode and a graphite anode are separated by an asbestos diaphragm, and sodium hydroxide accumulates in the cathode compartment; the resulting solution (containing about 10 per cent caustic soda, plus salt) is concentrated by evaporation. Alternatively, mercury is used as the cathode and is pumped away before the sodium which dissolves in it reacts with the aqueous electrolyte. The sodium amalgam is hydrolysed in a separate cell giving clean, concentrated solutions (ca. 50%), and the mercury is returned to the electrolysis cell. (Incidentally, the small losses incurred during this recycling process are one of the major causes of mercury-contamination of the environment, mercury and mercuric chloride being discharged with the waste.) Potassium hydroxide is manufactured similarly.

The major calcium compounds used are the chloride, the carbonate and the sulphate. The last of these occurs naturally as gypsum. Calcium chloride is a by-product from the Solvay process and the pure carbonate ('precipitated chalk') is obtained from this by treatment with sodium carbonate. The main uses of these compounds are for cements, as fillers in plastics, rubbers, and ceramics, and in refrigerator brines.

Magnesium is unique in that its major 'ore' is sea-water. Although there is almost ten times less magnesium than sodium in sea-water, the insolubility of magnesium hydroxide makes recovery fairly simple. The brine is treated with calcium hydroxide and the precipitated magnesium hydroxide is filtered off.

2.2   The elemental metals

The lighter metals of the s-block are best obtained by the electrolysis of chloride melts, although for beryllium this method is used only for small-scale production of very pure metal. The other metals are prepared by reaction of a halide or oxide with a reactive metal (see Table 2.2), usually under very low pressure so that the desired metal distils out from the mixture.

With the exception of magnesium, the metals are produced in relatively small quantities and are used primarily for their reactivity. Magnesium has proved to be an extremely useful structural metal, having a high strength:weight ratio, especially when alloyed with aluminium (10%) and zinc ($\frac{1}{2}$%), and being easy to form and work. It is rapidly becoming competitive with aluminium. In principle, beryllium would be even better, but has proved costly to isolate and difficult to process. It has found limited application in the nuclear industry (it has a low neutron-capture cross-section) and for special alloys in guidance systems. Magnesium hydroxide is converted to the chloride by treatment with hydrochloric acid. Electrolysis of the fused chloride with graphite electrodes gives the pure metal together with chlorine which is reconverted to hydrochloric acid.

Table 2.2

Metal	Method of Preparation	Uses
Li	Electrol, $LiCl/KCl$, 460 °C	Alloying with Al, Mg, Solders
Na	Electrol, $NaCl/CaCl_2$, 580 °C	Prep. of Et_4Pb, catalysts, coolant in nuclear reactors
K	$KCl + Na$	Prep. of KO_2, NaK
Rb	$RbCl + Ca$	Photocells, 'getter' in valves
	$CsCl + Ca$	'Getter' in valves, photoelectrodes, magnetohydrodynamic fluid
Be	$BeF_2 + Mg$, 900 °C Electrol, $BeCl_2/LiCl/KCl$	Nuclear industry, special alloys
Mg	Electrol, $MgCl_2/CaCl_2/NaCl$, 720 °C	Castings, automobiles
Ca	Electrol, $CaCl_2$, 800 °C $CaO + Al$, 1200 °C	Steel-additive
Ba	$BaO + Al(Si)$, 1200 °C	'Getter' in valves

All the metals are highly reactive, the reactivity increasing with increasing atomic number. Thus, lithium and sodium can be safely handled in air, although the latter tarnishes very rapidly. Lithium reacts slowly with water, sodium reacts considerably more rapidly, and the other metals react so exothermically that a hydrogen-fire and even an

$$2M + 2H_2O \rightarrow 2MOH + H_2$$

explosion may result. The alkaline earth metals are less reactive, being roughly comparable to sodium. Beryllium and magnesium are stable in air even at moderate temperatures, owing to the formation of a very adherent thin film of oxide which protects the underlying metal from attack. This film can be thickened and toughened by anodic oxidation of the metals (cf. aluminium). Magnesium and beryllium are, of course, attacked readily by acids which dissolve the oxide film.

A very interesting property of these metals is their solubility in liquid ammonia, to give intensely blue solutions from which the metals can be recovered, sometimes in the form of 'ammoniates', e.g. $Li(NH_3)_4$, $Ca(NH_3)_6$. Most of the metals dissolve readily but beryllium and magnesium require the presence of a strong base (e.g. KNH_2) or electrolysis. All the solutions are very similar, the properties seem to be independent of the particular metal used; thus, the absorption spectra show the same absorption bands, the solutions have very high electrical conductivity, associated mainly with the negative charge carriers, and very dilute solutions are paramagnetic. These properties have been explained in terms of ionisation of the metals, giving a normal metal cation, M^+ or M^{2+}, and electrons which are somehow stabilised by the solvent. The curious properties of these solutions are due to these so-called 'solvated' electrons. The solutions are used as reducing agents. In the presence of a catalyst (e.g. a transition metal salt) the blue colour is discharged, hydrogen is liberated, and the metal amide is formed:

$$Na(s) + NH_3 \rightarrow Na(NH_3)_x^+ + e(NH_3)_y^-$$

$$e(NH_3)_y^- \rightarrow H_2(g) + NH_2^-$$

2.3   Halides

Each metal forms all four halides, MX or MX_2. They are all colourless, crystalline solids, although BeF_2 is sometimes obtained as a glass. Since its structure is closely related to that of one form of silica, cristobalite, this is perhaps not surprising. The alkali halides are stable to air but those of the Group II metals all take up moisture (calcium chloride is a familiar desiccant) and form hydrates; with the beryllium compounds some hydrolysis to oxyhalides occurs.

With three exceptions (Table 2.3), the alkali metal halides have the NaCl-structure, i.e. the cations and anions form two interpenetrating fcc lattices, each ion being surrounded octahedrally by six of opposite charge. On a strict radius-ratio basis, the lithium ion appears too small to favour this arrangement, as it will not be in contact with all six anions. Presumably the extra electrostatic energy gained by having the lithium ion off-centre and close to three halide ions is greater than that gained by changing to a 4:4-structure. The chloride, bromide and iodide of caesium have the CsCl structure, i.e. a bcc arrangement with the metal ions surrounded by a cube of anions and vice versa. Again, a radius-ratio treatment would suggest a wider occurrence for the CsCl structure (for $r_+ : r_-$ 0·73). However, the Madelung constants for the NaCl and CsCl structures differ by less than one per cent (1·74756 and 1·76267), which is insufficient to offset the increase in interionic distance unless n (the exponent of distance in the Born repulsion term) is also large. As discussed in Section 1.4.4 (pp. 18–21) a covalent contribution to the bonding can also account for these apparent discrepancies e.g. the lithium ion is actually larger than the ionic radii suggest.

Table 2.3   Structures and radius-ratios for *s*-block halides, MX

M/X	F	Cl	Br	I
Li	NaCl	NaCl	NaCl	NaCl
	0·44	0·33	0·31	0·28
Na	NaCl	NaCl	NaCl	NaCl
	0·70	0·52	0·49	0·44
K	NaCl	NaCl	NaCl	NaCl
	0·98	0·73	0·68	0·62
Rb	NaCl	NaCl	NaCl	NaCl
	1·09(0·92)	0·82	0·76	0·69
Cs	NaCl	CsCl	CsCl	CsCl
	1·24(0·81)	0·93	0·87	0·76
Be	SiO_2	chain	chain?	chain?
	0·21	0·16	0·15	0·13
Mg	TiO_2	$CdCl_2$	CdI_2	CdI_2
	0·48	0·36	0·33	0·30
Ca	CaF_2	TiO_2d	TiO_2d	CdI_2
	0·76	0·55	0·51	0·46
Sr	CaF_2	CaF_2	$SrBr_2$	
	0·87	0·65	0·61	
Ba	CaF_2	$PbCl_2$	$PbCl_2$	$PbCl_2$
	1·03(0·97)	0·78	0·73	0·66

Radius-ratios are based on Pauling radii, figures in parentheses are the ratios $r_- : r_+$
d indicates a distorted version of the structure.

The Group II metal halides show more varied structures. The beryllium halides appear to be polymeric, covalent 'giant molecules', with the metal atoms bonded tetrahedrally to four halogen atoms each of which bridges between two metal atoms. Such behaviour is expected from a small, doubly charged, and therefore highly polarising, metal ion. Many of the other halides have metal ions in the octahedral holes of fcc or hcp anion lattices, but as the radius ratio increases (above 0·6) more complex structures occur with the metal ions surrounded by eight or nine halide ions. As the cation becomes larger, it is necessary to maximise electrostatic attraction by increasing the coordination number, to offset the effects of greater internuclear distance.

The energetics of these halides are also amenable to an ionic treatment (Fig. 2.1). As shown in Figure 2.2, for each metal the enthalpy of formation becomes more negative from iodide to

Fig. 2.1   Born–Haber cycles for formation of MX and MX_2 from the elements

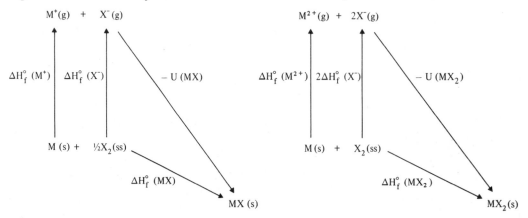

Fig. 2.2 Enthalpies of formation and lattice energies of *s*-block metal halides. (Note the difference in scale between the two plots)

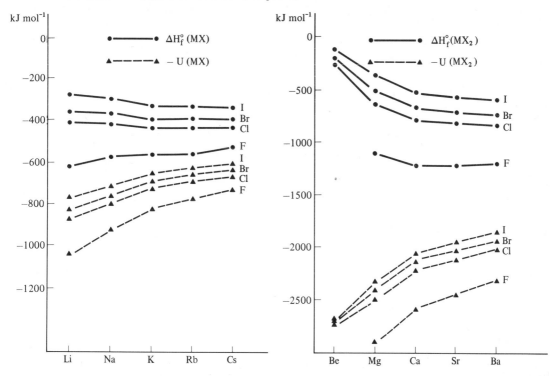

fluoride. Since the enthalpies of formation of the halide ions are very similar (-195 kJ mol^{-1} for I$^-$ to -260 kJ mol^{-1} for F$^-$), these trends represent mainly the increase in lattice energy as the anion becomes smaller. For any particular halogen, the enthalpies of formation normally become more negative as a Group is descended, reflecting the greater ease of formation of the cation (see Table 2.4). However, this effect is offset by the decrease in lattice energy as the metal ion becomes larger. The lattice energy is roughly proportional to $1/(r_+ + r_-)$ and will thus change most rapidly when the

Table 2.4 Some properties of the *s*-block metals

Metal	M.P.	ΔH^0_{sub}	$\Delta H^0_f(M^+)$	$\Delta H^0_f(M^{2+})$	$\Delta H^0_f(M^{3+})$	$r_{M^{n+}}$†
	°C			kJ mol^{-1}		pm
Li	181	161	681	7978	19788	60
Na	98	108	604	5165	12078	95
K	64	90	509	3568	7968	133
Rb	39	82	485	3135	7035	148
Cs	29	78	454	2874	–	169
Be	1283	326	1225	2983	18833	31
Mg	650	149	887	2337	10068	65
Ca	845	177	767	1913	6855	99
Sr	767	164	713	1777	–	113
Ba	707	178	680	1645	–	135

† Pauling radius of M$^+$ or M^{2+}

anion radius is small (Fig. 2.2). The lattice energy therefore decreases most rapidly for the fluorides, and this results in a reversal of the ΔH_f^0 trend.

The solubility of the halides also roughly parallels the lattice energies. All are soluble in water with the exception of the fluorides MF_2 (M = Mg, Ca, Sr, Ba). The beryllium halides all have high solubilities, presumably because the small cation is highly hydrated (see below).

2.4   Oxides

A variety of oxides is formed by the s-block metals the formulae of which, at first sight, suggest that a range of oxidation states is possible for the metals (Table 2.5). Thus, the heavier alkali metals give three oxides, M_2O, M_2O_2, and MO_2, while the alkaline earths form MO which, on heating under a pressure of oxygen, give MO_2. The properties and structures of these compounds show, however, that the oxidation state which varies is that of oxygen, and the compounds contain the oxide, O^{2-}, peroxide, O_2^{2-}, or superoxide, O_2^-, ions.

Table 2.5   Oxides of the s-block metals

Li₂O		
Na₂O	**Na₂O₂**†	
K₂O	K₂O₂	**KO₂**
Rb₂O	Rb₂O₂	**RbO₂**
Cs₂O	Cs₂O₂	**CsO₂**
BeO		
MgO		
CaO		
SrO	SrO₂	
BaO	BaO₂	

Formulae in bold type represent the product obtained on heating the metal in air.
† Usually contains about 10 per cent NaO_2

The alkali metal oxides M_2O react with water or carbon dioxide to give the hydroxide or carbonate and are very soluble in water, giving strongly alkaline solutions. All except Cs_2O have the anti-CaF_2-structure (i.e. the cations are four-coordinate and the oxide ions eight-coordinate); caesium oxide has the anti-$CdCl_2$-structure. The alkaline earth oxides MO are not soluble in water but react exothermically to give the sparingly soluble hydroxides. Beryllium oxide dissolves only in the presence of other beryllium salts to give solutions which probably contain condensed polymeric cations (see below). Beryllium oxide has the wurtzite-structure, while the other monoxides have the NaCl-structure.

The peroxides and superoxides react with water or dilute acids to give hydrogen peroxide and oxygen, e.g.

$$Na_2O_2 + 2H_2O \rightarrow 2NaOH + H_2O_2$$

$$KO_2 + 2H^+ \rightarrow H_2O_2 + O_2 + 2K^+$$

The superoxides are paramagnetic, showing the presence of one unpaired electron per O_2^- anion. A neutral O_2 molecule has two unpaired electrons (in $2p_\pi$-antibonding orbitals), one of which pairs with the electron added to form the anion. In the peroxides, a second (antibonding) electron has been added, and the anion is now diamagnetic. Crystal structure determinations have been made for the superoxides and for BaO_2, which have the calcium carbide (KO_2, RbO_2, CsO_2, BaO_2) or pyrites (NaO_2) structures. These structures are closely related to the NaCl-structure, with O_2^- or O_2^{2-} ions occupying the anion sites. The X-ray data show that as electrons are added to the antibonding orbitals of the O_2 molecule, the O-O bond length increases:

O_2, 121 pm; NaO_2, 133 pm; KO_2, 128 pm; BaO_2 149 pm.

The peroxides and superoxides become more stable down each Group, as is clearly shown by the products of direct oxidation of the alkali metals (Table 2.5). This does not necessarily mean that the enthalpies of formation become more negative, but indicates that the decomposition reactions become less favourable (Fig. 2.3). Consider the energy cycle shown in Fig. 2.4 for the decomposition of the peroxides MO_2. The enthalpy of the reaction

$$MO_2(s) = MO(s) + \tfrac{1}{2}O_2(g)$$

is given by

$$\Delta H^0 = U(MO_2) - U(MO) + D$$

Fig. 2.3   Enthalpies of formation and decomposition of s-block metal oxides

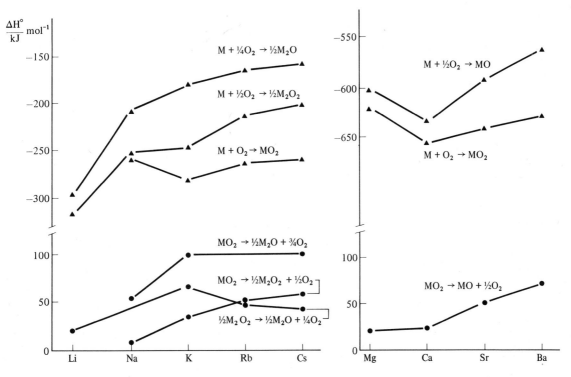

As Figure 2.3 shows, ΔH^0 is positive for each metal, and increases from magnesium to barium. The term D does not depend on the identity of the metal, so that changes in ΔH^0 are due entirely to the differences in lattice energies, $U(MO_2) - U(MO)$. Since the peroxide ion is larger than the oxide ion, this quantity must be negative. It will, however, become less negative as the cation becomes larger, because the lattice energies of the peroxides will decrease more slowly than those of the oxides.

Fig. 2.4   Energy cycle for decomposition of alkaline-earth peroxides

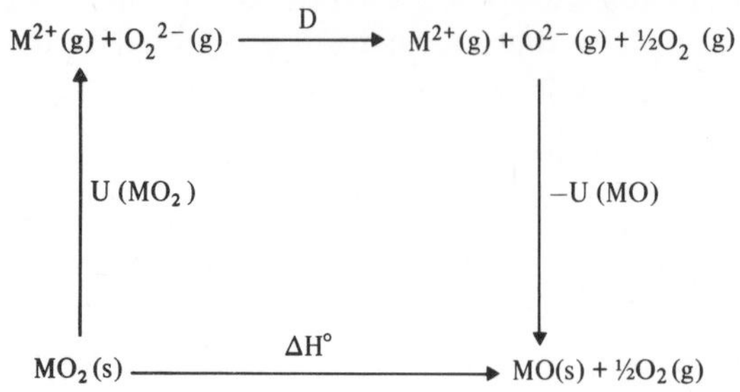

$$M^{2+}(g) + O_2^{2-}(g) \xrightarrow{\ D\ } M^{2+}(g) + O^{2-}(g) + \tfrac{1}{2}O_2\ (g)$$

$U\,(MO_2)$ $-U\,(MO)$

$$MO_2\,(s) \xrightarrow{\ \Delta H^\circ\ } MO(s) + \tfrac{1}{2}O_2\,(g)$$

The positive ΔH°-values for these reactions do not guarantee the (thermodynamic) stability of the peroxides, since there is also a positive entropy term. The major contribution to the entropy change is due to the formation of gaseous oxygen, so that ΔS^0 will be roughly independent of the metal. As the temperature is raised, the free energy of the decomposition reaction, ΔG^0, will eventually become negative ($\Delta G^0 = \Delta H^0 - T\Delta S^0$), and the reaction will proceed, but higher temperatures will be needed for the larger cations. For example, the pressure of oxygen in equilibrium with solid SrO_2 reaches one atmosphere at 357° C, but 840° C is required for BaO_2.

This treatment shows that a large anion is best stabilised by a large cation. A precisely similar argument can be applied to the alkali metal peroxides and superoxides, and also to many other salts of large anions. Thus, the decomposition of carbonates, nitrates, hydroxides, sulphates, sulphites, tri-iodides, etc. all require increasing temperatures with increasing atomic number of the metal.

2.5   Aqueous solution chemistry

All the metals give simple aquated cations, $M^{n+}(aq)$, although for beryllium this form is found only in strongly acid solution. In weakly acidic solutions, the four-coordinate cation dissociates with loss of a proton, and a complex series of equilibria is set up involving a range of polymeric species. The beryllium ion is presumably four-coordinate

$$Be(OH_2)_4^{2+} \rightarrow Be(OH_2)_3(OH)^+ + H^+$$

$$Be(OH_2)_4^{2+} + Be(OH_2)_3(OH)^+ \rightarrow (H_2O)_3Be\!-\!O\!-\!Be(OH_2)_3^{2+} + H^+$$

and adjacent beryllium ions are linked by hydroxide or oxide ions, Be—OH—Be or Be—O—Be, as in the $Be_3(OH)_3^{3+}$-species shown, in which the terminal groups may be coordinated water

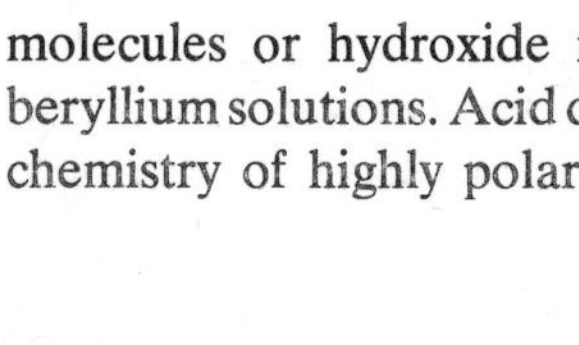

molecules or hydroxide ions. Similar species are formed when beryllium oxide dissolves in beryllium solutions. Acid dissociation and condensation of this type is a characteristic feature of the chemistry of highly polarising cations. The O—H bond of the coordinated water molecule or hydroxide ion is weakened by polarisation of the oxygen electrons towards the cation, facilitating loss of a proton:

$$Be \leftarrow O\begin{smallmatrix}H\\\\H\end{smallmatrix} + H_2O \rightarrow Be-O^- \begin{smallmatrix}\\\\H\end{smallmatrix} + H_3O^+$$

$$Be \leftarrow O\begin{smallmatrix}H\\\\H\end{smallmatrix} + ^-O-Be \rightarrow Be-O-Be + H_3O^+$$

If the pH is raised further, $Be(OH)_2$ is precipitated (i.e. condensation has proceeded so far that macroscopic particles are formed). The precipitate redissolves in concentrated alkali giving the beryllate anion, $Be(OH)_4^{2-}$. Beryllium is thus unique in this group of elements in having an amphoteric oxide, behaviour which results from the high charge density on the Be^{2+} cation.

The other metals of the s-block all appear to give simple aquated cations, although the actual numbers of water molecules directly coordinated to the metal ions are not well established. Lithium, sodium and potassium are probably four-coordinate, magnesium and (presumably) calcium are six-coordinate. However, the influence of the cation undoubtedly extends well beyond the first coordination sphere, and large numbers of water molecules are associated with each cation. The smallest, most highly charged cations will be most effective in attracting solvent molecules, as is clearly shown by the data of Table 2.6. The hydration of the gaseous cations is a highly exothermic process, especially for M^{2+}, and the entropy of this process is large and negative, indicating that a considerable degree of structuring of the solvent is occurring. In each series the

Table 2.6 Some properties of aquated ions

	$\Delta H^0_{hydr}(M^{n+})$†	$\Delta S^0_{hydr}(M^{n+})$†	apparent vol M^{n+}‡	effective radius M^{n+}_{aq}§	$E^0(M^{n+}/M)$
	kJ mol^{-1}	J K^{-1} mol^{-1}	10^6 pm^3	pm	V
Li	−519	−119	−5·7	230	−3·04
Na	−406	−88	−6·6	179	−2·71
K	−322	−51	+10·3	122	−2·92
Rb	−293	−44	+18·7	117	−2·92
Cs	−264	−37	+30·9	117	−2·92
Be	−2494	—	—	—	−1·85
Mg	−1921	−267	−44·0	344	−2·37
Ca	−1577	−210	−36·3	305	−2·87
Sr	−1443	−204	−37·8	304	−2·89
Ba	−1305	−158	−28·8	283	−2·90

† For the process $M^{n+}(g) \rightarrow M^{n+}(aq)$, relative to $\Delta H^0_{hydr}(H^+) = -1091$ kJ mol^{-1} and $\Delta S^0_{hydr}(H^+) = -109$ J K^{-1} mol^{-1}.

‡ The apparent volume of a salt is the change in volume produced by its dissolution. These volumes can be apportioned between the cation and anion.

§ Deduced from ionic mobilities.

smallest ion has the largest effect, as is also shown by the volume reduction on dissolution (the 'apparent volume' of the ion). The electric mobilities of the ions suggest that the lighter ions have larger effective radii, their large sheath of water molecules impeding their progress through the solution.

These effects also operate on the redox potentials. The values quoted in Table 2.6 show that all the metals are strong reducing agents. Normal chemical considerations would suggest that the heavier metals should be the most reducing, and that caesium should be more effective than barium. These expectations are only partly confirmed by the data. The last three members of each Group all have very similar redox potentials, while the most negative value is shown by lithium. These apparent anomalies arise because the redox measurements are made in aqueous solution, so that hydration energies play an important role. The relevant energy cycle is shown in Fig. 2.5.

Fig. 2.5   The relation between gaseous and aquated cations

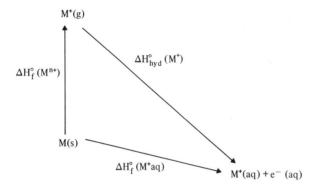

Although more energy is required to produce $Li^+(g)$ than $Na^+(g)$ (681 *vs* 604 kJ mol^{-1}) this is more than offset by the more negative enthalpy of hydration of Li^+ (-519 *vs* -406 kJ mol^{-1}), so that the enthalpy of the process

$$M(s) \rightarrow M^+(aq) + e^-$$

is $+162$ kJ mol^{-1} for lithium but $+198$ kJ mol^{-1} for sodium.† A similar effect might be expected for beryllium, but in this case the enthalpy of formation of $Be^{2+}(g)$ is so high (2983 kJ mol^{-1}) that it is not offset sufficiently by the hydration enthalpy (-2494 kJ mol^{-1}) to make beryllium a stronger reductant than magnesium. The similarity of the remaining metals is due to an almost exact balancing between the enthalpies of ion-formation and of ion-hydration.

2.6. Conclusion

2.6.1   Oxidation states

The most obvious generalisation from the chemistry of the s-block metals is the constancy of oxidation state, the characteristic oxidation number being equal to the Group number.

---

† To compare these figures with the redox potentials, the enthalpy of the reaction $\frac{1}{2}H_2(g) \rightarrow H^+(aq) + e^-$ (438 kJ mol^{-1}) must be subtracted, and appropriate entropy corrections made ($T\Delta S = -15$ kJ mol^{-1} for lithium and -22 kJ mol^{-1} for sodium at 298 K).

In the case of the alkali metals, the removal of a second electron is clearly a very unfavourable process. Although the lattice energies and hydration energies are much more favourable for M^{2+} ions, they cannot compensate sufficiently. The most likely candidate for the formation of a +2 state is caesium, which has the lowest second ionisation energy. By making some assumptions about lattice and hydration energies, it is possible to estimate the enthalpy of formation or redox potential for some hypothetical caesium(II) systems (Table 2.7). The 'best' simple compound of caesium(II) would be the fluoride, as this would have the largest lattice energy. The radius of Cs^{2+} would presumably be slightly larger than that of Ba^{2+}, but the lattice energy of BaF_2 could be used as an optimistic estimate of that of CsF_2. It then appears that this compound might just be exothermic (there is also a negative $T\Delta S^0$ term which will make ΔG^0 greater than ΔH^0). It would however, be very unstable to dissociation with loss of fluorine; the enthalpy of the reaction

$$CsF_2(s) \rightarrow CsF(s) + \tfrac{1}{2}F_2(g)$$

would be -612 kJ mol^{-1}. A similar computation of $E^0(Cs^{2+}/Cs)$, using the hydration enthalpy of Ba^{2+}, shows that the Cs^{2+} ion would be strongly oxidizing in aqueous solution (cf. $E^0(F_2/F^-)$, $+2\cdot9$ V). It is just possible that unstable caesium(II) compounds might be prepared, but this oxidation state seems very unlikely for the other metals of this Group.

Table 2.7 Thermochemical calculations for hypothetical caesium(II) systems: (*a*) $\Delta H_f^0(CsF_2)$, (*b*) $E^0(Cs^{2+}/Cs)$.

		ΔH^0/kJ mol^{-1}
	$Cs(s) \rightarrow Cs^{2+}(g) + 2e^-$	$+2874$
	$F_2(g) + 2e^- \rightarrow 2F^-(g)$	-520
(*a*)	$Cs^{2+}(g) + 2F^-(g) \rightarrow CsF_2(s)$	-2348
	$Cs(s) + F_2(g) \rightarrow CsF_2(s)$	$+6$
	$Cs(s) \rightarrow Cs^{2+}(g) + 2e^-$	$+2874$
	$Cs^{2+}(g) + \infty H_2O \rightarrow Cs^{2+}(aq)$	-1305
(*b*)	$Cs(s) \rightarrow Cs^{2+}(aq) + 2e^-$	$+1569$
	$2H^+(aq) + 2e^- \rightarrow H_2(g)$	-876
	$Cs(s) + 2H^+(aq) \rightarrow Cs^{2+}(aq) + H_2(g)$	$+693$

$$\frac{E^0(Cs^{2+}/Cs)}{V} \gtrsim +\frac{693}{2 \times 96\cdot5}$$

$$= +3\cdot6$$

Similar considerations would explain the inability of the Group II metals to achieve oxidation states higher than +2, but why are they never univalent? With the (slightly pessimistic) assumption that Mg^+ would be similar to Na^+ and Ba^+ to Cs^+, the enthalpies of formation of the hypothetical fluorides and iodides can be calculated (Table 2.8). These compounds are not endothermic, even allowing for the entropy terms, so that they would be stable with respect to dissociation into their constituent elements. In every case, however, the compounds are unstable to disproportionation:

$$MX(s) \rightarrow \tfrac{1}{2}MX_2(s) + \tfrac{1}{2}M(s)$$

The enthalpies of these reactions $\Delta H_{disp}^0(MX)$, are shown in Table 2.8; these are sufficiently negative to ensure that these compounds are unlikely to be obtained except perhaps as transient

Table 2.8   Estimated thermochemical data for hypothetical magnesium(I) and barium(I) systems

M	$\Delta H_f^0(MF)$	$\Delta H_f^0(MI)$	$\Delta H_{disp}^0(MF)$	$\Delta H_{disp}^0(MI)$	$E^0(M^+/M)$
	kJ mol^{-1}				V
Mg	−292	−11	−263	−169	+0·44
Ba	−310	−116	−291	−185	−0·23

species at extremely high temperatures. Similarly the redox potentials $E^0(M^+/M)$ are quite modest but would again lead the aquated ions to disproportionate. There is some evidence that the Mg^+ ion exists as a transient species when magnesium is oxidised electrolytically in pyridine solution.

The stability of the various oxidation states depends on the relative rates of increase with n (the oxidation state) of $\Delta H_f^0(M^{n+})$ and of $U(MX_n)$ or $\Delta H_{hyd}^0(M^{n+})$. Kapustinskii's treatment suggests that the lattice energies of MX_2 and MX should lie in the ratio $6:2$ (neglecting the change in cation radius), and this seems to be roughly true for the halides (although the observed ratio is only about $2:1$ for some fluorides). For the alkali metals the energy required to form the cation increases much more sharply than this, showing the 'stability of the closed-shell electron configuration.' For the Group II metals, on the other hand, the enthalpy of formation of M^{2+} is little more than twice that for M^+, i.e. it rises less steeply than the lattice energy, and it pays to remove both electrons. These trends are illustrated in Fig. 2.6.

2.6.2   Covalency

Most of the chemistry of the *s*-block metals can be explained, as above, in terms of the ionic model of bonding. There are, however, some covalent compounds and, as would be expected, these are most common for the metals which give the most strongly polarising cations. The major examples, therefore, occur with beryllium, for which even the oxide and halides are covalent. For instance, $BeCl_2$ has a low melting point (about 430 °C, cf. $MgCl_2$ 715 °C), and gives a virtually non-conducting melt. For the electrolytic preparation of beryllium metal, other halides have to be added (e.g. LiCl and KCl, or NaCl and $SrCl_2$). The other halides of beryllium are similar, while those of all the other metals in the block appear to be ionic.

The hydrides also display some tendency to covalency. All the metals give stoicheiometric hydrides, MH or MH_2. Beryllium hydride, BeH_2, appears to be a covalent 'giant molecule', with a structure probably similar to that of the chloride, although the bonding is of the electron-deficient, polycentric type. Magnesium hydride has the rutile structure, which may indicate a relatively large contribution from ionic bonding, but its thermal stability is much lower than those of the alkaline earth hydrides. Thus, BeH_2 decomposes at about 125 °C and MgH_2 at about 290 °C, while CaH_2, SrH_2 and BaH_2 are stable to temperatures of several hundred degrees. These last compounds appear to have ionic lattices, with slightly distorted hcp arrays of metal ions. The alkali metal hydrides all seem to be ionic, with the NaCl-structure. All are extremely reactive materials, being oxidised rapidly and even inflaming in air, and reacting vigorously with water. These reactions are essentially those of the hydride ion, and these compounds are sometimes used as reducing agents or as drying agents to remove the last traces of moisture from organic solvents.

The greatest tendency to covalency is shown, not surprisingly in organometallic compounds. Alkyl and aryl derivatives are formed by all the metals, but those of lithium, beryllium, and magnesium (the well-known Grignard reagents) have electron-deficient, polymeric structures. For instance, methyl lithium is tetrameric in the solid state and in solution in benzene. The other alkyls

Fig. 2.6   Proportional enthalpies of formation of gaseous metal ions and proportional lattice energies: $\frac{1}{n}\Delta H_f^0(M^{n+})$ and $\frac{1}{n}U(MCl_n)$

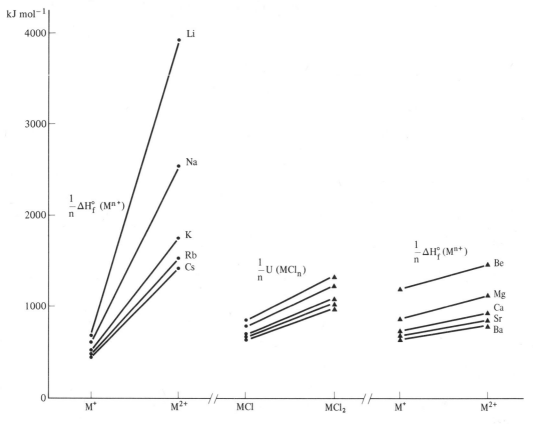

are ionic, but all are extremely reactive and must always be handled in the absence of water and oxygen. Their reactivity makes them useful reagents, particularly in the replacement of halogen atoms by organic groups in the synthesis of organometallic compounds of other elements.

Bibliography

BENT, 7–10; **CW**, 6–7; **D**, 3; **HJ**, 13–14; **J**, 3; **MM**, 9.

Advances in Chemistry Series, No. 19, 'Handling and Uses of Alkali Metals', American Chemical Society, 1957. A review of the manufacture and handling of the metals lithium, sodium, and potassium, and their hydrides and oxides.

E. K. Hyde, *J. Chem. Educ.*, **36**, 15 (1959), and H. J. Eméleus and J. S. Anderson, '*Modern Inorganic Chemistry*', 3rd edn., Routledge and Kegan Paul, 1960, Ch. 17. The chemistry of francium.

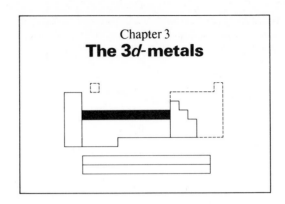

Chapter 3
The 3*d*-metals

The *d*-block is the largest block of the Periodic Table, containing at least 32 elements (elements 104 and 105 have been characterised, and 106 has been claimed recently). It would clearly be impractical to attempt to discuss such a large number of elements in a single chapter. Fortunately, a division can easily be made on chemical grounds, since the 3*d*-metals are sharply differentiated from the 4*d*- and 5*d*-metals, which display close similarities. In this block (and the *f*-block, Chapters 6 and 7), there is greater uniformity of behaviour within the Periods than within the Groups. Many properties (e.g. radii, ionisation energies) vary relatively smoothly along each Period, but within any one Group there is a large increase in radius and decrease in ionisation energy between the first row (3*d*) and the second (4*d*). This results in very different chemistry for the two rows, e.g. in the range of oxidation states exhibited and the nature of the compounds. The second and third rows (4*d* and 5*d*) are much more closely related owing to the effects of the lanthanide contraction. This chapter will therefore be confined to the 3*d* elements and the 4*d*- and 5*d*-metals will be treated together in Chapter 5. One further exclusion is also useful in that the first of the 3*d*-metals, scandium, (along with yttrium and lanthanum) bears a much closer resemblance to the 4*f*-metals and all these metals are more conveniently treated with the latter in Chapter 6.

3.1   Occurrence, extraction and uses

The 3*d*-metals are widely distributed and are among the more common elements. Deposits are chiefly in igneous rocks and the secondary minerals derived from them by weathering (Table 3.1). All occur in oxides or mixed oxides but sulphides become increasingly important for the later metals. This is not to imply that sulphides are the most abundant form, but only that they occur in relatively large, commercially workable deposits, while oxide minerals are often more sparsely distributed. Only copper and manganese occur native, the latter on the Pacific Ocean bed, but the Earth's core is believed to consist principally of elemental iron and nickel.

Titanium is used mainly in the elemental form or as the oxide. The metal has excellent corrosion resistance, especially to chloride ion, in which respect it is superior to stainless steel and aluminium. Its lightness combined with good mechanical strength, especially when alloyed with aluminium, makes it an excellent material for aircraft construction, and its corrosion-resistance makes it valuable in jet-engines, turbine blades and chemical reactors. The oxide, TiO_2, is extremely white, when pure, and chemically inert. It is therefore a valuable pigment, having very good 'covering power' owing to its high refractive index; it is also used extensively as a 'filler' in plastics, rubbers and paper.

Titanium dioxide cannot be reduced to the metal with carbon, because of the formation of a stable carbide, and at the temperatures which would be required the metal is very reactive and

Table 3.1.   Natural occurrence of the 3*d*-metals

	Abundance (%)	Principal Ores	Occurrence
Ti	0·63	Rutile, TiO_2 Ilmenite, $FeTiO_3$	Canada, Australia USA, Scandinavia
V	0·02	Carnotite, $K(UO_2)VO_4, 1·5H_2O$ Oil	USA, S. Africa, Scandinavia Venezuela
Cr	0·01	Chromite, $FeCr_2O_4$	USSR, S. Africa, Philippines, Turkey
Mn	0·085	Pyrolusite, MnO_2	USSR, S. Africa, Brazil, India, China
Fe	5·1	Haematite, Fe_2O_3 Magnetite, Fe_3O_4 Limonite, $Fe_2O_3 . 3H_2O$ Siderite, $FeCO_3$	USSR, USA, France Australia, Canada
Co	0·01	Smaltite, $CoAs_2$ Cobaltite, CoAsS	Germany, Canada Morocco, Norway
Ni	0·016	Pentlandite, $(Ni, Fe)_9S_8$ Various sulphides	Canada, S. Africa USSR
Cu	0·007	Chalcopyrite, $CuFeS_2$	USA, USSR, Zambia, Chile, Canada
Zn	0·01	Zinc blende, ZnS Calamine, $ZnCO_3$	Canada, USSR Australia, USA, Peru

combines readily with hydrogen, nitrogen and oxygen. Since the presence of even traces of any of these elements markedly affects the mechanical properties of the metal, they must be rigorously excluded, and elemental titanium is normally obtained by reducing the tetrachloride with sodium or magnesium in an atmosphere of argon or helium (the Kroll process). This makes the metal rather expensive, although this is somewhat offset by its low density. The tetrachloride is obtained by reaction of the dioxide with carbon and chlorine at 1 000 °C. In the purification of rutile, the chloride (a volatile liquid) is separated from other chlorides (chiefly $FeCl_3$) by distillation and then burnt in oxygen at 1 000 °C; the resulting chlorine is recycled. Ilmenite can be treated more

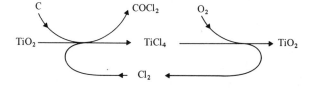

conventionally, being soluble in sulphuric acid (rutile is insoluble). Iron is largely removed by reduction to the ferrous [iron(II)] state, by adding scrap iron, and crystallisation of ferrous sulphate; the resulting solution of 'titanyl sulphate' is hydrolysed by boiling, giving hydrated TiO_2 (Fe_2O_3 would also precipitate at this stage but iron(II) stays in solution). The oxide is filtered off, washed to remove ferrous sulphate, and calcined.

Table 3.2.   Applications of the $3d$-metals and their principal compounds

Ti	Air-frames, jet engines, turbine blades, chemical reactors
TiO_2	Pigments, opacifiers, fillers (paper, etc.)
$TiCl_4$	Ziegler polymerisation catalyst
V	Steel-additive (toughening)
V_2O_5	Oxidation catalyst
Cr	Stainless steel, chromium plate
$Na_2Cr_2O_7$	Oxidant, leather tanning, other chromium compounds
Chromates	Pigments
Mn	Steel-additive (hardness)
MnO_2	Batteries, oxidant
$KMnO_4$	Oxidant
$MnSO_4$	Fertilisers
Fe	Steel
$FeSO_4$	Pharmaceuticals, reductant, other iron compounds
Cyanides	Pigments
Co	Non-ferrous alloys (hardness), magnetic alloys, catalysts
CoO	Enamels (colour, adherence)
Ni	Stainless steels, nickel plate, coinage and special alloys, hydrogenation catalysts
Cu	Conductors, water pipes, brasses and bronzes
$CuSO_4$	Fungicides, electroplating
CuO	Oxidation catalyst
Zn	Galvanising, brass, batteries
ZnO	Pigment, filler (rubber, paints, ceramics), emollients, fluorescents (TV screens)

Vanadium is also difficult to isolate in the pure state, being very reactive when hot. Its principal commercial application is as an additive to steels for grain refinement (by carbide formation) and hardening, and in titanium and aluminium alloys. Vanadium steels are used in cutting-tools, dies and springs. The metal is therefore usually prepared as an alloy with iron, ferrovanadium (35–95% V), obtained by reduction of the crude oxide with ferrosilicon and lime (to remove the silica as slag) or with aluminium and scrap iron. Vanadium is now mostly obtained as a by-product in the processing of carnotite for uranium, and also from the flue dusts of some oil-burning plants. Roasting with sodium carbonate gives water-soluble sodium metavanadate, $NaVO_3$, which is leached out. Uranium is removed from the solution by solvent extraction (e.g. with tributyl phosphate) and the pH is lowered to 2–3 when sodium hexavanadate ($Na_4V_6O_{17}$, 'red cake') crystallises out. This is sintered, giving technical grade, black vanadium pentoxide. The pure, orange pentoxide is obtained by dissolving the 'red cake' in sodium carbonate, precipitating the impurities (mainly iron and silica) by adjusting the pH, and then crystallising and calcining ammonium metavanadate, NH_4VO_3. The pentoxide is used as a catalyst in oxidation reactions, e.g. in the manufacture of sulphuric acid ($SO_2 \rightarrow SO_3$), of acrylonitrile (propene plus ammonia), and of phthalic acid (naphthalene), and in afterburners for car exhausts.

The chief use of elemental **chromium** is as an additive to steels. In small amounts (2–6%) it improves the mechanical properties while larger quantities (10–20%) give corrosion resistance – the 'stainless steels'. For these applications, ferrochromium is usually used, which is conveniently obtained by direct carbon-reduction of the ore chromite, $FeCr_2O_4$, in the blast furnace. The pure metal is made by reduction of the oxide Cr_2O_3 with aluminium or by electrolysis of chrome alum solution. The latter is obtained by dissolving ferrochromium in sulphuric acid and removing iron as ferrous ammonium sulphate – see below (section 3.5) for the chemistry of this separation. Most chromium compounds are prepared from sodium dichromate, which is by far the most important single compound of chromium. It is obtained by roasting chromite with sodium carbonate and leaching the product with water. This solution is concentrated and acidified, either with sulphuric acid or by passing carbon dioxide (which gives sodium bicarbonate as a valuable by-product), when the dichromate crystallises out.

Manganese is also produced in large quantities as the iron-alloy ferromanganese (ca. 80% Mn), which is used in steel making. Nearly all types of steel contain some manganese, which improves the mechanical properties by combining with dissolved oxygen and sulphur which cause brittleness. Large proportions of manganese (ca. 12%) give a very tough, hard steel, used for railway points and crushing- or grinding-machinery. The ferromanganese is obtained by blast-furnace reduction of the naturally occurring dioxide, pyrolusite, and iron oxide. The pure metal is made by aluminium-reduction of Mn_3O_4; the dioxide reacts too vigorously and must first be heated to give the lower oxide. Principal manganese compounds are the dioxide (used in batteries and as an oxidant) and potassium permanganate. The latter is a powerful oxidant used, for example, in the manufacture of saccharin (from o-toluenesulphonamide) and vitamin C (ascorbic acid, from diacetone-sorbose, obtained from glucose). Manganese sulphate and the oxides are also valuable additives to fertilisers, manganese being a vital trace element.

Iron is the most abundant metal in the Earth's crust after aluminium, and also constitutes much of the Earth's core. It is certainly the most widely used metal and is produced in vast quantities (several hundred million tons per year). The major application is, of course, in steel-making. Direct coke-reduction of the ores (all oxides) in the blast furnace gives pig iron which usually contains some carbon, silicon, phosphorus and manganese, and a little sulphur. To obtain steel these impurities are removed by oxidation – oxygen is blown into the molten metal to which some lime has been added to take up the oxidised impurities (especially phosphorus) as slag. Many detailed descriptions of these processes are available. Many other transition metals are added to iron in forming steels to give improved properties, either by removing impurities (manganese) by improving grain structure (vanadium carbide precipitates at the grain boundaries, preventing their movement) or giving corrosion resistance (chromium and nickel). The most readily available iron compound is ferrous [iron(II)] sulphate, which is a by-product of many other processes, particularly nickel extraction. It is one of the cheapest chemicals available and is the source of many other iron compounds, as well as being used in its own right, e.g. in pharmaceuticals.

Alone in the series, **cobalt** is worked chiefly from arsenical ores which usually also contain nickel, copper or lead, the cobalt being recovered as a by-product. Consequently, a variety of methods are used for its recovery, but most involve some form of smelting, e.g. with sodium carbonate followed by silica, to give an oxide, Co_3O_4, which is reduced with aluminium or carbon. Alternatively, the oxide is dissolved in sulphuric acid and reprecipitated as the hydroxide, which is calcined, or the solution is electrolysed. Cobalt finds little application as the elemental metal, but is used in hard, non-ferrous alloys for cutting-machinery, high-temperature alloys and special-purpose steels, and magnetic alloys for loudspeakers, magnetos, etc. Compounds of cobalt are widely used as colouring agents for glass, enamels and ceramics, and as catalysts in a variety of organic reactions.

The commercial ores of **nickel** (sulphides) contain copper and cobalt, in addition to the ubiquitous iron, and sometimes silver and other precious metals. Oxide minerals are more widespread but occur in less workable deposits. Metallic nickel also forms much of the Earth's core. After concentration, nickel ores are roasted with silica to obtain a sulphide melt (matte) from which nickel and copper sulphides crystallise independently and may be separated physically. The nickel sulphide is converted to oxide by roasting and smelted to obtain the crude metal. Refining is usually by electrolysis (of sulphate or chloride solutions) or by treatment with carbon monoxide at 50 °C, which gives the volatile (and highly toxic) carbonyl, $Ni(CO)_4$. This is distilled and pyrolysed at 150–300 °C, giving very pure nickel and carbon monoxide, which is recirculated (Mond process). Elemental nickel is used as a protective and decorative plating on baser metals and also, with chromium, as an additive to iron, giving stainless steels. A variety of other alloys have many applications, e.g. cupronickel (25% Ni, 75% Cu) in coinage, nichrome (60% Ni, 20% Fe, 20% Cr) for electric heating elements, and the nimonic alloys (Ni and Cr with small amounts of Ti and Al or Mo) in jet-turbine engines. The pure metal is also a useful catalyst, e.g. in the hydrogenation of fatty oils (to margarine) and in cracking methane in the presence of steam to generate hydrogen used in the synthesis of ammonia and methanol.

Copper is produced in very large quantities (ca. 6 million tons per annum), coming after iron (ca. 600 million tons p.a.) and aluminium (ca. 9 million tons p.a.). Being an excellent conductor both of heat and of electricity, and also resistant to corrosion, copper is widely used as an electrical conductor, and for water and steam piping. Its softness and ductility make for easy working, but it tends to harden on repeated working. It is miscible with many other metals and is used in several alloys which are tougher and better for working than pure copper, notably the brasses (with zinc) and bronzes (with tin) and the coinage metals (with small quantities of both tin and zinc). The metal is widely but sparsely distributed, occurring occasionally in elemental form but more usually as the sulphide (often with iron, nickel and silver) or as basic chlorides or carbonates. Over half the world production now involves ores containing less than 5 per cent of copper (and many have only $\frac{1}{2}$–1%), which has resulted in drastic price rises in recent years. Sulphide ores are roasted, often with silica to remove iron, and then smelted with coke. Very pure copper is obtained by electrolysis of solutions of copper sulphate which is also produced on a large scale in its own right (from scrap metal and residues), being used in agriculture as a fungicide and to a lesser extent in electroplating, dyeing and as a wood preservative.

Although not of very high abundance, **zinc** is readily available because it occurs in concentrated deposits of sulphide ores, usually with iron, lead and many other metals, from which it is easily recovered. Roasting in air gives the oxide which is smelted with coke and the zinc is obtained as a vapour (the boiling point is 908 °C), which is collected in a stream of molten lead, from which it separates on cooling. Alternatively, the crude oxide is treated with sulphuric acid and the resulting solution electrolysed after the removal of the other metals. Elemental zinc is mainly used for galvanising iron (under corrosive conditions the zinc dissolves first by electrochemical action) and in alloys, e.g. the brasses (with copper) and die-casting metals (with a little aluminium and some copper and magnesium). The principal compound is the oxide, ZnO, which finds application as a pigment, in ceramics and rubbers, and as an emollient ('zinc ointment').

3.2   The elemental metals

These are the familiar metals and several of them are found in everyday use. Iron and steel are widespread, copper water pipes abound, nickel and copper constitute most of our coinage, chromium and nickel plate are common, and galvanised iron is still widely used. Various steels contain vanadium, chromium, manganese or nickel. Many of these materials are used for their corrosion-resistance, which is chemically rather surprising, since all the metals are expected to be very reactive; indeed, when finely divided, many of them are pyrophoric (i.e. spontaneously inflammable in air). On thermodynamic grounds, all the metals are expected to react with oxygen and all except copper with water, and yet with the exception of iron and manganese all are found to

Table 3.3.   Properties of the 3*d*-metals

	M.P.	B.P.	ρ	Properties
	°C	°C	g cm^{-3}	
Ti	1 677	3 277	4·51	Silvery. Ductile, hard, strong, light. Resists corrosion. Insol. mineral acids and alkalis. Sol. HF, organic acids.
V	1 919	3 400	6·1	Grey-silver. Malleable, strong. Fair corrosion resistance. Insol. non-oxidising acids, alkali. Sol. HF, HNO$_3$, conc. H$_2$SO$_4$.
Cr	1 903	2 642	7·14	Silvery. Stable in air. Reactive when pure. Sol. acids. Passivated by oxidants.
Mn	1 244	2 095	7·44	Grey. Very reactive. Reacts with water. Sol. acids.
Fe	1 535	3 000	7.87	Silvery-white. Soft, malleable, ductile. Corroded by moist air. Passivated by oxidants. Sol. acids.
Co	1 493	3 100	8·90	Silvery-white. Harder than Fe, malleable, ductile. Stable to air. Sol. acids.
Ni	1 453	2 732	8·91	Silvery-white. Strong, ductile. Corrosion resistant. Passivated by oxidants. Sol. dil. acids, aq. ammonia.
Cu	1 083	2 595	8.95	Red. Soft, malleable, ductile. Stable to air and water. Insol. non-oxidising acids. Sol. HNO$_3$, aq. KCN.
Zn	420	908	7·14	Silvery-white. Soft. Stable to air and water. Sol. acids and alkalis.

be stable to both air and water (Table 3.4). This apparent anomaly is due to the formation of a closely adherent layer of oxide which protects the underlying metal (cf. magnesium and aluminium). The same phenomenon is presumably responsible for the 'passivation' which occurs when the metals, including iron, are treated with oxidising agents, e.g. concentrated nitric acid or dichromate solution. The metal will then only react if the surface is reduced (e.g. by hydrogen) or treated with reagents which remove the oxide film or interfere with its formation (e.g. titanium is soluble in many organic acids with which it forms complexes in solution). Manganese and iron react

Table 3.4.   Oxidation states produced by reaction of the 3*d*-metals with acid in the absence and presence of air.

	Ti	V	Cr	Mn	Fe	Co	Ni	Cu	Zn
H$^+$	NR(+3)	NR(+3)	+2(+3)	+2	+2	+2	+2	NR	+2
H$^+$/O$_2$	NR(+4)	NR(+5)	+3	+2	+3	+2	+2	NR(+2)	+2

NR—No reaction.
Oxidation states in parentheses are those expected on thermodynamic grounds.

with water, in the presence of air, at ordinary temperatures because the oxide films produced are porous and non-adherent. The addition of chromium to iron allows the formation of a protective layer of chromium oxide, resulting in a 'stainless' steel. The protective action of the zinc coating on galvanised iron, however, is not entirely due to the covering of the surface. Even if pores and cracks allow water to reach the iron, zinc reacts preferentially by an electrochemical action, 'cathodic' protection. The same effect is used in facilitating the dissolution of zinc in an acid by adding a little copper sulphate; copper is deposited on the surface of the zinc, which then dissolves cathodically. This has only become necessary in recent years as the purity of commercial zinc has improved. Occasionally, atmospheric corrosion is of value, as in the formation of the patina of basic carbonate or chloride on the copper roofing used by Victorian architects (in modern cities, the basic sulphate is also formed).

Those metals which are attacked by acids, i.e. all except titanium, vanadium and copper, dissolve to give bipositive cations which, for chromium and iron, are further oxidised by air (Table 3.4). Bivalent chromium is also slowly oxidised by water, liberating hydrogen. Only zinc is soluble in alkali, giving hydrogen and the 'zincate' ion, ZnO_2^{2-}, probably more correctly formulated as $Zn(OH)_4^{2-}$. If species are present which are capable of forming coordination complexes with the metal ion, solubility of the elemental metal may be achieved under otherwise unexpected conditions. Thus, nickel is unaffected by caustic alkalis but is attacked by aqueous ammonia, forming $Ni(NH_3)_6^{2+}$. Similarly, copper is resistant to mineral acids but dissolves in a cyanide solution, liberating hydrogen and giving the $Cu(CN)_3^{2-}$ ion (note the oxidation state: +1). Titanium and vanadium will dissolve in hydrofluoric acid to give anionic fluoro-complexes.

All the metals react readily with oxygen or halogens at moderate temperatures (200–300 °C), the temperature required depending on the degree of subdivision of the metal. Freshly prepared metal powders are often pyrophoric and even aged samples will in many cases react with halogens in organic solvents (e.g. ether or chloroform) at room temperature or on gentle refluxing – a convenient preparative method for the halides.

The pure metals, except titanium and vanadium, can be readily obtained by electrolysis of aqueous solutions of sulphates or chlorides, although for the production of zinc by this method other metals must be assiduously removed from the solution. Small quantities of titanium and vanadium (and the other metals) are best obtained by the van Arkel–de Boer process in which a volatile halide is decomposed on a hot filament in a vacuum.

3.3   Halides and oxyhalides

The 3*d*-metal halides and oxyhalides are very varied materials, ranging from air-stable, sparingly water-soluble, high-melting solids (the later difluorides) to volatile, readily hydrolysed liquids (the tetrachlorides) and explosive gases (MnO_3Cl). The diversity of oxidation state which characterises the *d*-block is well demonstrated, the range +1 (copper) to +7 (manganese) being covered (see Table 3.5,7). High oxidation states (i.e. those greater than +3) are found at the beginning of the series, where the Group oxidation state is found in compounds such as TiX_4 (X = F to I), VF_5, VOX_3 (X = F to Br), VO_2X (X = F, Cl), CrO_2X_2 (X = F, Cl), CrF_6, and MnO_3X (X = F, Cl). Nearly all these compounds are thermally unstable, becoming more so along the series, e.g. CrF_6 decomposes above −100 °C, and MnO_3Cl explodes at room temperature. The highest oxidation states are always found in the fluorides and oxyhalides, and the derivatives of the heavier halogens are the more susceptible to thermal instability. For these high oxidation states the compounds are highly covalent, usually forming simple tetrahedral or octahedral molecules, are easily volatile and

Table 3.5. Halides of the 3d-metals

Ti	V	Cr	Mn	Fe	Co	Ni	Cu	Zn
		(CrF_6)						
	VF_5	CrF_5						
TiF_4	VF_4	CrF_4	MnF_4					
TiF_3	VF_3	CrF_3	MnF_3	FeF_3	CoF_3			
	VF_2	CrF_2	MnF_2	FeF_2	CoF_2	NiF_2	CuF_2	ZnF_2

Ti	V	Cr	Mn	Fe	Co	Ni	Cu	Zn
$TiCl_4$	VCl_4	$(CrCl_4)$						
$TiCl_3$	VCl_3	$CrCl_3$	$(MnCl_3)$	$FeCl_3$				
$TiCl_2$	VCl_2	$CrCl_2$	$MnCl_2$	$FeCl_2$	$CoCl_2$	$NiCl_2$	$CuCl_2$	$ZnCl_2$
							$CuCl$	

Ti	V	Cr	Mn	Fe	Co	Ni	Cu	Zn
$TiBr_4$								
$TiBr_3$	VBr_3	$CrBr_3$		$FeBr_3$				
$TiBr_2$	VBr_2	$CrBr_2$	$MnBr_2$	$FeBr_2$	$CoBr_2$	$NiBr_2$	$CuBr_2$	$ZnBr_2$
							$CuBr$	

Ti	V	Cr	Mn	Fe	Co	Ni	Cu	Zn
TiI_4								
TiI_3	VI_3	CrI_3						
TiI_2	VI_2	CrI_2	MnI_2	FeI_2	CoI_2	NiI_2		ZnI_2
							CuI	

are very susceptible to hydrolysis. Hydrolysis presumably occurs by coordination of water molecules, which are thereby polarised, followed by elimination of hydrogen halide:

The tendency to hydrolysis thus increases with increasing oxidation state.

With the more modest +2 and +3 oxidation states the halides appear more ionic, usually having layer structures based on close-packing of anions, and discrete molecules cannot be discerned. These structures are reflected in increased melting points and decreased volatility.

However, these compounds are by no means involatile, and they can usually be purified by sublimation.

In large measure, all the halides of a given stoicheiometry have similar structures, the major exceptions being the fluorides which, for high oxidation states, usually give more condensed structures than the other halides, in which the metal is always octahedrally coordinated. The structures will now be surveyed type by type. The properties of the halides and oxyhalides are summarised in Tables 3.6 and 3.7.

Monohalides are formed only by copper (CuCl, CuBr, CuI; CuF is not known). They have cubic structures of the zinc blende type, i.e. cubic close-packing of anions with Cu^+ ions occupying half the available tetrahedral holes. All are very insoluble in water and are readily obtained by reduction of Cu^{2+} in the presence of the appropriate halide. Reduction by iodide is spontaneous.

Difluorides are known for all the metals except titanium. The basic crystal structure is of the rutile type in which the metal ions occupy slightly distorted octahedral sites; usually two fluoride ions are a little farther from the metal than the other four (Table 3.8). In CrF_2 and CuF_2 the irregularity is greater. A similar effect is found in the mixed-valence compound Cr_2F_5 (formed by heating CrF_2 with CrF_3 in a sealed tube at 950 °C), in which the Cr^{2+} ions have an irregular, $4+2$ environment, while the Cr^{3+} ions have regular octahedral coordination.

Vanadium and chromium difluorides are readily oxidised by air, but all the other difluorides are stable. All are only sparingly soluble in water.

All the other **dihalides** can be obtained except CuI_2. The addition of iodide ion to a copper(II) solution gives CuI and iodine, which forms the basis of a well-known method of determining copper. Most of the dihalides have the CdI_2-structure and a few have the $CdCl_2$-structure; both are built up from close-packed arrays of anions (fcc for $CdCl_2$ and hcp for CdI_2) with the cations occupying all the octahedral holes in alternate layers (Fig. 3.1). In the chromium dihalides

Fig. 3.1   Structures of di- and tri-halides. The only known examples of the $CdCl_2/CrCl_3$ type are $FeCl_2$, $CoCl_2$, $NiCl_2$, $CrCl_3$, $CrBr_3$ (?) and CrI_3. The hexagonal structure has been found for TiX_2, VX_2 (X = Cl, Br, I), $MnCl_2$, FeI_2 and CoI_2

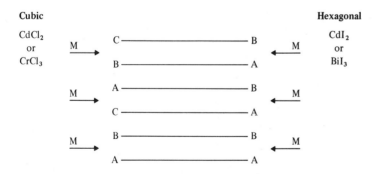

distorted structures are again found; the orthorhombic crystals contain six-coordinate metal ions but two metal-halogen distances are considerably greater than the other four (Table 3.8). Distortion from octahedral geometry is even more marked in the copper dihalides, in which planar chains are formed (Cu-X distances 230 (Cl) and 318 (Br) pm), which are packed together so that each copper ion has two more halide ions completing a distorted octahedron (295 (Cl) and 318 (Br) pm) (Fig. 3.2). All the dihalides are readily soluble in water and may be obtained as hydrates by evaporation of the solution, except for the titanium dihalides, which are violently oxidised by water

Table 3.6.   Properties of 3d-metal halides.

	Colour	M.P. /°C	ΔH_f^0 /kJ mol⁻¹	Structure	C.N.	Preparation	Properties
TiF₄	white		−1699		6?	Ti/F₂/200°/flow	V. hygroscopic. Sublimes.
TiCl₄	col. less	−23	−805	SnBr₄	4	TiO₂/C/Cl₂/500°, Ti/Cl₂/flow	BP 136°. Mobile, volatile liquid. V. readily hydrolysed. Sol. organic solvents.
TiBr₄	amber	39	−618	SnBr₄	4	Ti/Br₂/400°/flow	BP 233°. Readily hydrolysed. Sol. organic solvents.
TiI₄	orange	150	−425	SnBr₄	4	Ti/I₂/150°	BP 377°.
TiF₃	blue		−1436	rhombic	6	Ti/H₂/HF/700°/flow	
TiCl₃	violet	dec	−722	layer	6	TiCl₄/H₂/600°	$\xrightarrow{475°}$ TiCl₂ + TiCl₄. Sol. H₂O.
TiBr₃	grey	dec	−550		6?	TiBr₄/H₂/750°, TiBr₄/Ti/500°	$\xrightarrow{350°}$ TiBr₂ + TiBr₄. Sol. H₂O.
TiI₃	black	dec	−335		6?	Ti/I₂/750°	$\xrightarrow{300°}$ TiI₂ + TiI₄.
TiCl₂	red	dec	−515	CdI₂	6	TiCl₃/475°/vac	$\xrightarrow{600°}$ Ti + TiCl₄. Reacts violently with H₂O giving H₂.
TiBr₂	black	dec	−397	CdI₂	6	TiBr₃/350°/vac	$\xrightarrow{400°}$ Ti + TiBr₄. Reacts violently with H₂O giving H₂.
TiI₂	black	dec	−255	CdI₂	6	TiI₃/350°/vac	$\xrightarrow{450°}$ Ti + TiI₄.
VF₅	col. less	19	−1473	MoOF₄	6	V/F₂/300°	BP 48°. Viscous, associated liquid. Readily hydrolysed.
VF₄	green	dec	−1343		6?	VCl₄/HF(l), V/F₂/200°	$\xrightarrow{150°}$ VF₃ + VF₅. Hydrolyses.
VCl₄	red	−28	−598	SnBr₄	4	V/Cl₂/200°	BP 150° $\xrightarrow{130°}$ VCl₃. Mobile, volatile liquid. Readily hydrolysed. Sol. organic solvents.
VBr₄	purple	dec	−393		4	V/Br₂/325°/s.t.	$\xrightarrow{-23°}$ VBr₃.
VF₃	yellow-green	~1400		hcp	6	(NH₄)₃VF₆/500°	Involatile. Sl. sol. H₂O.
VCl₃	violet		−586	FeCl₃	6	VCl₄/150°	$\xrightarrow{400°}$ VCl₂ + VCl₄. V. hygroscopic. Sol. H₂O.
VBr₃	black		−494	FeCl₃	6	V/Br₂/550°	$\xrightarrow{375°}$ VBr₂ + Br₂. V. hygroscopic. Sol. H₂O.
VI₃	brown		−280		6?	V/I₂/200°	$\xrightarrow{300°}$ VI₂ + I₂. V. hygroscopic. Sol. H₂O.
VF₂	blue				6?	VF₃/H₂/HF/1150°	Oxidises rapidly in air.
VCl₂	green	1350	−460	CdI₂	6	VCl₃/H₂/500°	Hygroscopic. Oxidised by air. Sol. H₂O with oxidation.
VBr₂	red		−348	CdI₂	6	VBr₃/H₂/450°	
VI₂	violet		−264	CdI₂	6	VI₃/400°	

Table 3.6 (Continued)

	Colour	M.P. /°C	ΔH_f° /kJ mol^{-1}	Structure	C.N.	Preparation	Properties
CrF_6	yellow	dec			6?	$Cr/F_2/400°/200$ atm	$\xrightarrow{-100°}$ CrF_5.
CrF_5	red	30			6?	$Cr/F_2/400°/flow$	$\xrightarrow{ht}$ CrF_4. Viscous liquid. Powerful oxidant.
CrF_4	green				6?	$Cr/F_2/400°/flow$	Sublimes at 100°. Hydrolyses readily.
CrF_3	green	1 404	−1 112	rhombic	6	Cr_2O_3/HF	$\xrightarrow{600°}$ $CrF_2 + CrF_5$.
$CrCl_3$	violet		−560	monoclin.	6	$Cr/Cl_2/1\,000°$	Sublimes 850°. Sol. H_2O with difficulty.
$CrBr_3$	black				6?	Cr/Br_2	
CrI_3	black		−204	$CrCl_3$	6	Cr/I_2	$\xrightarrow{200°}$ $CrI_2 + I_2$.
CrF_2	blue	894	−757	TiO_2d	6	$CrF_3/Cr/1\,000°/bomb$	V. hygroscopic. Sol. H_2O.
$CrCl_2$	white	ca 820	−397	orthorh.	6	$CrCl_3/H_2/500°$	Sol. H_2O.
$CrBr_2$	white	842	−302	orthorh.	6	$Cr/HBr/750°/flow$	Sublimes at 700°.
CrI_2	red	868	−159	orthorh.	6	$Cr/I_2/600°/s.t.$	
MnF_4	blue	dec			6	$MnX_2/F_2/250°/flow$	$\xrightarrow{RT}$ $MnF_3 + F_2$. V. hygroscopic.
MnF_3	purple		−996	monoclin.	6		Good fluorinating agent. Hydrolysed very rapidly.
$MnCl_3$	black	dec			6?	$MnO_2/HCl/EtOH/-63°$	$\xrightarrow{-40°}$ $MnCl_2 + Cl_2$.
MnF_2	pink	920	−795	TiO_2	6	$MnCO_3/HF_{aq}$	Sp. sol. H_2O.
$MnCl_2$	pink	652	−481	CdI_2	6	$Mn/Cl_2/EtOH$	V. sol. H_2O. Hygroscopic.
$MnBr_2$	pink	695	−385	hexag.	6	$MnCO_3/HBr_{aq}/100°$	Hygroscopic. Readily sol. H_2O.
MnI_2	pink	613	−243		6?	$Mn/I_2/Et_2O$	Readily sol. H_2O.
FeF_3	white		−1 045		6?	Fe/F_2	
$FeCl_3$	green	303	−399	layer	6	$Fe/Cl_2/300°$	BP 330°. Sublimes readily. Hygroscopic. Sol. H_2O, organic solvents.
$FeBr_3$	brown	dec	−265	$FeCl_3$	6	$Fe/Br_2/200°$	$\xrightarrow{120°}$ $FeBr_2 + Br_2$. Hygroscopic. Readily sol. H_2O.
FeF_2	white		−706	TiO_2	6	$Fe/HF/900°$	Sp. sol. H_2O.
$FeCl_2$	white	676	−342	$CdCl_2$	6	$Fe/HCl/500°,$ $FeCl_3/Fe/THF$	V. hygroscopic. Sol. H_2O. Oxidised slowly in air.
$FeBr_2$	yellow	689	−250	hcp	6	$FeBr_3/200°$	Hygroscopic. Sol. H_2O.

	Colour	m.p./°C	Structure type	ΔH_f	Coord. no.	Preparation	Properties
FeI_2	red	590	CdI_2	−110	6	$Fe/I_2/500°$/s.t.	Hygroscopic. Sol. H_2O.
CoF_3	brown		rhombic	−811	6	$CoF_2/F_2/250°$	V. hygroscopic. Vigorous oxidant.
CoF_2	pink	ca 1 200	TiO_2	−692	6	$CoCl_2/HF/300°$	Mod. sol. H_2O.
$CoCl_2$	blue	730	$CdCl_2$	−313	6	$Co/Cl_2/Et_2O$	V. hygroscopic. Sol. H_2O.
$CoBr_2$	green	678	hcp	−221	6	$Co/Br_2/EtOH$	Sol. H_2O.
CoI_2	black	ca 500	CdI_2	−89	6	$CoCO_3/HI_{aq}$/dehd, 200°	Sublimes ca. 500°. Sol. H_2O.
NiF_2	yellow	1 450	TiO_2	−651	6	$Ni/HF/225°$, $NiCl_2/F_2/350°$	Sl. sol. H_2O.
$NiCl_2$	yellow	1 010	$CdCl_2$	−316	6	$Ni/Cl_2/EtOH$	V. hygroscopic. Readily sol. H_2O.
$NiBr_2$	yellow	965		−226	6?	$Ni/Br_2/Et_2O$, $NiBr_26H_2O/140°$	Sol. H_2O.
NiI_2	brown	780	hexag	−86	6	$Ni^{2+}/I^-/EtOH$	Deliquescent. Readily sol. H_2O.
CuF_2	white	785	TiO_2d	−543	6	$Cu/F_2/400°$	
$CuCl_2$	brown	dec	monoclin.	−206	'4'	$CuCl_2 . 2H_2O/SOCl_2$	$\xrightarrow{300°}$ $CuCl + Cl_2$. Volatile. Hygroscopic. Readily sol. H_2O.
$CuBr_2$	black	dec	monoclin.	−142	'4'	$CuCO_3/HBr_{aq}$	$\xrightarrow{150°}$ $CuBr + Br_2$. V. sol. H_2O.
$CuCl$	white	434	cubic	−135	4	$Cu^{2+}/HCl_{aq}/SO_2$	Insol. H_2O.
$CuBr$	white	490	ZnS blende	−105	4	$Cu^{2+}/HBr_{aq}/SO_2$, $CuBr_2/200°$	Insol. H_2O.
CuI	white	600		−68	4?	$Cu^{2+}_{aq}/I^-/SO_2$	Sublimes. Insol. H_2O.
ZnF_2	white	872	TiO_2	−764	6	$ZnCO_3/HF_{aq}$/dehydr	Sl. sol. H_2O. Mild fluorinating agent.
$ZnCl_2$	white	262		−415	4	$Zn/HCl_{aq}/30°$	Deliquescent. V. sol. H_2O. Melts to viscous, conducting liquid.
$ZnBr_2$	white	394	$CdCl_2$	−328	6	$Zn/HBr/Br_2$/sublime	V. sol. H_2O. Melts to viscous liquid.
ZnI_2	white	446	CdI_2	−209	6	$Zn/I_2/Et_2O$	V. sol. H_2O. Sublimes ca. 400°. Decomp. 625°.

d = distorted, s.t. = sealed tube; dehyd = dehydrate
Structure types are given where known.

Table 3.7. Oxyhalides of the 3d-metals

	Colour	Preparation	Properties
$TiOF_2$	yellow	$TiF_2Cl_2/Cl_2O/4°/$polar solv.	
TiO_2Cl_2	yellow	$TiCl_4/O_3$ or $Cl_2O/130°$	$\xrightarrow{180°} TiO_2 + TiCl_4$. Hygroscopic. Hydrolyses (to TiO_2).
TiO_2Br_2	yellow	$TiBr_4/O_3$ or $Cl_2O/130°$	$\xrightarrow{150°} TiO_2 + TiBr_4$.
TiO_2I_2	orange	$TiI_4/O_3/$cyclohexane	$\xrightarrow{125°} TiO_2 + TiI_4$.
$TiOF$	black	$TiF_3/Ti_2O_3/1\,000°/60$ kbar	
$TiOCl$	yellow	$TiCl_4/TiO_2/700°/$s.t.	Stable to H_2O. Oxidised by air.
VOF_3	yellow	$V_2O_5/F_2/450°$	Sublimes readily.
VO_2F		$VO_2Cl/F_2, N_2/80°$	$\xrightarrow{300°} VOF_3 + V_2O_5$. Instantly hydrolysed by moisture.
$VOCl_3$	yellow	$V_2O_5/C/Cl_2/350°$	MP $-79°$. BP $126°$. Very moisture sensitive.
VO_2Cl	orange	$VOCl_3/O_3/125°$	$\xrightarrow{150°} VOCl_3 + V_2O_5$. Hygroscopic.
$VOBr_3$	red	$V_2O_5/C/Br_2/500°$	MP $-59°$. Bp $170°$. Decomposes at room temperature.
VOF_2	yellow	$VOBr_2/HF/650°$	
$VOCl_2$	green	$V_2O_5/VCl_3/600°/$s.t.	$\xrightarrow{300°} VOCl_3 + VOCl$.
$VOBr_2$		$V_2O_3/Br_2/600°$	
VOF	black	$VF_3/V_2O_3/1\,000°/65$ kbar	
$VOCl$	brown	$VOCl_2/N_2/300°$	
$CrOF_4$	red	$Cr/F_2/$glass (by-product)	Very readily hydrolysed. MP $55°$.
CrO_2F_2	violet	CrO_3/HF	Very reactive (attacks glass). MP $32°$.
CrO_2Cl_2	red	$K_2Cr_2O_7/Cl^-/$conc. H_2SO_4	MP $-96°$.BP $117°$. $\xrightarrow{200°} Cl_2 +$ oxides.
CrO_2Br_2	red	$CrO_2Cl_2/HBr/-70°$	Decomposes below room temperature.
$CrOF_3$		CrO_3/BrF_3	Never obtained pure.
$CrOCl_3$	red	$CrO_3/SOCl_2$	$\xrightarrow{RT} CrO_2Cl_2 + Cr^{III}$ compounds.
$CrOCl$	green	$Cr_2O_3/CrCl_3/840-1\,040°$	Insol. H_2O. Stable to hot H_2O. $\xrightarrow[\text{vac.}]{\text{heat}} Cr_2O_3 + CrCl_3$.
$CrOBr$		$Cr_2O_3/CrBr_3/380°/$s.t.	
MnO_3F	green	$KMnO_4/HSO_3F$	Mp $-78°$. Explodes at room temp. $\longrightarrow$ $MnF_2 + MnO_2 + O_2$. Instantly hydrolysed to MnO_2.
MnO_3Cl	green	$KMnO_4/HCl/$conc. H_2SO_4	BP $-50°$. Decomposes violently at room temp.
MnO_2Cl_2	brown		Hydrolyses readily.
$MnOCl_3$	green		Decomposes above $0°$.
$FeOF$	white	$FeF_3/Fe_2O_3/O_2/850°$	
$FeOCl$	brown	$Fe_2O_3/HCl/300°$	$\xrightarrow{400°} FeCl_3 + Fe_2O_3$.

Table 3.8.   Metal halogen internuclear distances (pm)

CrF$_2$	198(2)	210(2)	243(2)
Cr$_2$F$_5$†	196(2)	201(2)	257(2)
MnF$_2$	211(4)	214(2)	
FeF$_2$	199(2)	212(4)	
CoF$_2$	204(4)	205(2)	
NiF$_2$	198(4)	201(2)	
CuF$_2$	193(4)	227(2)	
ZnF$_2$	203(4)	204(2)	
CrCl$_2$	240(4)	292(2)	
CrBr$_2$	254(4)	300(2)	
CrI$_2$	274(4)	324(2)	
MnF$_3$	179(2)	181(2)	209(2)

† Cr^{II}-F distances; Cr^{III}-F distances are all in the range 188–190 pm.

Fig. 3.2   Polymeric structure of CuX$_2$ (X = Cl, Br)

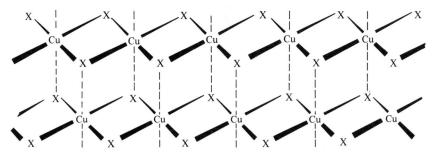

even in the absence of air, and the vanadium dihalides, which oxidise slowly. The hexahydrates of the di-iodides probably contain the M(H$_2$O)$_6^{2+}$ ions but the other dihalides contain *trans*-[M(H$_2$O)$_4$Cl$_2$]-units, with the other two molecules of water in the crystal lattice. Dihydrates are polymeric materials with planar chains similar to those in anhydrous CuCl$_2$, with water molecules coordinating to the metal ions to give an overall octahedral arrangement (Fig. 3.3).

Fig. 3.3   Polymeric structure of metal dihalide dihydrates, MX$_2$.2H$_2$O

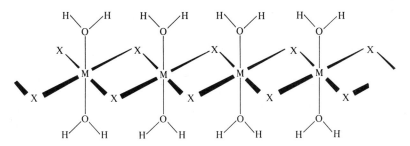

The **trifluorides** (titanium to cobalt) show a variety of crystal structures, but all are based on fairly close packing of fluoride ions with metal ions in octahedral holes. Manganese trifluoride is exceptional in that the Mn-F distances are irregular (Table 3.8). The manganese and cobalt

compounds lose fluorine readily and are good fluorinating agents, but chromium trifluoride decomposes only above 600 °C; the titanium and vanadium compounds are very stable.

The other **trihalides** show similar trends. The titanium compounds disproportionate to TiX_2 and TiX_4 at 300–500 °C, and the vanadium derivatives are similarly unstable to heat, giving VX_2 and either VCl_4 or the halogen (since VBr_4 is very unstable and VI_4 unknown). The remaining trihalides lose halogen with increasing ease with increase in atomic number both of the halogen and of the metal. All, except CrX_3, are readily soluble in water. With the exception of $CrCl_3$, all have layer structures of the BiI_3-type; this is the same as the hexagonal CdI_2-structure adopted by the dihalides (Fig. 3.1) except that only two-thirds of the available octahedral holes of alternate layers are occupied by metal ions. The chromium trihalides appears to be unique in making a similar adaptation of the $CdCl_2$ structure, i.e. cubic arrays of anions with Cr^{3+} ions in two-thirds of the octahedral holes of alternate layers.

The structures of the **tetrafluorides** (titanium to manganese) are not known with certainty but probably consist of condensed chains in which octahedral MF_6 units share edges. All are very readily hydrolysed and all except TiF_4 are thermally unstable; MnF_4 decomposes slowly even at room temperature, losing fluorine, while VF_4 disproportionates.

The **tetrahalides** and the oxyhalides of composition MO_nX_{4-n} all have simple, tetrahedral, molecular structures, although in the solid state these could equally well be described as fcc anion lattices with metal ions occupying one-eighth of the tetrahedral holes in a regular array. Being molecular, all are soluble in organic solvents, and $TiCl_4$ and VCl_4 are liquids at room temperature (cf. $GeCl_4$ and $SnCl_4$), and all are very susceptible to hydrolysis, the chlorides fuming on exposure to air. The vanadium compounds are thermally unstable; VBr_4 loses bromine well below room temperature and VCl_4 loses chlorine when refluxed (150 °C).

The **highest halides** are all fluorides. The pentafluorides of vanadium and chromium are viscous, highly associated liquids at room temperature, which hydrolyse very readily. In the solid state, VF_5 has a zig-zag chain structure in which octahedral VF_6 units share *cis* corners. On warming, CrF_5 loses fluorine to CrF_4. As might be expected, CrF_6 is even less stable, decomposing above -100 °C except under a high pressure of fluorine. The same oxidation state is found in the chromyl halides, CrO_2X_2, of which the chloride is the familiar red volatile liquid formed in testing for chromates or chlorides by heating the mixture with sulphuric acid. All are very reactive and the bromide decomposes below room temperature. The only oxyhalides reported for manganese are MnO_3F, a green liquid, and MnO_3Cl, a green gas, both of which decompose explosively at room temperature.

There are several points worth noting about this vast array of compounds:

(*a*) copper is exceptional in the series in being the only metal to form monohalides;

(*b*) the number of derivatives formed by each halogen decreases with increasing atomic number of the halogen, i.e. fluorides cover the largest range of oxidation states ($+2$ to $+6$) and iodides the smallest ($+1$ to $+4$);

(*c*) the higher oxidation states are obtained, even for fluorides, only in the early Groups, and fall away rapidly with increasing atomic number of the metal;

(*d*) consistently with (*c*), the Group oxidation state is found in stable compounds only for titanium and vanadium;

(*e*) it is not only the achievement of high oxidation states which becomes more difficult as the series is traversed; the thermodynamic data (Fig. 3.4) show that, within a series of compounds of the same stoicheiometry (e.g. MCl_2), enthalpies of formation become less negative with increasing atomic number of the metal. For example, $TiCl_4$ is quite stable to heat, VCl_4 loses chlorine at 150 °C and $CrCl_4$ has never been isolated;

(*f*) the one exception to the regular trend of (*e*) is that iron(III) seems to be easier to obtain than manganese(III).

Fig. 3.4   Enthalpies of formation of 3*d*-metal halides

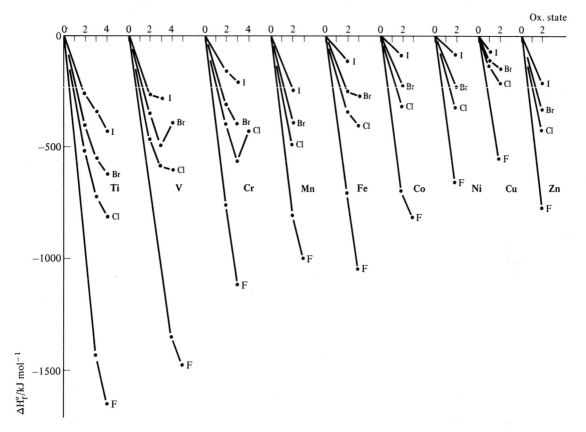

Many of these features, being functions of the metal rather than of the halogen, should appear in other systems and their further consideration will be deferred. The trend described in item (*b*) depends only on the halogen and is the same for all metals, and may usefully be discussed at this point.

For metals which show several oxidation states (except titanium, which is readily oxidised to the +4 state by all of the halogens) the highest oxidation state is attained with fluorine and the other halogens achieve progressively lower states. Even for the same oxidation state, the fluoride is the most thermodynamically stable of the series (i.e. has the most negative enthalpy of formation) and the iodide the least. It is, of course, well known that fluorine is the best oxidising agent of the halogens, and this is often attributed to the weakness of the F–F bond in F_2 and the high electronegativity (or electron affinity) of the fluorine atom. However, these factors actually play only a relatively small rôle. Consider the Born–Haber cycle shown in Fig. 3.5 for the formation of a halide MX_n. For any given metal, the only factors which change as the halogen is varied are $\Delta H_{at}^0(X_2)$, the enthalpy of converting the halogen in its standard state into atoms, E_A, the electron affinity, and U, the lattice energy. The first two of these terms may conveniently be taken together as the enthalpy of formation of the gaseous halide ion, $\Delta H_f^0(X^-)$. As Table 3.9 shows, although the various terms contributing to $\Delta H_f^0(X^-)$ differ from halogen to halogen, the total spans only a narrow range (-260 to -195 kJ mol^{-1}). Although these values lie in the right order to explain the trend in $\Delta H_f^0(MX_n)$, the variation is far too small to explain the observed differences. This leaves only the lattice energy, which is also dependent on the identity of the halogen. To a good

Fig. 3.5   Born–Haber cycle for the formation of a halide MX_n from the elements

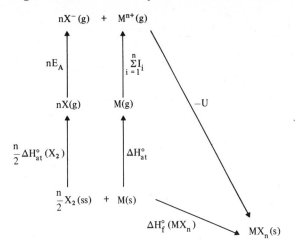

approximation, lattice energies are inversely proportional to the sum of the radii of cation and anion

$$U \propto \frac{1}{r_+ + r_-}$$

and will thus decrease as the anion becomes larger, making the enthalpy of formation of the halide less negative. This effect is quite significant. Taking a typical value of about $2\,800\,kJ\,mol^{-1}$ for $U(MF_2)$ and a cation radius of about 80 pm (the range of observed radii is about 70–80 pm), an increase of radius of the anion from 136 pm (F^-) to 216 pm (I^-) would imply a loss of lattice energy of about $750\,kJ\,mol^{-1}$. Actual differences are rather less than this because the iodides are not completely ionic. Nevertheless, it is true to say that the 'oxidising power' of a halogen is dependent more on the size of its anion than on its electron affinity or electronegativity.

Table 3.9.   Terms contributing to $\Delta H_f^0(X^-)$ $(kJ\,mol^{-1})$

	F	Cl	Br	I
$\frac{1}{2}X_2(ss) \rightarrow \frac{1}{2}X_2(g)$	0	0	15	31
$\frac{1}{2}X_2(g) \rightarrow X(g)$	79	122	97	75
$X(g) + e^- \rightarrow X^-(g)$	-339	-354	-330	-301
$\Delta H_f^0(X^-)$	-260	-233	-218	-195

The oxidation state plots of Fig. 3.4 are typical of *d*-block compounds. Usually a series of compounds is obtained differing by unit oxidation state, with progressively more negative enthalpies of formation. However, the decrease in enthalpy per unit of oxidation state is not uniform but becomes smaller as the oxidation state increases, i.e. the plots are concave upwards. Thus, for instance, $-\Delta H_f^0(VCl_4)$ is less than twice $-\Delta H_f^0(VCl_2)$. This effect occurs because the increase in lattice energy (or bond energy) with oxidation state is less rapid than the increase in the sum of the ionisation energies or the promotion energy.

Non-existent compounds do not necessarily have to be endothermic, with $\Delta H_f^0 > 0$, e.g. the unknown VCl_5 is presumably unstable relative to $VCl_4 + \frac{1}{2}Cl_2$. For this to occur, $\Delta H_f^0(VCl_5)$ need only be slightly less negative than $\Delta H_f^0(VCl_4)$. Similar instability may be induced in other compounds by raising the temperature, e.g. VCl_4 loses chlorine at 150 °C. Strictly, of course, these reactions are governed by the free-energy changes, $\Delta G_f = \Delta H_f - T \Delta S_f$, and it is the entropy term which becomes increasingly important as the temperature is raised. In the formation reaction

$$M(s) + \frac{n}{2} X_2(g) \rightarrow MX_n(s)$$

the entropy change is negative and arises mainly from the removal of the gaseous halogen. As the temperature is raised, ΔG_f becomes less negative and this effect becomes more pronounced as n becomes larger. (Section 1.6, p. 27). That is, on raising the temperature, all compounds are destabilised, but the effect is greatest for the highest oxidation states. The oxidation-state diagram for the higher temperature is more curved and shallower and may eventually begin to curve upwards. At this stage the final compound of the series has become unstable relative to the penultimate one (Fig. 3.6). If the temperature is raised further, the next member of the series becomes unstable. In some cases (VCl_5, CrF_6) the decomposition temperature is below room temperature.

The temperature required for this type of instability will depend on the shallowness of the room-temperature oxidation-state curve, i.e. iodides should be the least thermally stable halides, as is observed in practice. Consider the two reactions

$$Fe(s) + Br_2(l) \rightarrow FeBr_2(s) \qquad \Delta H_f^0 = -236 \text{ kJ mol}^{-1}$$

$$Fe(s) + \tfrac{3}{2}Br_2(l) \rightarrow FeBr_3(s) \qquad \Delta H_f^0 = -263 \text{ kJ mol}^{-1}$$

Fig. 3.6   Schematic free-energy diagrams for two temperatures, $T_2 > T_1$. As the temperature is raised ΔG_f becomes less negative more rapidly the greater the oxidation state. At T_1 all the compounds are stable. At T_2, MX_4 is unstable relative to $MX_3 + \tfrac{1}{2}X_2$

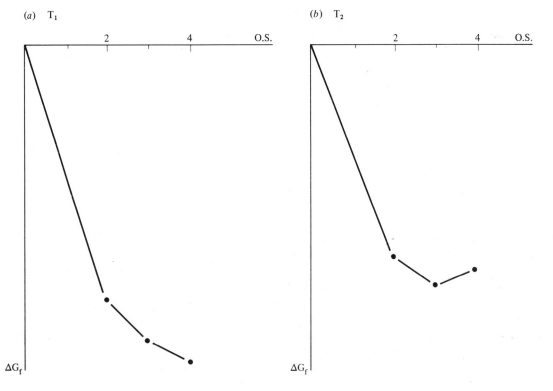

These imply that the conversion of iron(III) bromide to iron(II) bromide and bromine is endothermic by about 30 kJ mol^{-1}:

$$FeBr_3(s) \rightarrow \tfrac{1}{2}Br_2(l) + FeBr_2(s) \qquad \Delta H = +30 \text{ kJ mol}^{-1}$$

Hence, when $T\,\Delta S$ becomes greater than 30 kJ mol^{-1} this reaction is expected to proceed as written. The enthalpy of the corresponding reaction for the chlorides is about 50 kJ mol^{-1}, so that a higher temperature is required before iron(III) chloride becomes unstable relative to FeCl$_2$, and FeCl$_3$ can be heated at 330 °C without decomposition. On the other hand, iron(III) iodide cannot be formed at all at room temperature.

3.4 Oxides and hydroxides

The oxides show just as much variation in properties as the halides, ranging from high-melting, non-stoicheiometric, ionic solids to an explosive liquid as the oxidation state of the metal changes from +2 to +7. The known oxides are listed in Table 3.10, and some of their properties are

Table 3.10. Oxides of the 3d-metals

Ti	V	Cr	Mn	Fe	Co	Ni	Cu	Zn
			Mn_2O_7					
		CrO_3						
	V_2O_5							
†TiO_2	†VO_2	CrO_2	†MnO_2					
Ti_2O_3	V_2O_3	Cr_2O_3	Mn_2O_3	Fe_2O_3	(Co_2O_3)			
†TiO	†VO	CrO	MnO	†FeO	CoO	NiO	CuO	ZnO
							Cu_2O	

Other oxides known are:
Ti_3O_5 V_3O_5 Cr_3O_8 Mn_3O_8
Cr_5O_{12} Mn_3O_4 Fe_3O_4 Co_3O_4
Cr_2O_5

† denotes oxides known to have wide composition ranges.

summarised in Table 3.11. Considerable generalisation is again possible if the oxides are classified by oxidation state of the metal.

The only **dimetal heptoxide** is Mn$_2$O$_7$, which is a dangerously explosive green liquid, obtained by treating potassium permanganate with concentrated sulphuric acid. In a vacuum it explodes at −10 °C, forming Mn$_2$O$_3$, while at atmospheric pressure rapid decomposition to MnO$_2$ sets in at about 55 °C and becomes violent at 95 °C. Oxygen is lost slowly on standing at room temperature. The compound is molecular and its structure has been shown by electron diffraction of the vapour to consist of two MnO$_4$-tetrahedra with a common oxygen atom forming a bent bridge between them.

Table 3.11. Properties of 3*d*-metal oxides

	Colour	M.P. °C	ΔH_f^0 kJ mol^{-1}	Structure	C.N.	Preparation	Properties
TiO	bronze	1 737	−518	NaCl	6	Ti/TiO$_2$/1 600°	Grossly non-stoich. Readily oxidised.
Ti$_2$O$_3$	violet	2 130	−1 536	Al$_2$O$_3$	6	Ti/3TiO$_2$/1 600°	Narrow comp. range.
Ti$_3$O$_5$	blue		−2 458	monoclin	6	TiO$_2$/H$_2$/1 200°	
TiO$_2$	white	1 800	−945	TiO$_2$	6	Ti/O$_2$	Very stable. Non-stoicheiometric, forming Ti$_n$O$_{2n-1}$.
VO	grey	dec	−420	NaCl	6	(higher oxide)/H$_2$	Grossly non-stoich. Disproportionates at 950°.
V$_2$O$_3$	grey	1 967	−1 238	Al$_2$O$_3$	6	V$_2$O$_5$/H$_2$	
V$_3$O$_5$							Very narrow comp. range.
VO$_2$	blue	1 637	−718	TiO$_2$ dist	6	V$_2$O$_5$/700°	
V$_2$O$_5$	orange	658	−1 560		"5"	V/O$_2$	Sl. sol. H$_2$O, acid. Sol. alkali. Loses O$_2$ reversibly 700–1 150°.
CrO	red			ZnO wustite	6	Cr$_2$O$_3$/NaF$_{melt}$/H$_2$	Insol. dil. acids. Pyrophoric if finely divided.
Cr$_2$O$_3$	green	2 275	−1 140	Al$_2$O$_3$	6	Cr/O$_2$	Dissociates below MP.
CrO$_2$	black		−598	TiO$_2$	6	Cr$_2$O$_3$/O$_2$/250°	Decomposes to Cr$_2$O$_3$ on heating.
Cr$_2$O$_5$				polymeric	4 & 6		Non-stoich. Decomposes in air at 380° to Cr$_2$O$_3$.
CrO$_3$	red	190	−590	polymeric	4	Na$_2$Cr$_2$O$_7$/conc. H$_2$SO$_4$	Sol. H$_2$O. Vig. oxidant. Loses O$_2$ above MP.
MnO	green	1 785	−385	NaCl	6	(salt or oxide)/H$_2$	Narrow comp. range.
MnO$_3$O$_4$	purple	1 560	−1 388	spinel	4 & 6	oxide/air/1 000°	
Mn$_5$O$_8$				Cd$_2$Mn$_3$O$_8$	6	Mn$_3$O$_4$/O$_2$/300°	
Mn$_2$O$_3$	black		−958	orthorhomb	4+2	MnO$_2$/800°	$\xrightarrow[\text{vac}]{350°}$ Mn$_3$O$_4$.
MnO$_2$	brown		−520	TiO$_2$	6	Mn(NO$_3$)$_2$/O$_2$/150°	Non-stoich. Oxidant. Disprop. in alkali to Mn(III)+Mn(V).
Mn$_2$O$_7$	green		−742	molecular	4	KMnO$_4$/conc. H$_2$SO$_4$	Explosive liquid. Hygroscopic. Hydrolyses to MnO$_2$+O$_3$+O$_2$. Slowly decomposes to MnO$_2$.
FeO	black	1 368	−266	NaCl	6	Fe/restrict O$_2$/600°	Grossly non-stoich. Limiting composition Fe$_{0.947}$O.
Fe$_3$O$_4$	black	1 600	−1 118	spinel	4 & 6	Fe/Air/	Insol. acids.
Fe$_2$O$_3$	red	1 565	−825	Al$_2$O$_3$	6	Fe/O$_2$	
CoO	green		−239	NaCl	6	Co/air	$\xrightarrow[\text{O}_2]{400°}$ Co$_3$O$_4$. Easily reduced. Sol. acids.
Co$_3$O$_4$	black		−900	spinel	4 & 6	Co/O$_2$/400°	
NiO	green	1 955	−240	NaCl	6	Ni/O$_2$	Sol. acids. Readily reduced.
Cu$_2$O	red	1 230	−159		2	CuO/1 000°	Sol. NH$_4$OH. H$_2$SO$_4$ gives Cu^{2+}+Cu.
CuO	black		−169		4	Cu powder/O$_2$	Sol. Acids. V. Easily reduced to Cu.
ZnO	white	1 975	−348	wurtzite	4	Zn/O$_2$	Sol. acids, NH$_4$OH.

Similarly, there is only one **trioxide**, CrO$_3$, also a vigorous oxidizing agent. It is rather more stable than Mn$_2$O$_7$, but begins to lose oxygen above its melting point (190 °C) giving a series of lower oxides (Cr$_3$O$_8$, Cr$_2$O$_5$, CrO$_2$) and, finally, Cr$_2$O$_3$. Being soluble in organic solvents (e.g. acetic acid) it is a useful oxidant. Chromium trioxide is familiar in laboratories as the red solid which often precipitates from concentrated 'chromic acid' cleaning baths, and it is best prepared by adding concentrated sulphuric acid to sodium dichromate. As might be expected, it has a highly covalent structure in which tetrahedral CrO$_4$-units form chains (Fig. 3.7).

Fig. 3.7   Structures of Mn_2O_7 and CrO_3

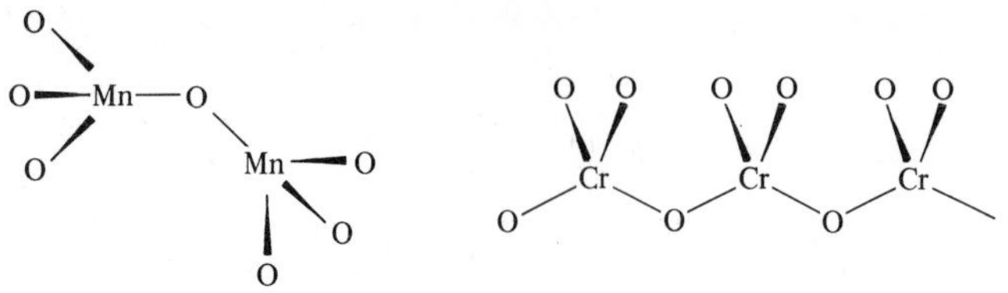

Chromium forms other oxide phases between CrO_3 and CrO_2, with compositions Cr_3O_8, Cr_5O_{12} and Cr_2O_5. These probably all contain mixtures of trivalent and hexavalent chromium; Cr_2O_5 is non-stoicheiometric, its composition range being $CrO_{2.385-2.430}$. Only for Cr_5O_{12} is the structure known: it consists of tetrahedral $Cr^{VI}O_4$ and octahedral $Cr^{III}O_6$ units linked in a continuous framework (Fig. 3.8). All these oxides lose oxygen on heating giving, ultimately, Cr_2O_3.

Fig. 3.8   Structure of the Cr_3O_{12} unit

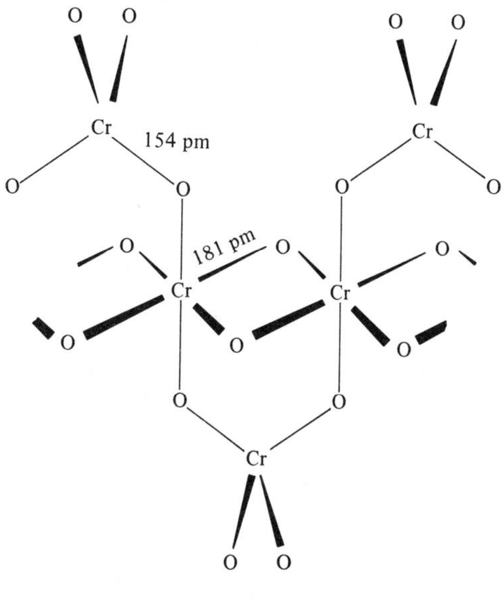

A stoicheiometric **pentoxide** is formed by vanadium, and results from direct reaction of the elements, the highest $3d$-metal oxide obtainable in this way. It is a mild oxidant, being fairly readily reduced to tetravalent vanadium and, at elevated temperatures loses oxygen reversibly. These properties are presumably responsible for its utility as a catalyst in oxidation reactions, e.g. in the oxidation of sulphur dioxide to the trioxide in the manufacture of sulphuric acid. It has the advantages of being cheaper and less easily 'poisoned' than other catalyst systems (e.g. platinum). Alone among the oxides so far mentioned, it is amphoteric, being soluble in alkalis to give the vanadate(V) ion, VO_4^{3-}, while in acids a cationic species, VO_2^+, is formed, usually coordinated by the anions of the acid.

The structure of V_2O_5 is curious and appears to represent a compromise between the tetrahedral molecular structures described above for CrO_3 and Mn_2O_7 and the ionic structures of the lower oxides which all contain octahedrally coordinated metal ions. The vanadium environment is probably best described as five-coordinate in a distorted trigonal-bipyramidal arrangement. The structure is most easily visualised as being composed of chains of VO_4-tetrahedra (like those in CrO_3, and also found in metavanadates, M^IVO_3, Fig. 3.9a) which are linked together in pairs (Fig. 3.9b), giving each vanadium atom an approximately trigonal-bipyramidal configuration with the 'trigonal' axis lying along the chain (this polymeric anion is found in $KVO_3.H_2O$). The double chains are fused to other double chains on either side by sharing oxygen atoms, giving a puckered layer structure. Each vanadium atom has a single terminal oxygen atom, with a bond distance of 154 pm corresponding to a double bond, $V=O$, and three bridging oxygen atoms at 178 and 188 (2) pm; the fourth bridging $V—O$ bond, that linking the chains, is longer, 204 pm. When the layers are stacked together to form the final crystal structure, there is another oxygen atom from an adjacent layer at 281 pm which could be considered as occupying the sixth position in a very distorted octahedral coordination, *trans* to the $V=O$ bond.

Fig. 3.9 (a) chain of VO_4–tetrahedra $[(VO_3^-)_n]$ (b) chains linking together $[(VO_3^-)_n]$ (c) layer structure of V_2O_5 (distances in pm). The starred oxygen atom is part of the next layer (after A. F. Wells (1975) *Structural Inorganic Chemistry*, 4th edn, OUP)

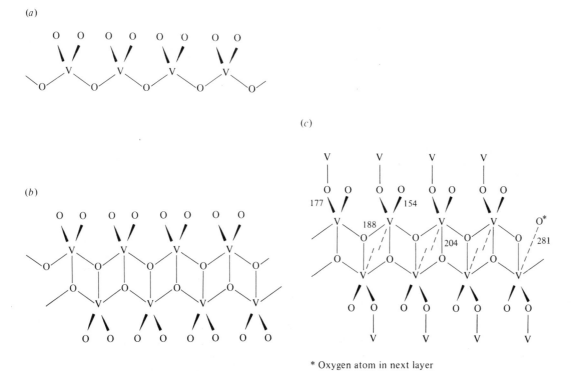

* Oxygen atom in next layer

The structures of the **dioxides** (titanium to manganese) are all related to that of rutile, TiO_2, in which the metal ions occupy half the octahedral holes in a distorted hcp anion lattice, the distortions being such as to allow the highly-charged cations to move away from each other. Alternatively, the structure may be regarded as being formed from chains of octahedral MO_6 units linked together by axial oxygen atoms. (Fig. 3.10). Vanadium dioxide has a similar structure above 70 °C, but below this temperature a different type of distortion occurs which allows the vanadium atoms to come together in pairs within each chain, so that the $V—V$ distances are alternately 265

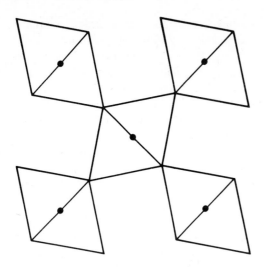

Fig. 3.10   The rutile (TiO$_2$) structure. Linked chains of octahedral MO$_6$ units run perpendicular to the page (after A. F. Wells (1975) *Structural Inorganic Chemistry*, 4th edn, OUP)

and 312 pm. The vanadium ion is also appreciably closer to one oxide ion (176 pm) than the others [186 (2) and 203 (3) pm], suggesting an embryonic V=O unit, as found in vanadyl compounds. The atom pairing represents the formation of localised V—V bonds by the coupling of the odd electrons, and the compound is diamagnetic. In its high-temperature form, this pairing does not occur, the *d*-electrons are delocalised over all the metal atoms, and in this form VO$_2$ is paramagnetic and a metallic conductor. The dioxides of titanium and vanadium are both non-stoicheiometric, but in a regular way; both form a series of phases of composition M$_n$O$_{2n-1}$ (Ti, n = 4 to 10; V, n = 4 to 8), in addition to the stoicheiometric MO$_2$. These phases have structures similar to the basic rutile structure with oxide ions missing in regularly spaced layers, so that blocks of the rutile structure are joined together (Magneli or shear phases, see Chapter 10).

Chromium dioxide appears to have the regular TiO$_2$-structure in which the two *d*-electrons of each metal ion are delocalised, giving metallic conduction. It is also ferromagnetic, and is finding application in high-quality recording tapes, being superior to the iron oxides (especially in high-frequency response). Manganese dioxide is a very variable material. Several crystalline phases have been reported but many are now known to contain Mn^{2+} with other metal ions to balance the charge. In the form in which it is normally precipitated from solution, manganese dioxide has a very open structure and acts as a cation-exchange medium. In its pure form, β-MnO$_2$, and the mineral pyrolusite, it has an undistorted rutile structure, as might be expected for a metal ion with a d^3 configuration; some interaction between the metal ions does occur, however, as the oxide is antiferromagnetic.

The dioxides become less stable to reduction with increasing atomic number of the metal. Thus, TiO$_2$ is a very stable material, being reduced only to Ti$_3$O$_5$ by hydrogen at 900 °C and even at 1 300 °C only Ti$_2$O$_3$ is formed, whereas VO$_2$ gives V$_2$O$_3$ readily with hydrogen at 400 °C, and CrO$_2$ and MnO$_2$ lose oxygen when heated alone. Manganese dioxide is a useful catalyst for the oxidation of carbon monoxide at room temperature (even better, in conjunction with CuO).

In the **sesquioxides**, M$_2$O$_3$, the range of metals is still wider, titanium (and scandium) to iron. Oxides of this composition have not been definitely established for cobalt or nickel, but each forms an oxyhydroxide, MOOH, by alkaline oxidation of the dihydroxides (the corresponding manganese compound probably contains Mn^{IV}). The anhydrous sesquioxides of chromium and iron are obtained by heating the metals in air or oxygen, but Mn$_2$O$_3$ is best prepared by reduction of MnO$_2$ (by heating to 900 °C in air or 250 °C in hydrogen). The vanadium compound is similarly obtained by reduction of V$_2$O$_5$ with hydrogen, but the best route to Ti$_2$O$_3$ seems to be reduction of TiO$_2$ with the metal at 1 600 °C. All these oxides have narrow composition ranges (e.g. TiO$_{1.49-1.51}$) and all except Mn_2O_3 crystallise with the α-Al_2O_3 (corundum) structure, which is an almost regular hcp array of oxide ions with metal ions in octahedral holes. Manganese sesquioxide has the C-M_2O_3 structure found most commonly for the lanthanides (p. 149), which is basically a fluorite-type lattice with one-quarter of the anions missing. The coordination of the Mn^{3+} is six-fold, with two long and four short bonds (cf. other d^4 systems). This compound and Fe_2O_3 can both be obtained in a second (γ) form, most readily by dehydration of the oxyhydroxides, MOOH. In this form, the oxide ions are in a ccp array (again tetragonally distorted for the Mn^{3+} compound) in which the metal ions are distributed randomly over octahedral and tetrahedral sites, and the structures are closely related to the spinel structures described below.

The **oxides M_3O_4** are formed by manganese, iron and cobalt. All have spinel-type structures (Fig. 3-11) with an fcc array of oxide ions and metal ions in tetrahedral and octahedral holes. In the basic face-centred cube of the oxide lattice, octahedral sites are found at the centre of the cube and at the centre of each edge, and the tetrahedral sites are at the centre of each octant of the cube.

Fig. 3.11   Spinel structure – a ccp array of oxide ions. Octahedral sites are at the centres of the cube edges and at the cube-centre (those on the top faces and the centre are shown). Tetrahedral sites are at the centre of each octant of the cube (those in the front four octants are shown). Each edge octahedral site is shared with three adjacent cubes, so that there are effectively 3 such sites per cube, plus the central one. There are eight tetrahedral sites per cube

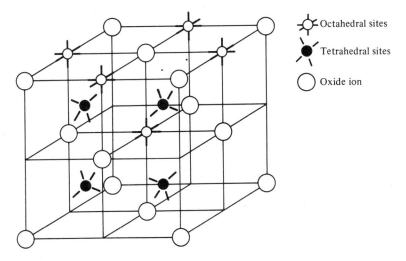

- $-\bigcirc-$ Octahedral sites
- $\bullet$ Tetrahedral sites
- $\bigcirc$ Oxide ion

Metal ions fill regularly half the octahedral sites and one-eighth of the tetrahedral sites (i.e. a 2:1 ratio), and two basic arrangements are possible. In the 'normal' spinel structure (e.g. Mn_3O_4, Co_3O_4) the octahedral sites are occupied by the tripositive ions and the tetrahedral sites by the dipositive ions. The alternative (Fe_3O_4) is the 'inverse' spinel structure, in which the octahedral sites are occupied randomly by the dipositive ions and half the tripositive ions, the remainder being on the tetrahedral sites. Which structure is adopted is determined, *inter alia*, by ligand-field effects (see Ch. 4). Intermediate distributions are also found in some mixed-oxide systems. The random arrangement of Fe^{2+} and Fe^{3+} ions on the octahedral sites allows ready transmission of electrons through the lattice, which functions as a metallic conductor. Oxidation of the Fe^{2+} ions gives the γ-Fe_2O_3 structure, and these two oxides (and Mn_3O_4 and γ-Mn_2O_3) are readily interconvertible.

Monoxides, MO, are formed by all the metals of the series. Those of the early members (titanium to chromium) are formed only under strongly reducing conditions (e.g. Ti+TiO_2 at

1 600 °C, $TiO_2 + H_2$ at 2 000 °C, 130 atm), while for the later members (nickel, copper, zinc) they are the normal products of oxidation of the metals. All except CuO and ZnO have basically the NaCl-structure, but many are non-stoicheiometric. The composition ranges of the monoxides are given in Table 3.12. The much wider ranges for TiO and VO reflect the fact that these phases are prepared at high temperatures (and are only metastable at room temperature) so that the configurational entropy arising from the randomisation of the defects is considerable. In TiO, for instance, both metal and oxide sublattices may be defective; even the apparently stoicheiometric oxide has 30 per cent of the ions missing and should be formulated $Ti_{0.85}O_{0.85}$. For iron, the composition range does not even include the stoicheiometric oxide, which cannot be made and is unstable with respect to a mixture of the metal and $Fe_{0.945}O$. The subject of non-stoicheiometry is discussed more fully in Chapter 10.

Table 3.12.   Extreme composition ranges of 3*d*-metal oxides.

Oxide	x in MO_x
TiO	0·62 –1·25
Ti_2O_3	1·501–1·512
TiO_2	1·992–2·000
VO	0·86 –1·27
MnO	1·00 –1·13
FeO	1·045–1·200
Fe_3O_4	1·336–1·381
CoO	1·000–1·012
NiO	1·000–1·001
Cu_2O	0·500–0·5016

The monoxides of copper and zinc have structures which differ from those of the other metals and from each other, although the metal ions are four-coordinate in both cases. Zinc(II) oxide has the wurtzite structure, a hcp array of oxide ions with the Zn^{2+} ions arranged regularly in half the tetrahedral holes. The adoption of a four-coordinate, tetrahedral arrangement is probably due partly to the small radius of Zn^{2+} and partly to covalency effects (cf. $ZnCl_2$). In the copper compound, as in many other derivatives of copper(II), the coordination about the metal is square-planar, giving a structure in which planar ribbons are linked perpendicular to each other by oxide ions, each oxide ion being coordinated tetrahedrally to four copper ions, two in each ribbon (Fig. 3.12).

Copper is also unique in that it gives the only **hemioxide** of the series, Cu_2O, although metallic titanium takes up oxygen to a composition corresponding to $TiO_{0.5}$. Red copper(I) oxide is precipitated when copper(II) solutions are reduced in the absence of coordinating anions, and is best obtained by reduction in alkaline solution (e.g. Fehling's mixture; an alkaline solution of copper sulphate and sodium tartrate) or by heating CuO to 1 000 °C. The structure is also unique, consisting of two independent, interlaced, three-dimensional frameworks, in which each copper atom is linearly coordinated to two oxygen atoms which are themselves tetrahedrally coordinated (Fig. 3.13).

The following points of interest may be noted about the 3*d*-metal oxides:

(*a*) the pattern of oxidation states is very similar to that of the fluorides and chlorides, viz. all metals give monoxides, MO, but higher oxidation states are progressively confined to the lighter metals;

(*b*) only copper gives a hemioxide, Cu_2O;

Fig. 3.12   Crystal structure of CuO (after A. F. Wells (1975) *Structural Inorganic Chemistry*, 4th edn, OUP)

Fig. 3.13   Crystal structure of Cu$_2$O (after A. F. Wells (1975) *Structural Inorganic Chemistry*, 4th edn, OUP)

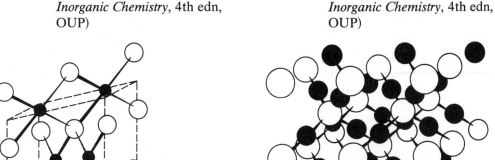

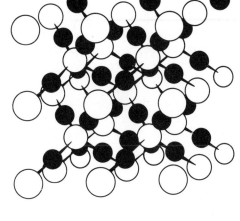

(*c*)   the stability of any given oxidation state decreases across the series, e.g. Ti$_2$O$_3$ is quite stable but readily oxidised to TiO$_2$, Fe$_2$O$_3$ is very familiar and readily formed, and Ni$_2$O$_3$ has never been properly characterised and probably does not exist;

(*d*)   these trends are reflected in the thermodynamic data (Fig. 3.14);

Fig. 3.14   Enthalpies of formation of 3*d*-oxides

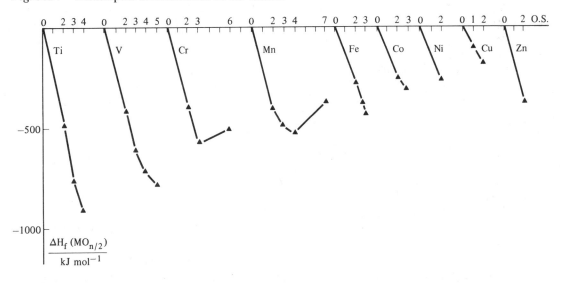

(*e*)   the highest oxidation states are found for chromium (+6) and manganese (+7), although these oxides cannot be formed directly from the elements (this is also evident from the enthalpies of formation). It is also evident that the salts from which these oxides are prepared are more stable than the oxides themselves, e.g. Mn$_2$O$_7$ is spontaneously explosive, but KMnO$_4$ is found on the shelves of most laboratories. This is a general phenomenon, that anionic species are more stable than the corresponding neutral compound when high oxidation states are involved (cf. also CrO_3 *vs* CrO_4^{2-} and $Cr_2O_7^{2-}$). Higher oxidation states of many metals can be stabilised in anionic species or mixed oxides, typical examples of which are shown in Table 3.13. Discrete anions are not found in the metallates(IV), which are stable only as solids, and have spinel or perovskite structures. The higher metallates form discrete tetrahedral anions, stable in strongly basic solutions. The greater stability of the anionic species is probably due to the lower coordination number of the oxygen atoms (one rather than two) and because the anionic charge to some extent resides on the metal; both these factors enable the metal atom to approach more closely to electroneutrality (see below).

Table 3.13.   Anionic oxo-complexes

	MnO_4^- purple			
CrO_4^{2-} yellow	MnO_4^{2-} green	FeO_4^{2-} red		
CrO_4^{3-} blue	MnO_4^{3-} blue		K_3CoO_4 blue-black	
Sr_2CrO_4 black	Ba_2MnO_4 black	Sr_2FeO_4 black	Ba_2CoO_4 black	$BaNiO_3$ black

Discrete anions are not discernible in the metallates(IV).

The highest oxides (M_2O_5 and above) are acidic, dissolving in alkalis to give tetrahedral anions. The monoxides, MO, are all entirely basic, dissolving in acids to give M^{2+}(aq), although for titanium, vanadium and chromium these are very readily oxidised. The sequioxides, M_2O_3, are usually rather inert to acids and alkalis, but there is some evidence to suggest that Cr_2O_3 and Fe_2O_3 may be amphoteric.

Despite the high electronegativity of oxygen, the enthalpies of formation of metal oxides (per mole of metal) are closer to those of the corresponding chlorides than the fluorides, although the range of oxidation states available is more similar to (and more extensive than) that for fluorides. It is instructive to compare the terms contributing to the enthalpies of formation in the normal Born–Haber cycle:

$$\Delta H_f^0(MO) - \Delta H_f^0(MF_2) = [\Delta H_f^0(O^{2-}) - U(MO)] - [2\,\Delta H_f^0(F^-) - U(MF_2)]$$

since the terms involving the formation of the metal ion cancel out. Rearranging,

$$\Delta H_f^0(MO) - \Delta H_f^0(MF_2) = [\Delta H_f^0(O^{2-}) - 2\,\Delta H_f^0(F^-)] - [U(MO) - U(MF_2)]$$

The formation of $2F^-$(g) is exothermic ($-520\,kJ\,mol^{-1}$), while formation of O^{2-}(g) is strongly endothermic ($+950\,kJ\,mol^{-1}$), mainly due to the difficulty of adding a second electron to O^- and the stronger bond in O_2. The oxide thus commences with a handicap. The lattice energies may be compared by Kapustinskii's formula, from which lattice energy is roughly proportional to vz_+z_- (see Ch. 1). The anions O^{2-} and F^- fortuitously have almost indentical radii (130 pm), so that the ratio of lattice energies $U(MO):U(MF_2)$ is about $2\times2\times2:3\times2\times1 = 4:3$. This means that MO gains about $1\,200\,kJ\,mol^{-1}$ over MF_2 simply because of the higher charge on the anion. Therefore, over all $\Delta H_f^0(MO)$ is expected to be about $300\,kJ\,mol^{-1}$ less negative than $\Delta H_f^0(MF_2)$, which is about what is observed, bringing the oxides closer to the chlorides (which have lower lattice energies by virtue of the larger radius of the anion).

3.5 Aqueous solution chemistry

A similarly wide range of oxidation states is attainable in aqueous solution (+2 to +7), and considerable variety is shown in the nature of the species formed. In this case, not only is the identity of the metal and its oxidation state important, but the pH of the solution exerts a large influence over whether cationic, anionic, or condensed species, or insoluble hydroxides are formed. The relative stabilities of the oxidation states in acidic and basic solutions are shown in Fig. 3.15, and some data for these systems are summarised in Table 3.14.

Fig. 3.15 Oxidation-state diagram for aqueous solutions of 3*d*-metal ions

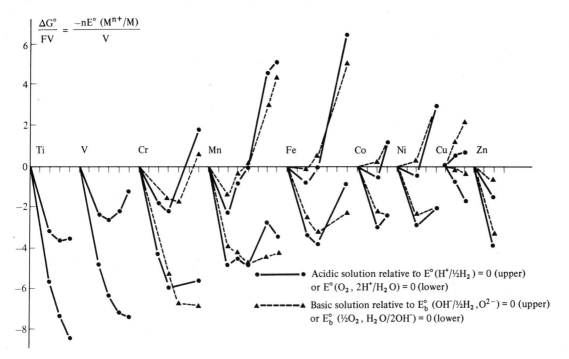

The **divalent ions** in acidic solution are almost certainly hexacoordinate, $M(OH_2)_6^{2+}$, with the exception of Cu^{2+} which probably has only four strongly bound water molecules. The stability of the divalent state increases with increasing atomic number of the metal: titanium(II) and vanadium(II) rapidly reduce water at room temperature, but for most of the other metals this state is the normal product of dissolving the metal in acid, although sometimes air must be excluded. The addition of alkali gives the insoluble hydroxides, $M(OH)_2$, which redissolve readily in acids but are unaffected by excess alkali. The only exception is $Zn(OH)_2$, which dissolves in alkali to give the zincate ion, probably $Zn(OH)_4^{2-}$. Freshly precipitated $Cu(OH)_2$ also dissolves in concentrated alkali to give purple-blue solutions probably containing polymeric species $[Cu_n(OH)_{2n-2}]^{2+}$.

Tripositive ions are formed by the metals titanium to iron; Mn^{3+} is unstable to disproportionation but the reaction is slow in moderately concentrated acid (>3M). The Co^{3+} ion is very unstable in aqueous solution, being reduced rapidly by the solvent with the evolution of oxygen. In strongly acidic solutions containing only non-coordinating anions (e.g. perchloric or nitric acids), the tripositive ions are also hexa-coordinate, $M(OH_2)_6^{3+}$, but with other acids there is a strong tendency in many cases for complexes with the anion to be formed. For example, iron(III) in nitric acid solution gives the pale purple hexa-aquo ion, but in hydrochloric acid bright yellow complexes are

Table 3.14. Properties of aquated metal ions.

	O.S.	Species	Colour	ΔG^0/FV	ΔG^0_O/FV	Species	Colour	ΔG^0_b/FV	ΔG^0_{bO}/FV	Preparation	Comments
Ti	+2	Ti^{2+}	violet	$-3{\cdot}26$	$-5{\cdot}71$	$Ti(OH)_2$	purple			TiO/H^+, ice-water	Oxidised rapidly by H_2O to Ti^{III}.
	+3	Ti^{3+}	none	$-3{\cdot}63$	$-7{\cdot}31$	$Ti(OH)_3$	none			$Ti^{IV}/Zn/H^+$	Oxidised by O_2 to Ti^{IV}.
	+4	$Ti(OH)_2^{2+}$	none	$-3{\cdot}53$	$-8{\cdot}44$	TiO_3^{2-}					Stable.
V	+2	V^{2+}	violet	$-2{\cdot}37$	$-4{\cdot}83$	$V(OH)_2$	green			$V^{n+}/Zn/H^+$	Oxidised by H_2O to V^{III}.
	+3	V^{3+}	green	$-2{\cdot}63$	$-6{\cdot}31$	$V(OH)_3$	yellow			$(V^V,V^{IV})/Zn/H^+$	Oxidised by air to V^{IV}.
	+4	VO^{2+}	blue	$-2{\cdot}27$	$-7{\cdot}18$	$VO(OH)_2$	none			$V^V/SO_2/H^+$	Stable in acid. Oxidised by air in alkali.
	+5	VO_2^+	none	$-1{\cdot}27$	$-7{\cdot}42$	VO_3^- / VO_4^{3-}		$-1{\cdot}63$	$-7{\cdot}77$	V^{n+}/O_2	Polymerises, pH 2–13. Readily reduced to V^{IV}.
Cr	+2	Cr^{2+}	blue	$-1{\cdot}82$	$-4{\cdot}28$	$Cr(OH)_2$	yellow	$-1{\cdot}54$	$-5{\cdot}22$	$Cr^{III}/Zn/H^+$	Oxidised rapidly by air.
	+3	Cr^{3+}	violet	$-2{\cdot}23$	$-5{\cdot}92$	$Cr(OH)_3$	green	$-1{\cdot}77$	$-6{\cdot}68$	$Cr^{VI}/$any reductant	Hydrolysed readily. Usually coordinated to anions.
	+4					CrO_2^-	black			$Cr(OH)_3/O_2/350\,°C$	
	+6	$Cr_2O_7^{2-}$	orange	$+1{\cdot}76$	$-5{\cdot}61$	CrO_4^{2-}	yellow	$+0{\cdot}56$	$-6{\cdot}82$	$Cr^{III}/S_2O_8^{2-}/H^+$	Strong oxidant. Dimeric in acid solution.
Mn	+2	Mn^{2+}	pl pink	$-2{\cdot}36$	$-4{\cdot}82$	$Mn(OH)_2$	white	$-1{\cdot}44$	$-3{\cdot}90$	$(MnO_2, MnO_4^-)/$reduce$/H^+$	Stable. Readily oxidised by air in alkali.
	+3	Mn^{3+}	red	$-0{\cdot}85$	$-4{\cdot}54$	$MnOOH$	brown	$-0{\cdot}46$	$-4{\cdot}15$	$(3Mn^{2+}+MnO_4^-)/H^+$	Reduced by H_2O. Disprop. to $Mn^{2+}+MnO_2$, but slowly in acid.
	+4	MnO_2	brown	$-0{\cdot}10$	$-4{\cdot}92$	MnO_2	brown	$+0{\cdot}12$	$-4{\cdot}80$	$MnO_4^-/$reduce$/$alkali	Found only as insol. MnO_2.
	+5	$(HMnO_3)$		$+2{\cdot}4$	$-3{\cdot}6$	MnO_3^-	blue	$+1{\cdot}8$	$-4{\cdot}3$	$MnO_4^-/XS\ SO_3^{2-}$	Stable only in conc. alkali. Disprop. to $Mn^{2+}+MnO_4^-$ in acid.
	+6	(H_2MnO_4)		$+4{\cdot}63$	$-2{\cdot}75$	MnO_4^{2-}	green	$+2{\cdot}97$	$-4{\cdot}40$	$MnO_2/KNO_3/KOH/$fuse	Stable only in conc. alkali. Disprop. to $Mn^{2+}+MnO_4^-$ in acid.
	+7	$HMnO_4$	purple	$+5{\cdot}19$	$-3{\cdot}41$	MnO_4^-	purple	$+4{\cdot}36$	$-4{\cdot}24$	MnO_4^{2-}/H^+, $Mn^{2+}/NaBiO_3$	Very strong oxidant.
Fe	+2	Fe^{2+}	pl green	$-0{\cdot}88$	$-3{\cdot}34$	$Fe(OH)_2$	white	$-0{\cdot}10$	$-2{\cdot}56$	$Fe^{3+}/Zn/H^+$	Oxidised by air, very rapidly in alkali.
	+3	Fe^{3+}	pl violet	$-0{\cdot}11$	$-3{\cdot}80$	$FeOOH$	redbrown	$+0{\cdot}44$	$-3{\cdot}25$	$Fe^{2+}/$any oxidant	Stable. Readily hydrolysed.
	+6	(H_2FeO_4)		$+6{\cdot}49$	$-0{\cdot}88$	FeO_4^{2-}	red	$+5{\cdot}08$	$-2{\cdot}29$	$Fe^{3+}/Cl_2/$conc. alkali	Stable only in conc. alkali. Very strong oxidant.
Co	+2	Co^{2+}	pink	$-0{\cdot}55$	$-3{\cdot}01$	$Co(OH)_2$	blue	$+0{\cdot}20$	$-2{\cdot}26$		Stable.
	+3	Co^{3+}	brown	$+1{\cdot}25$	$-2{\cdot}43$	$CoOOH$	black	$+1{\cdot}19$	$-2{\cdot}49$	$Co^{2+}/O_3/HClO_4$ aq	Reduced rapidly by H_2O. Strongly hydrolysed.
Ni	+2	Ni^{2+}	green	$-0{\cdot}50$	$-2{\cdot}96$	$Ni(OH)_2$	green	$+0{\cdot}22$	$-2{\cdot}42$		Stable.
	+4	(NiO_2)		$+2{\cdot}86$	$-2{\cdot}06$	NiO_2	black	$+2{\cdot}85$	$-2{\cdot}05$	$Ni^{2+}/OCl^-/$alkali	Found only as insol. oxide. Reduced by H_2O. Strong oxidant.
Cu	+1	Cu^+	none	$+0{\cdot}52$	$-0{\cdot}71$	Cu_2O	red	$+1{\cdot}18$	$-0{\cdot}04$		Disprop. to $Cu+Cu^{2+}$ unless complexed.
	+2	Cu^{2+}	blue	$+0{\cdot}67$	$-1{\cdot}78$	$Cu(OH)_2$	blue	$+2{\cdot}09$	$-0{\cdot}37$	Cu^{2+}/SO_2	Stable.
Zn	+2	Zn^{2+}	none	$-1{\cdot}53$	$-3{\cdot}98$	$Zn(OH)_2$	none	$-0{\cdot}83$	$-3{\cdot}29$		Stable.

The following conventions are used (cf. Section 1.6):

ΔG^0/FV $= -nE^0_O$/V, standard acid conditions, pH 0, in the absence of oxygen;

ΔG^0_b/FV $= -nE^0_b$/V, standard alkaline conditions, pH 14, in the absence of oxygen;

ΔG^0_O/FV $= -nE^0_O$/V, standard acid conditions, pH 0, in the presence of oxygen at 1 atm;

ΔG^0_{bO}/FV $= -nE^0_{bO}$/V, standard alkaline conditions, pH 14, in the presence of oxygen at 1 atm.

formed of composition $[FeCl_n(OH_2)_{6-n}]^{(3-n)+}$ ($n = 1-3$); the intense blood-red thiocyanate complexes are well-known indicators of the presence of iron(III). Chromium(III) also readily forms complexes, such as the familiar green $[CrCl_2(OH_2)_4]^+$ and $[Cr(OSO_3)(OH_2)_5]^+$ ions present in hydrated chromic salts.

When the pH is raised, precipitation of the hydroxides (or, more likely, hydrated oxides) occurs readily, and at much lower pH-values than for the divalent metals. The deprotonation which produces the hydroxide or oxide is, of course, a stepwise process:

$$[M(OH_2)_6]^{3+} \rightleftharpoons [M(OH_2)_5OH]^{2+} + H^+$$

$$[M(OH_2)_5OH]^{2+} \rightleftharpoons [M(OH_2)_4(OH)_2]^+ + H^+$$

that is, the aquo-complexes function as acids. For titanium, chromium and iron, the pK_a-values of the tripositive hexa-aquo ions are 3·89, *ca.* 4, and 3·05 respectively, corresponding to moderately strong acids (cf. hydrofluoric and acetic acids with pK_a-values of 3·45 and 4·75 respectively).

In addition to simple deprotonation, polymerisation may occur, leading ultimately to the precipitation of the hydrous oxide. For instance, the following equilibria are known to occur for chromium(III):

$$2[Cr(OH_2)_5(OH)]^{2+} \rightleftharpoons [(H_2O)_4Cr(OH)_2Cr(OH_2)_4]^{4+} + 2H_2O$$

$$[(H_2O)_4Cr(OH)_2Cr(OH_2)_4]^{4+} \rightleftharpoons [(H_2O)_5CrOCr(OH_2)_5]^{4+} + H_2O$$

$$2[Cr(OSO_3)(OH_2)_5]^+ \rightleftharpoons [(H_2O)_4(O_3SO)CrOCr(OSO_3)(OH_2)_4] + H_2O + 2H^+$$

These species are important in the refining of chromite, since the iron in solution is readily reduced to $Fe(OH_2)_6^{2+}$ leaving the chromium as $Cr(OH_2)_6^{3+}$. Addition of a little alkali preferentially deprotonates the chromium(III) complex and warming the solution induces the polymerisation ('olation'). The polymeric species remain in solution while iron is removed by crystallisation as ferrous ammonium sulphate; had the chromium been present as $Cr(OH_2)_6^{3+}$, chrome alum would also have crystallised out. After removal of the iron, the chromium solution is acidified and diluted, re-forming $Cr(OH_2)_6^{3+}$, and chrome alum is crystallised out and subsequently electrolysed.

The only metals found in the **tetrapositive state** in aqueous solution are titanium and vanadium, although chromium and manganese both form insoluble dioxides. Both titanium and vanadium were originally thought to form the MO_2(aq) ions in acid solution, but it is now known that this is true only for vanadium. The $V=O^{2+}$ unit behaves rather like a typical dipositive cation, e.g. on addition of alkali the hydroxide $VO(OH)_2$ is precipitated, which is insoluble even in concentrated alkali. Titanium(IV), on the other hand, seems to form the $Ti(OH)_2^{2+}$(aq) ion in acid solution, which readily forms complexes with anions, e.g. F^-, Cl^-, HSO_4^-, and which is readily deprotonated by raising the pH, when hydrated TiO_2 is precipitated. On addition of excess alkali, the oxide re-dissolves giving anionic titanate(IV) species, probably TiO_3^{2-}(aq).

A similar oxo-species is found for **pentavalent** vanadium in strongly acidic solution, but this appears to contain two oxo-ligands: VO_2^+(aq) in a non-linear arrangement. On raising the pH to about 2, V_2O_5 is precipitated, which dissolves readily in concentrated alkali to give vanadate(V) ions, VO_4^{3-}, above pH 13. At intermediate pH-values, a variety of polymeric species is formed by condensation of the tetrahedral VO_4-units and protonation of the eliminated oxide ions:

$$O_3VO^{3-} + OVO_3^{3-} \rightleftharpoons O_3VOVO_3^{4-} + O^{2-}$$

$$2H^+ + O^{2-} \rightleftharpoons H_2O$$

The second reaction is strongly exothermic and provides the driving force for the overall reaction. In principle this process could be repeated, giving chains of general formula $(VO_4)_nVO_3^{(3n+2)-}$. In practice, the formation of rings and three-dimensional structures involving

VO_6-units also occurs, but not all species are equally stable. Those which can be obtained in high enough concentration to be characterised are $V_2O_7^{4-}$, $V_3O_9^{3-}$, $V_4O_{12}^{4-}$ and $V_{10}O_{28}^{6-}$. The structures of these species, and indeed their accurate formulae, are not known. In particular, the number of water molecules associated with any given species cannot be determined. Crystalline salts may be obtained from the solutions, but there is no necessary relation between the nature of the species in solution and that which will crystallise out. It is quite possible for a species present in only small concentration at equilibrium to give rise to the least soluble salt, which will then crystallise out, while the solution equilibrium readjusts to restore the concentration. Similarly, the structures of the anions in the crystal are not necessarily the same as those in solution. The trivanadate ion is almost certainly cyclic but the precise number of VO_3 units in the polymer is not definitely established. It seems probable, however, that the decavanadate ion, $V_{10}O_{28}^{6-}$, has the same structure both in the solid and in solution. The structure in the solid salts is built up of VO_6-octahedra which share edges, as shown in Fig. 3.16.

The manganate(V) ion, MnO_4^{3-}, is formed by reduction of permanganate (with sulphite), or disproportionation of MnO_2, in concentrated alkali. This bright blue ion is stable only in strong alkali and disproportionates into MnO_4^- and MnO_2 on acidification. Little is known of its chemistry.

Fig. 3.16   The structure of the $V_{10}O_{28}^{6-}$ ion. The ion is formed by the condensation of ten octahedral VO_6-units; six pack together in the central plane and two more pairs fit over and under this plane (after A. F. Wells (1975) *Structural Inorganic Chemistry*, 4th edn, OUP)

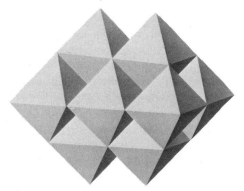

The **hexavalent state** is exhibited by chromium, manganese and iron in the tetrahedral anions MO_4^{2-}. The deep red ferrate(VI) ion is formed by vigorous oxidation of iron(III) in strongly basic solution, and is stable only in that medium or in solid salts. On acidification, it oxidises water rapidly, giving oxygen and iron(III). The green manganate(VI) ion is also stable only under alkaline conditions, but disproportionates into MnO_4^- and MnO_2 when the pH is lowered. For chromium, the +6 state is the highest attainable (as also for iron), and chromates(VI) can be obtained in acid solutions without disproportionation or reduction by the solvent. In very strong acid, CrO_3 is formed; presumably its precipitation is preceded by polymerisation, but only the familiar dichromate ion, $Cr_2O_7^{2-}$, has been characterised. There is some evidence for tri- and tetra-chromates, $Cr_3O_{10}^{2-}$ and $Cr_4O_{13}^{2-}$. Above pH 8 the only species present in solution is yellow CrO_4^{2-}, while between pH 2 and 6 $HCrO_4^-$ and $Cr_2O_7^{2-}$ are in equilibrium.

The only representative of the **heptapositive state** is the permanganate ion, one of the most powerful oxidants commonly available. It is, in principle, capable of oxidising water; fortunately, the reaction is slow, but it is catalysed by the product, MnO_2, and by light. Permanganate

$$4MnO_4^- + 2H_2O \rightarrow 4MnO_2 + 3O_2 + 4OH^-$$

solutions for quantitative work must therefore be boiled, to complete the oxidation of any impurities, filtered to remove MnO_2, and stored in the dark. No polymanganates(VII) are known.

The types of species obtained in aqueous solution are thus seen to depend on the oxidation state of the metal and on the pH of the solution. The transition from aquo- to hydroxo- to oxo-ligand is facilitated by a high formal charge on the metal ion, which may be regarded as repelling the proton, making it easier to remove. Alternatively, the charge on the metal atom may

$$M \leftarrow \overset{H}{\underset{H}{\ddot{O}}} \qquad M-\overset{H}{\underset{H^+}{\ddot{O}}} \qquad M=\overset{H^+}{\underset{H^+}{\ddot{O}}}$$

be regarded as polarising the oxygen atom; electrons are drawn towards the metal and away from the O–H bond. A third approach is to regard the metal ion and the proton as competing for charge donated by the oxide ion. As the metal ion becomes more polarising so the proton becomes easier to remove. The tripositive cations are therefore stronger acids than dipositive ions and polymerise more readily, and M_2O_3 is precipitated at a lower pH than $M(OH)_2$. With the highest oxidation states the polarisation of the oxygen ligands is so strong that only anionic oxo-complexes are formed, MO_4^{n-}, although protonated species can be detected. For intermediate oxidation states, $+4$ and $+5$, three additional features are found: (a) either cationic or anionic species are formed depending on the pH; (b) as the metal ion becomes more polarising, hydroxo-groups are replaced by oxo-groups even in the cationic species, $Ti(OH)_2^{2+}$, VO^{2+}, VO_2^+ (for still more polarising cations, anionic oxo-complexes are formed); (c) polymeric, condensed species are found, especially on the anionic side. The pH-range over which these species exist, and the number of species which can be detected, both depend on the polarising nature of the metal ion. The optimum appears to be V^{5+}. The charge on the cation must be high enough to allow easy formation of anionic oxo-species, but not so high that a polymeric structure is destabilised by repulsions between the metal ions or by weakening of the M–O–M bonds by polarisation effects. (With the larger ions of the $4d$- and $5d$-series, Mo^{6+} and W^{6+} give many polyanions.) That repulsion between adjacent metal ions is important is indicated by the fact that in fusing tetrahedra or octahedra together into polymeric structures, only corners or edges are shared, and not faces, which would bring the highly charged metal ions closer together.

The relative stabilities of the various oxidation states are best summarised in oxidation state diagrams, as in Fig. 3.14. Several points of interest may be seen:

(a) Minima represent the most stable species under the conditions shown. Thus the elemental metals will dissolve in acids (i.e. be oxidised by H^+) to give Ti^{3+}, V^{3+}, Cr^{3+}, Mn^{2+}, Fe^{2+}, Co^{2+}, Ni^{2+} and Zn^{2+}; copper will not dissolve. (The oxidation of Cr^{2+} by H^+/H_2O is very slow, so that the experimentally observed product is Cr^{2+}.) In the presence of oxygen, some metals are oxidised further: Ti^{4+}, V^{5+}, Fe^{3+}.

(b) Any given oxidation state becomes less stable (more oxidising) as the series of metals is traversed (note again that there is an irregularity at Mn^{2+}, which is not readily oxidised to Mn^{3+} whereas Fe^{2+} is oxidised by atmospheric oxygen).

(c) The highest oxidation states become progressively stronger oxidants in the series VO_4^{3-}, CrO_4^{2-}, MnO_4^-, FeO_4^{2-}.

(d) The relative stabilities of the oxidation states of any one metal are pH-dependent.

This last point is readily explained. Since the data are related to the elemental metal as the standard state, it is convenient to consider each species as being formed from the metal. The effect of changing the pH is then easily seen. Consider the manganese system. Manganese(II) appears to be more stable in acid than alkaline solution (relative to Mn^0), manganese(VII) is less stable, while the stability of manganese(IV) is not sensitive to change in pH. These differences in behaviour are related to the consumption or production of protons in the oxidation of the metal. If the reaction consumes protons, it will be inhibited by raising the pH, which restricts the supply of protons. Conversely, a reaction which produces protons will be facilitated by alkaline conditions. The reactions concerned here are:

$$Mn + 2H^+ \rightleftharpoons Mn^{2+} + H_2 \quad \text{(protons consumed)}$$

$$Mn + 4H_2O \rightleftharpoons MnO_4^- + \tfrac{7}{2}H_2 + H^+ \quad \text{(protons produced)}$$

$$Mn + 2H_2O \rightleftharpoons MnO_2 + 2H_2 \quad \text{(no protons involved)}$$

These trends may be expressed more formally via the relation

$$\Delta G = \Delta G^0 + RT \ln \left\{ \frac{\Pi_{products}}{\Pi_{reactants}} \right\}$$

where the Π terms are the products of the activities of the species concerned raised to the power corresponding to the stoicheiometry of the reaction. Thus, for the first reaction

$$\Delta G(1) = \Delta G^0(1) + RT \ln \left\{ \frac{[Mn^{2+}][H_2]}{[H^+]^2[Mn]} \right\}$$

$$= \Delta G^0(1) + RT \ln \left\{ \frac{[Mn^{2+}]}{[H^+]^2} \right\}$$

since Mn(s) and H_2(g) are in standard states and have unit activity. Hence, a rise in pH results in an increase in ΔG, i.e. a destabilisation. This will be so for all reactions which consume protons, i.e. those in which cationic species are formed. The converse effect is seen when anionic (or acid) species are formed, since protons are liberated, as in the second reaction above.

$$\Delta G(2) = \Delta G^0(2) + RT \ln \left\{ \frac{[MnO_4^-][H^+][H_2]^{\frac{7}{2}}}{[H_2O]^4[Mn]} \right\}$$

where ΔG is lowered by lowering $[H^+]$. Thus anionic species are favoured by alkaline conditions. The extent of this effect is obviously dependent on the number of protons involved in the reaction. Thus for the manganate(VI) ion

$$\Delta G(MnO_4^{2-}) = \Delta G^0(MnO_4^{2-}) + RT \ln \left\{ \frac{[MnO_4^{2-}][H^+]^2[H_2]^3}{[H_2O]^4[Mn]} \right\}$$

the effect of changing the pH will be roughly twice as great as for MnO_4^-, so that in concentrated alkali MnO_4^{2-} becomes stable to disproportionation. Clearly, in reactions in which solid oxides are the products (e.g. MnO_2, 'Co_2O_3'), changing the acidity will have little effect.

The destabilisation of anionic species by increased acid concentration may also be viewed as a polarisation effect. If an M=O bond is protonated, M–O–H$^+$, some electron density must be withdrawn from the M–O bond and hence from the metal ion. The metal ion thus becomes more positively charged, and becomes a stronger oxidant, a more avid acceptor of electrons. A similar competition effect explains the greater stability of the anions than the neutral oxides from which they may be (formally) derived; contrast permanganate with manganese(VII) oxide! In the anions, there are four M=O bonds, whereas in the oxides at least one of the bonds is a single bond, whence it follows that the positive charge on the metal ion is more effectively neutralised in the anion, resulting in greater stability.

3.6 Rationale

The three systems studied here in some detail have several features in common, which might reasonably be expected to have a common basis. Those features are:

(a) Any given oxidation state becomes thermodynamically less stable, relative to the elemental metal (and oxygen or the halogens), with increasing atomic number of the metal, but zinc(II) seems extra stable;

(b) high oxidation states ($\geqslant 4$) are found only in the early Groups;

(c) the Group oxidation state is found only for titanium, vanadium, chromium and manganese;

(d) the regular trend in stability of the +2 and +3 states is broken at manganese, which appears reluctant to form manganese(III) whereas iron(III) is common;

(e) copper is unique in forming the +1 oxidation state;

(f) the common coordination number is six, except for the high oxidation states in oxides and oxo-anions which have tetrahedral structures; the corresponding fluorides are six-coordinate;

(g) some metal ions (Cr^{2+}, Mn^{3+}, Cu^{2+}) frequently give distorted octahedral or even square planar structures.

The last two points may be dealt with separately from the others. Coordination numbers are governed by several factors. In purely electrostatic terms the attraction between the metal cation and the negative (or dipolar) ligands must outweigh the mutual repulsions of the ligands on each other. The attraction increases in direct proportion to the number of ligands and the repulsion (approximately) to its square. This difference clearly places an upper limit on the coordination number, although the limiting value will depend on the charge on the metal ion. For uni-negative or partially negative (i.e. dipolar) ligands, six-coordination is stable over a wide range of charge on the metal, relative to both higher and lower coordination numbers (Fig. 3.17). The introduction of a more highly negatively charged ligand, e.g. O^{2-}, increases the ligand–ligand repulsions, resulting in a drop in coordination number to four. Similar considerations apply to crystal systems with the additional constraint that a satisfactory packing of the ions into a symmetrical lattice must also be achieved.

The distorted structures shown by Cr^{2+}, Mn^{3+}, and Cu^{2+} are a result of repulsive interactions between the ligands and non-bonding d-electrons on the metal ion. This phenomenon, the Jahn–Teller effect, is most pronounced in systems with four or nine d-electrons, as is discussed in Chapter 4.

It is clear, however, that electrostatic interactions are not the only forces at work. Particularly for the more highly-charged metal ions, covalency effects are also important. These are most readily considered in terms of the formation of coordinate bonds by donation from lone pairs on the (anionic) ligands to the positively charged metal ion. Transfer of charge by donation will be expected to continue until the metal ion has become approximately electrically neutral. The number of ligands required to achieve this will depend on the charge on the metal ion, on its polarising power, and on the polarisability of the ligands. A hard, non-polarisable ligand, such as F^- or OH_2, will transfer charge sparingly, requiring a higher coordination number than a more polarisable ligand such as O^{2-} or the heavier halide ions.

Electroneutrality effects also play a part in determining the oxidation states which may occur in various systems. The factors at work may be expressed (very qualitatively) as shown in Fig. 3.18. The net charge on the metal ion is shown as the sum of the (positive) charge gained by ionisation to the appropriate oxidation state and the (negative) charge donated by the ligands. As the oxidation state of the metal increases, so does its polarising power (q/r), but the increase is not linear because of the decrease in radius. Stable compounds are expected in the region where the metal atom has a net charge of approximately zero (electroneutrality principle). It is immediately obvious that

Fig. 3.17   Net electrostatic energies of complexes $[M^{Z+}(X^-)_n]^{(Z-n)+}$ as a function of the charge, Z, on the metal atom. All M–X distances are assumed to be identical and shielding by the metal atom is ignored. Numbers on the lines are the values of n. (After R. V. Parish *Coord. Chem. Rev.*, **1**, 439 (1966))

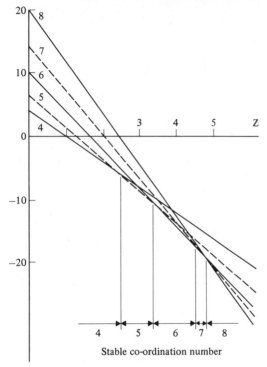

Fig. 3.18   Accumulation of charge on the metal atom with increasing oxidation state for (*a*) hard, non-polarisable ligands, or large, poorly polarising metal atom (*b*) soft, polarisable ligands, or small highly polarising metal atom

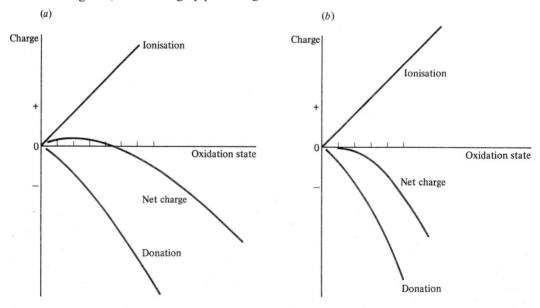

polarisable ligands, such as iodide, transfer relatively large amounts of charge to the metal, favouring the lower oxidation states. If the oxidation state is increased too far, the ligand is polarised so strongly that complete transfer of electrons occurs, with oxidation of the ligand and reduction of the metal, as in the reaction of Fe^{3+} or Cu^{2+} with iodide ion. The harder ligands transfer charge much less easily, and higher oxidation states are preferred. On this basis it seems curious that higher oxidation states should be attained in oxides and oxyanions (and oxyhalides) than in fluorides and fluoro–anions. This trend is presumably related to the capacity of oxygen to form double bonds with the metal, i.e. in the oxo-anions there are eight electron pairs to be polarised in four double bonds, rather than six in the fluoro-compounds.

An alternative, more quantitative approach to the relative stabilities of the oxidation states is the thermodynamic treatment. For any particular system, two major terms must be examined, viz. the energy of formation of the metal ion from the elemental metal (the enthalpy of atomisation plus the ionisation energies), and the chemical energy released on the formation of the compound or dissolution of the ion (lattice or hydration energies). Consideration of the variations in these quantities can give much insight into the behaviour of the $3d$-metals.

Lattice energies and hydration energies both increase with decreasing radius of the cation. The radii decrease with increasing oxidation state and also with increasing atomic number, although the latter trend is not entirely smooth across the series (see Section 4.6.2). Nevertheless, chemical energies are expected to increase with increasing oxidation state and with increasing atomic number of the metal. The latter trend is clearly against the experimental evidence, which shows that any given oxidation state becomes less thermodynamically stable across the series, and that high oxidation states become more difficult to obtain and cannot be achieved for the later metals. Obviously, there must be trends in the ion-formation energies which offset these favourable influences. Some relevant data are given in Table 3.15 and Fig. 3.19 and 20.

Table 3.15.   Enthalpies of formation of gaseous metal ions, $\Delta H_f^0(M^{n+})/kJ\ mol^{-1}$.

n =	0	1	2	3	4
Sc	326	957	2 192	4 581	11 711
Ti	473	1 129	2 438	5 088	9 261
V	515	1 165	2 579	5 407	10 007
Cr	397	1 049	2 641	5 627	10 527
Mn	281	998	2 507	5 785	10 779
Fe	416	1 178	2 739	5 695	11 197
Co	425	1 183	2 827	6 058	11 162
Ni	430	1 166	2 918	6 407	11 804
Cu	339	1 084	3 042	6 587	12 269
Zn	125	1 031	2 765	6 596	12 579

The enthalpies of atomisation are much greater than for the s- and p-block metals, being rather more than half the first ionisation energies. They reflect the variation in the strength of bonding of the metal lattice, which varies with the number of d-electrons, having maxima in Groups V and VIII and a minimum at manganese (Group VII; manganese also has a rather odd crystal structure). This effect should therefore make all manganese compounds more stable (by about $100\ kJ\ mol^{-1}$) than analogous compounds of the neighbouring elements, again at variance with experience.

The ionisation energies also vary rather irregularly, but two important trends may be discerned. Firstly, there is a general increase of ionisation energy with increasing atomic number, although this trend is interrupted in the middle of the series for each ionisation. The general

Fig. 3.20   Enthalpies of formation of $M^{n+}(g)$. ionisation energies

Fig. 3.20   Enthalpies of formation of $M^{n+}(g)$. Dotted lines represent approximately the sum of lattice energy and enthalpy of anion formation for oxides or chlorides

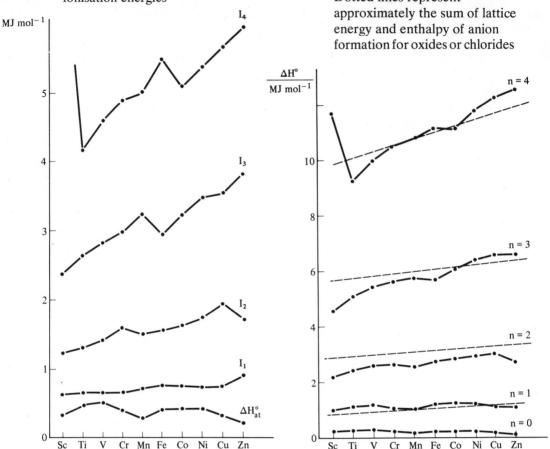

increase is the result of the steadily increasing nuclear charge, which is incompletely offset by the shielding effect of the additional electrons. Superimposed on this trend is the effect of exchange energy.

The exchange energy is a stabilising term roughly proportional to the number of pairs of electrons with parallel spin; it is the driving force behind Hund's rule which demands that as many electrons as possible have parallel spins.† However, exchange interactions between electrons of

---

† In physical terms, the exchange energy arises from the fact that electrons with parallel spins are constrained to keep slightly farther apart than those with opposite spins, i.e. the average electrostatic repulsion is lower. This in turn derives from the antisymmetric nature of the overall wavefunction with respect to the interchange (exchange) of electrons. Consider two electrons, a and b, two orbitals with space wavefunctions ψ_1 and ψ_2. The total wavefunction is the product of the space part and the spin part, and must change sign when the electrons are exchanged, i.e. either the space function or the spin function must be odd, but not both:

$$\text{either} \quad [\psi_1(a)+\psi_2(b)][\Sigma(a)-\Sigma(b)] \quad \text{spins opposed}$$

$$\text{or} \quad [\psi_1(a)-\psi_2(b)][\Sigma(a)+\Sigma(b)] \quad \text{spins parallel.}$$

If ψ_1 and ψ_2 are the same, that is both electrons are in the same orbital, it is immediately apparent that the spins must be opposed (Pauli principle). If the spins are parallel, the space function must be odd, which means effectively that there is zero probability that both electrons will simultaneously be at the same point. For the even space function there is a finite, albeit small, probability that the electrons will meet.

different l-value are very small; those between the d- and s-electrons contribute very little. In the first ionisation an s-electron is removed and this ionisation energy rises fairly smoothly across the series reflecting the increasing effective nuclear charge. For higher degrees of ionisation, the number of d-electrons changes, $d^n \rightarrow d^{n-1}$, and in these cases exchange effects will be important. Exchange energies will contribute to the energy of the metal ions both before and after ionisation, but will usually be less after ionisation because there are less electrons. The loss in exchange energy therefore appears as an increase in the ionisation energy, by the relative amounts shown in Table 3.16. Thus, the ionisation energy rises to a maximum at the d^5 configuration (the stable half-filled shell) and then falls for d^6, rising again towards d^{10}. The maxima in the ionisation energies in the centre of the series therefore occur for the ionisation of Cr^+, Mn^{2+} and Fe^{3+}.

Table 3.16. Loss of exchange energy in ionisation $d^n \rightarrow d^{n-1}$.

Configuration, d^n		No. of pairs	Configuration, d^{n-1}		No. of pairs	Loss of exchange energy
d^2	↑ ↑	1	d^1	↑	0	K
d^3	↑ ↑ ↑	3	d^2	↑ ↑	1	2K
d^4	↑ ↑ ↑ ↑	6	d^3	↑ ↑ ↑	3	3K
d^5	↑ ↑ ↑ ↑ ↑	10	d^4	↑ ↑ ↑ ↑	6	4K
d^6	↑↓ ↑ ↑ ↑ ↑	10	d^5	↑ ↑ ↑ ↑ ↑	10	0
d^7	↑↓ ↑↓ ↑ ↑ ↑	11	d^6	↑↓ ↑ ↑ ↑ ↑	10	K
d^8	↑↓ ↑↓ ↑↓ ↑ ↑	13	d^7	↑↓ ↑↓ ↑ ↑ ↑	11	2K
d^9	↑↓ ↑↓ ↑↓ ↑↓ ↑	16	d^8	↑↓ ↑↓ ↑↓ ↑ ↑	13	3K
d^{10}	↑↓ ↑↓ ↑↓ ↑↓ ↑↓.	20	d^9	↑↓ ↑↓ ↑↓ ↑↓ ↑	16	4K

The number of units of exchange energy is proportional to the number of distinct pairs of electrons with the same spin, i.e. the number of ways in which the electrons can be interchanged in pairs to give a different arrangement. For electrons of one spin sub-set this is $^nC_2$. For example, in the d^4 case there would be $4 \times 3/(1 \times 2) = 6$ such pairs; if the electrons are labelled a–d, a can be exchanged with b, c, or d, b with c or d (exchange with a has already been counted), and c with d.

The second obvious trend in ionisation energies is the marked increase for successive ionisations. This is expected, since electrons are being removed from ions with successively higher positive charges. As the data in Table 3.17 show, after the first ionisation the total energy required to form $M^{n+}(g)$ form $M(g)$ increases roughly as n^2. The ion-formation energy increases more

Table 3.17. Enthalpies of formation of gaseous ions from gaseous metal atoms ($kJ\,mol^{-1}$)

	Ti	Fe
$M(g) \rightarrow M^+(g)$	633	762
$M(g) \rightarrow M^{2+}(g)$	1 968	2 323
$M(g) \rightarrow M^{3+}(g)$	4 680	5 279
$M(g) \rightarrow M^{4+}(g)$	8 550	10 780

rapidly with increasing oxidation state than the chemical energy (e.g. on Kapustinskii's model, ignoring the change in radius of the cation, the lattice energies of the series MX_n increase with n in the ratio $1:3:6:10$), so that in every system there is a limiting, maximum oxidation state. When this trend is combined with the first, the increase in ionisation energies with atomic number, the inability of the later metals to attain high oxidation states appears very reasonable. A rough comparison of chemical energies with ion-formation energies is shown in Fig. 3.20, from which it is apparent that the uni-positive state is endothermic or only weakly exothermic for all metals except copper. The dipositive state is always exothermic but less so than the tripositive state at the beginning of the series and more at the end. The tetrapositive state is exothermic only for the early metals.

The variation in ion-formation energies with increasing oxidation state is fairly smooth, and rather faster than in the *p*-block, with the result that series of compounds may be obtained in which the oxidation state of the metal changes by one unit between successive members. (This is discussed further in Chapter 6 and Appendix D.) For the majority of the *d*-block metals, copper being the notable exception, only the +1 state is unstable; the first stable oxidation state is +2, corresponding to removal of all the *s*-electrons. Thereafter, the *d*-electrons can be ionised off singly, rather than in groups as happens in the *p* block.

The moderately regular trend in the pattern of oxidation states is broken in the region Cr–Mn–Fe: manganese appears reluctant to be oxidised to the tripositive state which can be attained easily for both chromium and iron. This could arise either because manganese is more difficult to oxidise than the regular trend would suggest, or because iron is unexpectedly easy to oxidise. An analysis in terms of the Born–Haber energy cycle should provide some useful pointers, and Table 3.18 gives data for the formation of the di- and tri-chlorides. Three of these compounds are known, $FeCl_2$, $MnCl_2$, and $FeCl_3$, and their enthalpies of formation have been measured. All the other terms in the energy cycle are known with the exception of the lattice energies, which may therefore be derived. In order to calculate a value for the enthalpy of formation of $MnCl_3$, a lattice energy value is needed. As a reasonable approximation, that of $FeCl_3$ may be used; this should be accurate to within 2–3 per cent. The calculated value of $\Delta H_f^0(MnCl_3)$ shows that this compound is not intrinsically unstable relative to the elements, but it is unstable to dissociation into $MnCl_2 + \frac{1}{2}Cl_2$.

Table 3.18.   Terms in the energy cycle for iron and manganese halides (kJ mol^{-1}).

	$\Delta H_f^0(MX_n)$	ΔH_{at}^0	Σ IE	$n\Delta H_f^0(Cl(g))$	$U(MX_n)$
$FeCl_2$	−301	+416	+2 323	−454	**+2 626**
$MnCl_2$	−473	+281	+2 225	−454	**+2 525**
Difference	−132	−135	−98		+101
$FeCl_3$	−405	+416	+5 279	−681	**+5 419**
$MnCl_3$	**−342**	+281	+5 477	−681	+5 419
Difference	+63	−135	+198		

Figures in bold type are derived values.

It appears then both that $MnCl_2$ is much more stable than $FeCl_2$ and that $MnCl_3$ is less stable than $FeCl_3$. The first observation is primarily a result of the low enthalpy of atomisation of manganese, with a smaller contribution form the lower ionisation energies. The lower lattice energy of $MnCl_2$ presumably reflects the larger radius of Mn^{2+} than Fe^{2+}. However, the destabilisation of $MnCl_3$ is clearly a result of the much bigger third ionisation energy: $d^5 \rightarrow d^4$ requires more energy than $d^6 \rightarrow d^5$, and this outweighs the difference in enthalpies of atomisation. A similar treatment may be applied to rationalise the univalency of copper; this is left as an exercise for the reader (the solution is given in Appendix E).

Bibliography

BENT, 27, 32, 34, 36–7, 40–2; **CW**, 19, 25; **D**, 3; **ES**, 18; **HJ**, 27, 32–6; **J**, 6; **L**, 16; **MM**, 11; **PW**, 23, 25–6; **W**, 12, 25.

A. Earnshaw and T. Harrington, *The Chemistry of the Transition Elements*, Oxford University Press, 1973. Some systematic chemistry and a good introductory treatment of coordination chemistry.

D. Nicholls, *Complexes and First-Row Transition Elements*, Macmillan, 1974. A useful, brief survey of the basic chemistry and coordination chemistry of the $3d$-elements.

R. Colton and J. H. Canterford, *Halides of the First-Row Transition Metals*, Wiley, 1969. Comprehensive treatment of halides and oxyhalides.

C. Rosenblum and S. L. Holt, *Transition Metal Chem.*, **7**, 87 (1972). Detailed account of structures of oxides and halides of $3d$-metals in high oxidation states.

R. A. Walton, *Prog. Inorg. Chem.*, **16**, 1 (1972). Review of the preparation, properties and structures of the halides and oxyhalides of the metals of Groups IV–VI.

R. J. H. Clark, *The Chemistry of Titanium and Vanadium*, Elsevier, 1968. Good survey of these two elements.

M. Barber, J. W. Linnett, and N. H. Taylor, *J. Chem. Soc.*, 3323 (1961). Simple ionic Born–Haber treatment of relative stabilities of mono-, di-, and tri-halides of the $3d$-metals.

R. V. Parish, *Coord. Chem. Rev.*, **1**, 439 (1966). Review of the factors influencing coordination numbers.

The metallic elements form a wide variety of coordination compounds, i.e. compounds in which other atoms or molecules are bound to the metal ion by the formation of donor-acceptor, or coordinate, bonds. In principle any group which possesses a lone pair of electrons can act as the donor, or **ligand,** an obvious example being the water molecule. A solvated (*aquated*) metal ion is a cationic complex, usually six-coordinate, $[M(OH_2)_6]^{n+}$, but even simpler ligands are possible, e.g. halide ions as in TiF_6^{2-}, $SnCl_3^-$ or the neutral halides. Equally, ligands may be extremely complex molecules, particularly those found in biological systems such as chlorophyll (which contains magnesium), haemoglobin (iron), vitamin B_{12} (cobalt), and the enzyme carboxypeptidase (zinc). The metal atoms appear to play vital rôles in the functioning of these materials and their replacement by other metals often accounts for the toxicity of those metals (e.g. cadmium replaces zinc very readily, but the resulting complex is not an active enzyme).

Except under very special circumstances (the vapour phase at low pressure) metal atoms and ions are always coordinated. The nature of the ligands can have a profound effect on the properties which the metal ion appears to exhibit, e.g. on the relative stabilities of its oxidation states, on its colour, on the ease with which the ligands can be replaced by other ligands, on the magnetic properties, etc., etc. The study of coordination compounds is thus a wide and important field, and one which cannot be divorced from systematic chemistry, since even 'ordinary' compounds are often conveniently regarded as coordination compounds.

4.1 Bonding in coordination compounds

A large part of the bond energy in many coordination compounds is electrostatic in origin – the attraction of the positively charged metal ion for the electron pairs of the ligands. For many purposes this ion-dipole description is quite adequate, for instance in the majority of cases the stereochemistry and to some extent the coordination number can be rationalised on this basis, as described in Chapter 3. Frequently, the stereochemistry is that which minimises the repulsions between the ligands. However, it is clear that there is also a covalent contribution to the metal–ligand bond, which becomes increasingly important as the charge on the metal ion increases [or decreases, since several instances are known where the metal has an oxidation state of zero or less, e.g. $Ni(CO)_4$, $Fe(CO)_4^{2-}$].

A covalent bond is most simply described in valence-bond terms as arising from the interaction of an orbital on the ligand, containing the lone pair of electrons, with an empty hybrid orbital on the metal ion directed towards the ligand. The common hybridisation schemes are shown in Table 4.1. While such descriptions are frequently convenient and are often quite adequate, there are some instances in which difficulties occur. For instance, TiF_6^{2-} is adequately described in terms of

Table 4.1   Hybridisation schemes

Coordination number	Stereochemistry	Hybridisation	Example
2	linear	sp	$Ag(CN)_2^-$
3	trigonal	sp^2 ($p_{x,y}$)	HgI_3^-
4	tetrahedral	sp^3	$SnCl_4$
		d^3s ($d_{xy,xz,yz}$)	MnO_4^-
	square planar	dsp^2 ($d_{x^2-y^2}$)	$Ni(CN)_4^{2-}$
5	trigonal bipyramidal	dsp^3 (d_{z^2})	$CuCl_5^{3-}$
	square pyramidal	dsp^3 ($d_{x^2-y^2}$)	$Ni(CN)_5^{3-}$
6	octahedral	d^2sp^3 (d_{z^2,x^2-y^2})	$Co(NH_3)_6^{3+}$
	trigonal prismatic	d^2sp^3 ($d_{xz,yz}$)	
		d^5s ($d_{xy,x^2-y^2,xz,yz}$)	$V(S_2C_2Ph_2)_3$
7	pentagonal bipyramidal	d^3sp^3 ($d_{x^2-y^2,z^2,xy}$)	IF_7
	capped trigonal prism	d^3sp^3 ($d_{z^2,xy,xz}$)	NbF_7^{2-}
8	square antiprismatic	d^4sp^3 (d_{xz,yz,xy,x^2-y^2})	TaF_8^{3-}
	dodecahedral	d^4sp^3 ($d_{z^2,x^2-y^2,xz,yz}$)	$Mo(CN)_8^{4-}$
9	face-centred trigonal prismatic	d^5sp^3	ReH_9^{3-}

$2p$-orbitals (or sp^3-hybrids) containing the lone pairs of the F^- ions overlapping with octahedral hybrids formed from the $3d_{x^2-y^2}$, $3d_{z^2}$, $4s$, $4p_x$, $4p_y$, and $4p_z$ orbitals of a Ti^{4+} ion. In AlF_6^{3-} or GeF_6^{2-}, however, the d-orbitals used in the octahedral hybrids would have to be those of the same quantum shell as the s- and p-orbitals, e.g. $3s$, $3p$, and $3d$ for aluminium, and there is some doubt as to whether these d-orbitals have suitable energies and overlaps to contribute significantly to the bonding. A similar difficulty arises in the case of complexes such as FeF_6^{3-}, in which all the $3d$-orbitals appear to be occupied by the non-bonding electrons (in this case, five) of the metal ion, the same orbitals which are believed to contribute to the metal–ligand bonds. These difficulties can be overcome by the molecular-orbital description (see below).† Nevertheless, the hybridisation approach is very useful, being conceptually simple and leading in many cases to perfectly satisfatory descriptions.

4.2   Colours of coordination compounds

Nearly all compounds of the d-block elements are highly coloured, whereas in the s- and p-blocks colour is relatively rare. Thus, compounds of the alkali and alkaline earth metals are coloured only if they contain coloured anions. A few examples are known among the p-block elements, e.g. SnI_4, PbI_2, and some other iodides, NO_2, ClO_2 and the halogens, but these are relatively isolated examples. On the other hand, the colours displayed by most of the compounds of the d-block metals are one of their most striking attributes, and colourless compounds are rare. This marked difference in properties can be related to the incomplete filling of the d sub-shell which characterises the transition metals.

---

† The valence-bond approach is also capable of giving a detailed, correct description of coordination compounds if it is applied rigorously, rather than in the oversimplified way given here. Such a rigorous treatment is beyond the scope of this book.

The compounds of the *d*-block metals exhibit a wide variety of colours, but the colour observed depends not only on the identity of the metal but also on its environment. A familiar example is the deepening of the blue colour observed when ammonium hydroxide is added to a copper(II) solution. A more dramatic change occurs when ammonia is added to a nickel(II) solution: green to purple. A more delightful example of the dependence of colour on environment is afforded by gemstones; both rubies and emeralds owe their colour to chromium(III) ions which substitute for aluminium(III) ion in either aluminium oxide (ruby) or in a beryllium aluminium silicate (emerald). In both cases the metal ions are surrounded by six oxide ions, but the distances and geometries are slightly different.

Despite the variety of colours exhibited, some systematisation is possible. Although different colours are shown by different metals, the effect of changing one set of ligands for another, say an aqueous medium for an ammoniacal one, does show some consistency. The best way to compare colours is to examine the absorption spectra of the substances concerned, that is to plot the intensity of the light absorbed by the sample as a function of its wavelength, as shown in Fig. 4.1. The copper(II) solution appears blue because the $Cu(OH_2)_4^{2+}$ ions absorb a little light at the red end of the spectrum (and also some of the near infra-red radiation to which the human eye is not sensitive). On addition of ammonia, the complex $Cu(NH_3)_4^{2+}$ is formed which absorbs rather more of the red light, and the solution appears to have a richer blue colour. The region of absorption has moved to shorter wavelength, higher frequency. A similar effect is seen in the nickel case. The aquo-complex, $Ni(OH_2)_6^{2+}$, absorbs red and blue light and transmits green, whereas the ammine, $Ni(NH_3)_6^{2+}$,

Fig. 4.1   Absorption spectra of copper(II) and nickel(II) complexes

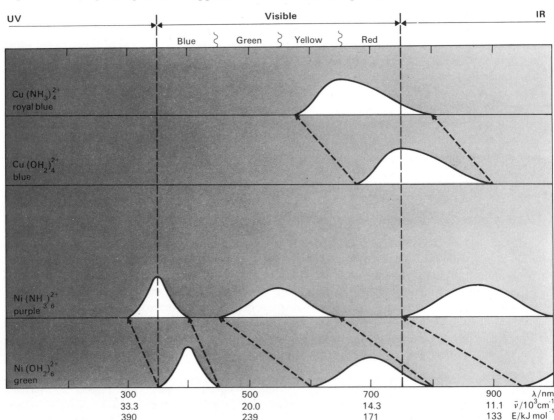

absorbs in the ultra-violet, the green and the near infra-red, and thus appears purple. The absorption bands have again shifted to higher frequency.

These effects can be explained in terms of a simple model of the coordination complex. The absorption of light is the absorption of energy, so that some mechanism must be found for transferring energy from the light beam to the complex. The energies involved, 200–400 kJ mol^{-1}, are comparable to those involved in chemical reactions, which normally involve redistribution of electrons between the reactants. Similarly, absorption of light involves redistribution of electrons within one molecule. Since the behaviour currently under examination concerns the d-block metals, it seems likely that d-electrons will be involved. Consider the nickel case. In aqueous solution the nickel ion is surrounded by six tightly held water molecules, which are bound largely by the electrostatic attraction between the positive metal ion and the lone pairs. However, these lone pairs will interact with the valence-shell electrons of the metal ion, repelling them and raising their energy. For s- and p-electrons, all electrons of any one sub-group would be repelled equally, but this is not true of d electrons. The five d-orbitals are not equivalently situated relative to the six ligands, but divide into two sub-sets. The d_{xy}, d_{xz}, and d_{yz} orbitals have their lobes directed between the x, y and z axes, on which lie the ligands; electrons in these orbitals are thus repelled less by the ligands than those in the $d_{x^2-y^2}$ and d_{z^2} orbitals, which are directed along the axes (Fig. 4.2).† Under the influence of the ligands, the degeneracy of the d-orbitals is thus removed and the two sub-sets

Fig. 4.2 Shapes of the d-orbitals (the square of the angular function is shown)

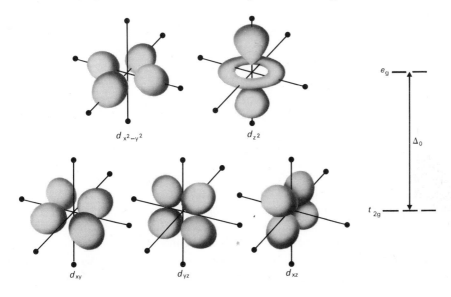

e_g

Δ_0

t_{2g}

$d_{x^2-y^2}$

d_{z^2}

d_{xy}

d_{yz}

d_{xz}

---

† It is not immediately apparent from their shapes that the d_{z^2} and $d_{x^2-y^2}$ orbitals are equivalent. On symmetry grounds two further orbitals like $d_{x^2-y^2}$ would be expected, lying in the xy and yz planes, i.e. $d_{z^2-x^2}$ and $d_{z^2-y^2}$. However, the form of the wave equation allows only five independent d-orbitals, so that these two are combined (any two acceptable solutions of the wave equation may be combined linearly to give another acceptable solution). If $d_{z^2-x^2}$ and $d_{z^2-y^2}$ are added together, the positive lobes reinforce along the z-axis and the negative lobes along the x- and y-axes combine to give a ring in the xy-plane. The d_{z^2}-orbital thus behaves as 1 : 1-combination of these two orbitals and is therefore equivalent to $d_{x^2-y^2}$ in all respects except orientation.

have different energies. This splitting of the orbital energy levels is known as **ligand-field splitting** (or **crystal field splitting**†) and the separation between the two subsets is the **ligand- (or crystal-) field splitting energy**, often symbolised Δ_o, sometimes 10Dq.

The complex can absorb energy by promoting electrons from the lower level (labelled t_{2g}) to the upper level (e_g). For example, the purplish-red colour of titanium(III) solutions is due to the absorption of light around 240 kJ mol^{-1} (500 nm) by promotion of the single electron; the value of Δ_o is thus 240 kJ mol^{-1}. If there were no d-electrons present, no transitions of this type could occur, so that in general titanium(IV), scandium(III), calcium(II) and potassium(I) solutions are colourless. (The colours of other d^0 systems with metals in higher oxidation states are discussed below.) In the majority of cases, at least one such electronic transition can occur, giving rise to absorption bands in or near the visible region of the spectrum. If the d-orbitals are completely occupied, as in zinc(II) (d^{10}, cf. Fig. 4.3), no promotion is possible as there is no orbital in the e_g set which can accommodate the promoted electron. Thus zinc compounds and those of the other p-block metals are not usually coloured.

Fig. 4.3   Orbital filling for d^1, d^5 and d^{10} configurations. Excitation is possible for d^1 but not for d^{10}. Excitation for d^5 is spin-forbidden

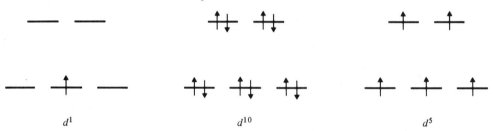

One further restriction on electron promotion has been observed. In the d^5 case there is one electron in each of the d-orbitals, and Hund's rule suggests that all should have the same spin. To promote an electron from the t_{2g} to the e_g set would involve reversal of spin, since an orbital can accommodate two electrons only if they have opposite spin. Such a process appears to be very improbable, and these transitions are designated *spin-forbidden*. Complexes with d^5-configurations therefore exhibit very weak colours, e.g. manganese(II), iron(III).

The energy absorbed from the light beam, and hence the colour of the complex, depends on the value of Δ_o which in turn is governed by the interaction between the ligands and the d-electrons. Different ligands will differ in the extent of interaction, and thus give rise to different colours. Thus, for both copper(II) and nickel(II), replacement of water as a ligand by ammonia shifted the absorption bands to higher energies, i.e. Δ_o for Ni(NH$_3$)$_6^{2+}$ is larger than Δ_o for Ni(OH$_2$)$_6^{2+}$ (129 and 102 kJ mol^{-1} respectively). This is a perfectly general effect and ligands can be ranked in order of ligand-field splitting energy independently of the metal, i.e. the same ordering is found for each metal, even though the actual Δ_o-values differ from metal to metal. The order of some common ligands is:

$$I^- < Br^- < Cl^- < F^- < OH^- < OH_2 < NH_3 < NO_2^- < PR_3 < CN^-$$

This sequence is known, for obvious reasons, as the **spectrochemical series**.

---

† The term crystal field is usually used for the purely electrostatic approach described above, by analogy with other electrostatic treatments, e.g. of the lattice energies of ionic crystals. The ligands are effectively considered as negative point charges. It would be more realistic to take account of the covalency of the metal-ligand bonds (see below); when this is done, the term ligand-field is normally employed.

4.3   Molecular-orbital approach to bonding in complexes

The above description of crystal-field effects is somewhat unrealistic in that the only type of metal–ligand interaction considered is electrostatic. While the electrostatic attraction between metal and ligand contributes greatly to the bond energy, there must also be covalent character to the bond, becoming more important the higher the oxidation state of the metal. Several experimental techniques demonstrate that there is often considerable covalency in the metal–ligand bond. The inadequacy of the electrostatic approach is also revealed by detailed inspection of the spectrochemical series. The four halide ions appear in the order expected, i.e. increasing interaction with the metal (as measured by Δ_o) with decreasing radius, but it is by no means obvious why OH^-, bearing a negative charge, should give a smaller Δ_O-value than the neutral OH_2 molecule. Similarly, it is curious that the large CN^- ion should be high in the series.

These difficulties can be surmounted by adopting a molecular-orbital description of the bonding. In this method, the orbitals on the central metal atom are combined with those of the ligands to give bonding and antibonding molecular orbitals which cover all of the atoms involved. Purely on symmetry grounds it should be obvious that only the $d_{x^2-y^2}$, d_{z^2}, s, p_x, p_y, and p_z orbitals are suited to form σ-bonds with the ligands (note that this is again a d^2sp^3 set). The remaining three d-orbitals do not have the correct symmetry, since overlap of the ligand orbital with the positive lobe is exactly cancelled by overlap with the negative lobe (Fig. 4.4). Thus, there are six orbitals on

Fig. 4.4   Overlap of ligand σ-orbitals with (a) $d_{x^2-y^2}$ and (b) d_{xy}

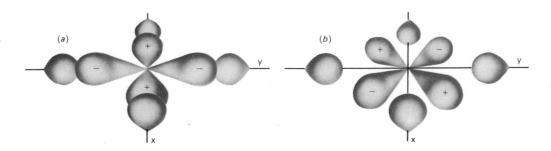

the metal atom capable of forming bonds with the six ligand orbitals; combination of these gives six bonding and six anti-bonding orbitals (Fig. 4.5). The other three d-orbitals, having no suitable ligand orbitals with which to combine, remain unaffected in energy as non-bonding orbitals localised on the metal atom. The bonding orbitals are just sufficient to accommodate the six electron pairs forming the metal-ligand bonds. The next two sets of molecular orbitals, t_{2g} and e_g^*, are available to house the remaining electrons of the complex, i.e. the 'd-electrons' of the metal. These five orbitals form the same pattern as was deduced from the crystal-field approach, and this is a general result. The major difference is that the e_g^* orbitals are now anti-bonding molecular orbitals delocalised over the entire complex; these latter orbitals are, however, associated more with the metal atom than the ligands, the converse being true of the bonding orbitals.

The magnitude of Δ_o, the ligand-field splitting energy, is now seen to represent the strength of the metal–ligand bonds, since the greater the metal–ligand interaction the greater the separation between corresponding bonding and anti-bonding orbitals. That is, strong bonding will raise the energy of the e_g^* orbitals and increase Δ_o. In general it is found that Δ_o increases when the oxidation

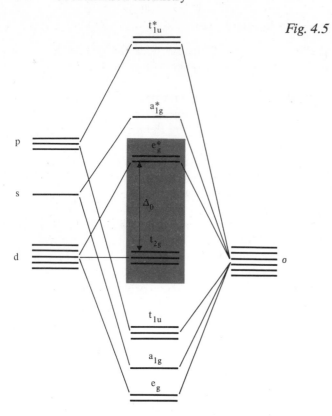

Fig. 4.5 Molecular-orbital scheme for an octahedral complex. Degenerate orbitals are drawn closely-spaced for convenience. The orbitals in the shaded area (t_{2g} and e_g^*) correspond to the crystal-field splitting pattern of d-orbitals

state of the metal is raised, indicating the increased covalency of the bonds. Similarly, Δ_0 is larger for corresponding complexes of the $4d$- and $5d$-metals than for the $3d$-metals, representing increased overlap of ligand orbitals with the larger metal orbitals.

In some cases it is possible for the t_{2g} orbitals also to interact with the ligands. Many ligands possess valence-shell electrons or orbitals other than those involved in the metal–ligand σ-bonds, e.g. halide ions have a total of four electron pairs in the valence-shell. While these orbitals do not have the correct symmetry to form σ-bonds, they may have the same symmetry (π-symmetry) as the t_{2g} orbitals (Fig. 4.6). It is then possible to form additional bonding and anti-bonding molecular orbitals by interaction between these orbitals (the combinations of ligand orbitals in excess of the three which interact with the t_{2g} orbitals remain non-bonding, localised on the ligands). The effect which this interaction has on Δ_0 depends on the type of ligand.

Fig. 4.6 d_π – p_π overlap

Ligands such as halide and hydroxide ions, and the water molecule have filled, low-energy π-orbitals, which interact with the metal orbitals as shown in Fig. 4.7a. The t_{2g}-orbitals and the

Fig. 4.7   Partial molecular-orbital scheme for octahedral complexes with π-bonding ligands. The a_{1g}, a_{1g}^*, t_{1u} and t_{1u}^* orbitals are omitted. Figures in parentheses are orbital degeneracies. (*a*) π-donor ligands – the e_g, t_{2g} and π-orbitals are filled by 'ligand' electrons (*b*) π-acceptor ligands – only the e_g orbitals are filled with 'ligand' electrons

(*a*)   (*b*)

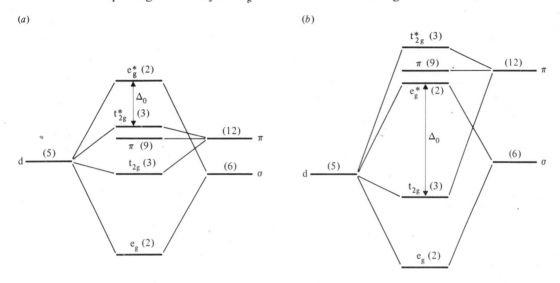

non-bonding π-orbitals accommodate the ligand electrons and the next available orbitals are t_{2g}^* and e_g^*, in which the '*d*-electrons' must be housed. The splitting energy, Δ_o, is thus reduced. This interaction between t_{2g} metal orbitals and filled ligand π-orbitals represents further donation of electrons from the ligands to the metal. Thus, good π-*donor ligands* will give low Δ_o-values (note that a small Δ_o-value does not mean that the metal–ligand bonds are necessarily weak; in this case the π-bonding represents additional bonding, and reinforces the σ-bonding). By virtue of its negative charge and extra lone pair of electrons, OH^- is a better π-donor than OH_2, and therefore lies lower in the spectrochemical series.

Other ligands have the opposite effect on Δ_o by virtue of their possessing vacant, higher-energy orbitals of π-symmetry (Fig. 4.7*b*). Such ligands are the tertiary phosphines, R_3P, in which the $3d$-orbitals of the phosphorus are available, or carbon monoxide and cyanide ion, in which the vacant orbitals are effectively the antibonding orbitals of the ligand π-system. In these cases, the bonding t_{2g} molecular orbital is available for the '*d*-electrons', and the delocalisation of these electrons from the metal to the ligands is sometimes called **back-donation**. The value of Δ_o is now greater than it would have been in the absence of the π-interaction, so that π-*acceptor ligands* lie high in the spectrochemical series. It is the ability of ligands such as these to accept as well as donate charge which allows low oxidation states (zero or negative) to be achieved, e.g. the metal carbonyls.

(Note that many ligands are potentially capable of both π-donation and π-acceptance, but normally one type of behaviour predominates. Thus the chloride ion also has vacant $3d$-orbitals and could function as a π-acceptor, but does not appear to do so to any great extent.)

The colours of d^0 complexes such as CrO_4^{2-} and MnO_4^- are due to electronic transitions between non-bonding π-electrons on the ligands and the t_{2g}^*-orbitals. This type of transition is commonly called a 'charge-transfer' transition because the electron moves from an orbital on the ligand to one centred mainly on the metal, representing transfer of charge from ligand to metal. In many cases such transitions are of relatively high energy and occur in the ultraviolet, but as the metal atom becomes a better acceptor, i.e. as its oxidation state increases, the transition energy decreases. This is shown by the colours of titanium(IV) (white), vanadium(V) (yellow-orange) and chromium(VI) (orange-red) species, reprsenting the absorption of progressively more of the blue end of the spectrum by the 'tail' of the ultraviolet absorption band moving closer to the visible region. In manganese(VII) the absorption band lies in the visible region, giving the intense purple colouration of permanganate ion.

4.4   Magnetic properties

All substances interact with a magnetic field by virtue of the motion of their electrons. An electron moving in its orbital is like an electric current and has an associated magnetic field. There is also another contribution to the magnetic field arising from the spin of the electron. In the majority of compounds all electrons are paired and the spin contributions cancel to zero. If an external magnetic field is applied, the orbital motion of the electrons is modified to produce a field in opposition (cf. the motor effect of a current in a wire), so that the sample is repelled by the magnet. Such substances are said to be **diamagnetic**.

In many compounds of the d-block elements there are one or more unpaired electrons. For such materials the opposite effect can occur; they will often be attracted by a magnet. This happens because the magnetic field due to the spin of the electrons can interact cooperatively with the applied field, i.e. the electron, with its spin and orbital momenta, acts like a small magnet. This phenomenon is known as **paramagnetism**. In the majority of compounds with unpaired electrons the paramagnetism of these electrons considerably outweighs the diamagnetism due to all the other, paired, electrons.

These properties can be quantified and used to determine experimentally the number of unpaired electrons, and such measurements are of great value in confirming the oxidation state and stereochemistry of a metal ion in a complex.

The magnetic flux density, B, within a material placed in a magnetic field, H, is given by

$$B = \mu H$$

where μ is the magnetic permeability of the material. For diamagnetic materials $B < H$ and μ is negative, while for paramagnets $B > H$ and μ is positive. The quantity of interest to the chemist is the **magnetic susceptibility**, χ, given by

$$\chi = \frac{\mu}{\mu_0} - 1$$

where μ_0 is the permeability of a vacuum ($4\pi \times 10^{-7}$ kg m s^{-1} A^{-2}). For diamagnetic substances, χ is negative and independent of temperature. Paramagnetism, however, is dependent on the alignment of the magnetic fields of the individual electrons with the external field, which process is resisted by thermal agitation of the atoms. The susceptibility therefore decreases with increasing temperature in a linear fashion. In normal use, the **molar susceptibility** is employed,

$$\chi_M = \chi M / \rho$$

where M is the molar mass and ρ the density; this figure is further corrected for the diamagnetism of all the other electrons and the corrected molar susceptibility, χ'_M, is then usually quite closely inversely proportional to temperature,

$$\chi'_M \propto \frac{1}{T}$$

In many other cases, χ'_M is inversely proportional to the absolute temperature plus a small fixed increment

$$\chi'_M \propto 1/(T+\theta)$$

The proportionality constant is $N_A\mu_{eff}^2/3k$, where N_A is Avagadro's number, k is the Boltzmann constant, and μ_{eff} is the **effective magnetic moment**. Where one of these relationships is obeyed μ_{eff} is independent of temperature and may be related to the number of unpaired electrons.

For the $3d$-metals the magnetic moment is determined almost entirely by the spin contribution, and that from the orbital motion of the unpaired electrons is small. The spin-only magnetic moment is given by

$$\mu_{eff}^{so} = \sqrt{4S(S+1)}\mu_B = \sqrt{n(n+2)}\mu_B$$

where S is the total spin quantum number, n is the number of unpaired electrons ($S = \frac{1}{2}n$), and μ_B is the Bohr magneton, a convenient unit equal to $eh/4\pi m_e$ ($= 9\cdot27 \times 10^{-2}$ A m^{-2}). The values of μ_{eff}^{so} calculated on this basis are shown in Table 4.2 with some experimental data.

Table 4.2 Magnetic moments

n	$\mu_{eff}^{so} = \sqrt{n(n+2)}$	Example	μ_{eff}^{obs}/μ_B
1	1·73	$[Ti(OH_2)_6]Cs(OH_2)_6(SO_4)_2$	1·80
		$K_2[VF_6]$	1·76
		$[Cu(NH_3)_4]SO_4.H_2O$	1·93
2	2·83	$K_3[VF_6]$	2·79
		$K_2[CrF_6]$	2·80
		$[Ni(NH_3)_6]Cl_2$	3·32
		$(Et_4N)_2[NiCl_4]$	4·10
3	3·87	$[Cr(NH_3)_6]Br_3$	3·77
		$K_3[Cr(CN)_6]$	3·87
		$[Co(OH_2)_6]Cl_2$	4·82
		$(Et_4N)_2[CoCl_4]$	4·59
4	4·90	$[Cr(OH_2)_6]SO_4$	4·82
		$K_3[MnF_6]$	4·95
		$[Fe(OH_2)_6](ClO_4)_2$	5·11
		$K_3[CoF_6]$	5·53
5	5·92	$[Mn(OH_2)_6](NH_4)_2(SO_4)_2$	5·88
		$(Et_4N)_2[MnCl_4]$	5·87
		$[Fe(OH_2)_6](NH_4)(SO_4)_2.6H_2O$	5·80
		$K_3[Fe(C_2O_4)_3].3H_2O$	5.90

In the majority of cases, the observed magnetic moment is close to or a little larger than that calculated on the spin-only formula. The differences are attributable to the orbital contribution, which is small and negative for ions with less than five $3d$-electrons and positive and rather larger for those with more than five (and zero for exactly five). [This is a function of the magnitude of the spin-orbit coupling constant, which increases rapidly with atomic number (roughly proportional to Z^4) and changes sign at the half-filled shell. Orbital contributions are therefore much more important for $4d$- and $5d$-metals (and for $4f$- and $5f$-metals), and the spin-only treatment cannot be used in these cases.] Very rarely does the orbital contribution become large enough to cause confusion over the number of unpaired electrons, and this relatively simple measurement provides a convenient check on the oxidation state of the metal. In favourable cases [e.g. nickel(II)] the magnitude of the orbital contribution can give information on the stereochemistry of the complex.

For some compounds much lower magnetic moments are found than would be expected on the basis of the above treatment. For instance, most cobalt(III) complexes (only two exceptions are known to the author) are diamagnetic, i.e. contain no unpaired electrons, despite the $3d^6$ configuration. Some iron(II) complexes (also d^6) are similarly diamagnetic, e.g. the hexacyanoferrate(II) ion, $Fe(CN)_6^{4-}$; the corresponding iron(III) complex has an effective magnetic moment of $2\cdot25\ \mu_B$, corresponding to a single unpaired electron, although there are five d-electrons present.

The spin-only moments quoted above were calculated on the assumption that, in accordance with Hund's rule, there would be the maximum number of electrons with parallel spin. In an octahedral complex this is a reasonable assumption for d^1, d^2 and d^3 configurations, and also for d^8 and d^9, but for d^4 to d^7 configurations there are two possibilities. Maximisation of the number of electrons with parallel spin will require some electrons to be in the anti-bonding e_g^*-orbitals. While this **high-spin** (or **spin-free**) configuration is favourable from the point of view of maximising the exchange energy, it is less so in terms of the orbital energy. Clearly, if Δ_o is large enough it will be preferable to have all the electrons in the lower-energy t_{2g}-orbitals (a **low-spin** or **spin-paired** configuration), the energy thus gained off-setting the loss in exchange energy (Fig. 4.8). The value of K, the unit of exchange energy, is roughly constant within the $3d$-series (8 000–11 000 cm^{-1}, 100–300 kJ mol^{-1}), so that the d^6 configuration should spin-pair for relatively low values of Δ_o, while the d^4 and d^5 configurations will be more resistant. (The figures for the d^7 configuration are approximate owing to the effects of configurational interaction in the high-spin arrangement and a large Jahn–Teller effect in the low-spin form.)

For each metal ion there will be a critical Δ_o-value at which spin-pairing will occur; all ligands higher in the spectrochemical series will give low-spin complexes while those lower in the series will form high-spin complexes. Owing to the large values of Δ_o, all complexes of the $4d$- and $5d$-metals are spin-paired. In some cases, when the ligands can be chosen to give a ligand-field splitting close to the critical value, both forms may be present in thermal equilibrium. In other systems an increase in the ligand field may be brought about by increasing the coordination number. This is important,

Fig. 4.8   Electron-configurations for the high- and low-spin d^4, d^5, d^6 and d^7 cases

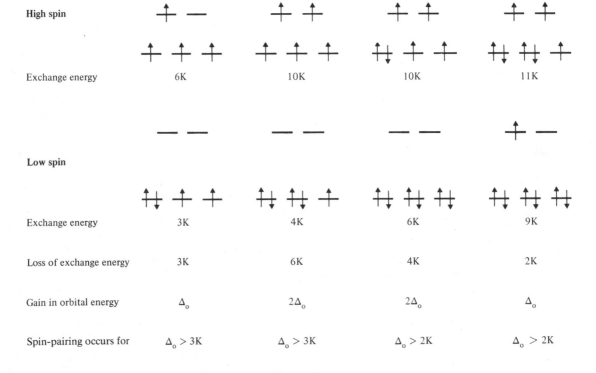

High spin			
Exchange energy	6K	10K	10K	11K
Low spin			
Exchange energy	3K	4K	6K	9K
Loss of exchange energy	3K	6K	4K	2K
Gain in orbital energy	Δ_o	$2\Delta_o$	$2\Delta_o$	Δ_o
Spin-pairing occurs for	$\Delta_o > 3K$	$\Delta_o > 3K$	$\Delta_o > 2K$	$\Delta_o > 2K$

for instance, in the oxygen-carrying ability of haemoglobin; in the de-oxygenated form the iron(II) ion is five-coordinate and high-spin, but the coordination of the oxygen gives a diamagnetic, low-spin species. An additional characteristic of low-spin complexes is that they undergo dissociation slowly (see below), thus the oxygen, once bound, remains coordinated during its journey through the blood-stream.

4.5   Geometries other than octahedral

The type of interaction which gives rise to the difference in energy between t_{2g} and e_g orbitals must occur in all complexes, of whatever coordination number or stereochemistry, but the detailed splitting pattern will depend on the geometry. Some common examples will now be examined.

4.5.1   Tetrahedral

In tetrahedral geometry the d-orbitals again form two sub-sets which interact differently with the ligands. In this case the d_{xy}, d_{xz}, and d_{yz} orbitals are directed more nearly towards the ligands (t_2 sub-set), while $d_{x^2-y^2}$ and d_{z^2} have their lobes farther away from the ligands (e sub-set; note that these two orbitals are still equivalent) (Fig. 4.9). The splitting pattern is thus the inverse of that for

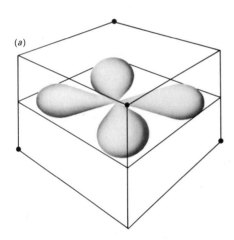

(a)

Fig. 4.9   The relationship between a tetrahedral set of ligands and (*a*) the d_{xy}-orbital, (*b*) the $d_{x^2-y^2}$-orbital and (*c*) the ligand-field splitting pattern

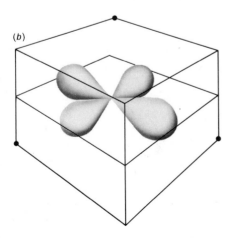

(b)

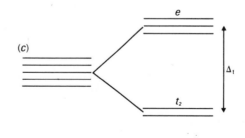

(c)

the octahedral case. (Both stereochemistries are sometimes called cubic since they can be related in complementary fashion to the geometry of a cube, as in Fig. 4.10. The presence of a ligand at the face-centre is thus equivalent to the absence of a ligand at the cube corner.) However, since the orbitals are less well directed towards the ligands than for the octahedron, the interaction, and hence the ligand-field splitting energy Δ_t, is less. On a purely electrostatic model (treating the ligands as point charges), if the metal–ligand bond distances were the same in both cases, Δ_t would be $\frac{4}{9}\Delta_0$. (In practice, the bond length would be rather less in the tetrahedral case, and it is usually sufficient to assume that $\Delta_t \approx \frac{1}{2}\Delta_0$.) All known tetrahedral complexes have spin-free configurations.

Fig. 4.10   The relationship of the octahedron and the tetrahedron to the cube. The cubes are scaled so that the metal–ligand distances are the same in both cases

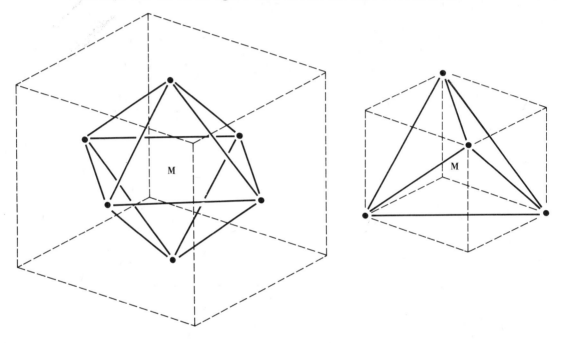

4.5.2   Tetragonal and square planar

If in an octahedral complex, two *trans* metal-ligand bonds, say those along the z-axis, are lengthened, the interaction between these ligands and orbitals which have z-components is lessened. The two-fold degeneracy of the e_g-orbitals is lifted. The d_{z^2}-orbital will be relatively stabilised and the d_{xz}- and d_{yz}-orbitals will be similarly lowered in energy but to a lesser extent since they are less directly influenced by the ligands. The remaining orbitals will be slightly raised in energy (Fig. 4.11).† The same effect would be achieved if two *trans* ligands were lower in the spectrochemical series than the other four. A similar splitting pattern would be obtained by the complete removal of one or two ligands, so that a square-planar complex may be regarded as an extreme case of tetragonal bond-lengthening.

---

† On a purely electrostatic model this is because the centre of gravity (baricentre) of the energy levels must be preserved (as in the $t_{2g} - e_g$ splitting). In the real complex, distortion of the octahedron by lengthening of a pair of *trans* bonds reduces ligand–ligand repulsion and allows the remaining ligands to move towards the metal slightly, increasing the interaction with $d_{x^2-y^2}$ and d_{xy}.

Fig. 4.11   Orbital splitting patterns for two types of tetragonal distortion. For the extreme cases, the precise sequence of orbitals depends on the nature of the ligands

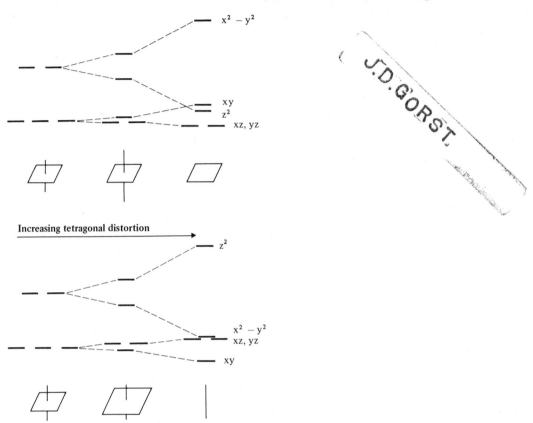

If the two *trans* bonds were shortened (or the four equatorial bonds lengthened), the splitting of the t_{2g} and e_g subsets would each be inverted. The extreme case would now be a linear two-coordinate (or one-coordinate) system.

4.5.3   Trigonal bipyramidal

With a trigonal arrangement of ligands, two of the axes (x and y, say) are no longer distinguishable since the ligands lie symmetrically between them. The d_{xz}- and d_{yz}-orbitals thus remain degenerate, and d_{xy} and $d_{x^2-y^2}$ are also degenerate. The orbital splitting pattern is therefore as shown in Fig. 4.12.

Fig. 4.12   Ligand-field splitting for trigonal-bipyramidal geometry

4.6   Effects of ligand-field splitting†

The splitting of the energy of the d-orbitals is responsible not only for the colours and magnetic behaviour of complexes of the d-block metals but may affect other properties also, a small selection of which is now examined.

4.6.1   Jahn–Teller effect

The ligand field partially lifts the degeneracy of the d-orbitals but in many cases, particularly those of cubic symmetry (octahedral and tetrahedral) some degeneracy remains. A theorem due to Jahn and Teller states that a system which is orbitally degenerate will achieve a lower energy by distorting in such a way as to remove that degeneracy. This theorem is very often quoted in relation to complexes of the transition metals, but applies to any non-linear orbitally-degenerate system. Orbital degeneracy occurs whenever a set of energetically-degenerate orbitals is neither completely filled nor half-filled with electrons, i.e. there is conceptually more than one way of arranging the electrons in the orbitals. Thus, for octahedral complexes with high-spin d^3, d^4 and d^5 configurations (Fig. 4.13), the d^3 and d^5 cases are orbitally non-degenerate, since there is only one

Fig. 4.13   Jahn–Teller effect for the d^4-configuration

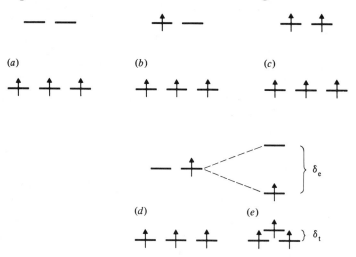

distinct way in which three electrons can be distributed between three (t_{2g}) orbitals or five electrons between five orbitals. (Note that, since electrons are indistinguishable, permuting the electrons between the orbitals does not give a recognizably different configuration.) The d^4 configuration, however, is orbitally degenerate since the odd e_g electron can be assigned to either orbital (Fig. 4.13b and d). By the Jahn–Teller theorem the system can be stabilised by distortion which removes the degeneracy; the simplest such distortion (which is also required to maintain the centre of symmetry) is a tetragonal lengthening of two (or four) metal–ligand bonds. As discussed above, this will result in a splitting of the two subsets of orbitals and the energy of the system is lowered by $\frac{1}{2}\delta_e$ by placing the odd electron in the lower of the two orbitals (Fig. 4.13e). Since the additional splitting retains the original energy baricentre, no net stabilisation will occur if the orbitals are equally occupied.

† The same splitting patterns and ligand-field stabilisation effects are found regardless of whether the simple crystal-field approach or the more rigorous molecular-orbital method is used.

Clearly, the greater the distortion, the greater the stabilisation, but this is offset by loss of metal–ligand bond energy as the bonds lengthen, and eventually an energy minimum is reached beyond which further distortion would raise the net energy of the system. The configurations most prone to Jahn–Teller distortions are the high-spin d^4 and d^9 systems [chromium(II), manganese(III), copper(II)], for which much structural evidence is available (see Ch. 3). It is found that the majority of systems (though not all) undergo a lengthening of two bonds; this may be because this results in a smaller loss of bond energy for the same gain in splitting energy. In some cases the distortion is carried to the extreme of giving a four-coordinate square-planar system, as is common for copper(II) complexes. A similar effect should occur for low-spin cobalt(II) (d^7) but structural evidence is lacking; cobalt(II) does, however, form several square-planar complexes with ligands relatively low in the spectrochemical series (e.g. the anions of dimethylglyoxime and various Schiff bases). Since the splitting of the t_{2g} orbitals, δ_t, is much smaller than that of the e_g orbitals (see section 4.5.2 above), Jahn–Teller distortions in compounds with degenerate t_{2g} configurations are much less, and have not been observed.

It should also be noted in passing, that the Jahn–Teller effect applies also to the excited states of complexes, and this sometimes gives rise to the appearance of extra bands in the absorption spectra. For instance, copper(II) complexes generally show broad absorptions consisting of several bands resulting from electronic transitions to the half-empty $d_{x^2-y^2}$-orbital from the other orbitals which are non-equivalent in the ground state (Fig. 4.14). For the d^1 case, however, Jahn–Teller effects in the ground state are small but the excited state (e_g^1) will be much more affected, so that the absorption spectrum of, say, titanium(III) complexes consist of two broad envelopes arising from transitions to the d_{z^2} and $d_{x^2-y^2}$ orbitals. Similar effects are found for high-spin d^6 systems (e.g. iron(II)).†

Fig. 4.14 Electronic transitions in a tetragonal copper(II) (d^9) complex

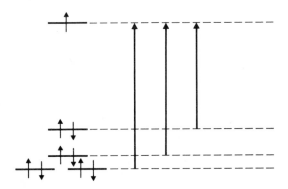

4.6.2 Ionic radii

Ions in crystal lattices are usually treated as incompressible spheres, the radii of which are governed by the balancing of inter-electronic repulsions and electron–nuclear attractions and shielding effects. For a series of isoelectronic closed-shell ions, the radius decreases smoothly as the nuclear charge increases. For a series of, say, dipositive ions of the $3d$-group, the increasing nuclear charge

---

† Note that, for many properties, high-spin d^n and d^{5+n} configurations exhibit the same behaviour; low-spin d^n and d^{3+n} systems are similar. An inverse correlation is also found between high-spin d^n and d^{10-n} configurations, so that an octahedral d^n configuration has similar properties to a tetrahedral d^{10-n} configuration, and vice versa.

would still be expected to produce a decrease in radius since the mutual shielding of d-electrons is relatively inefficient, and this trend is indeed found. There is, however, another effect superimposed on the general decrease and, as Fig. 4.15 shows, the variation of radii along the series is not completely regular. The irregularities arise because the majority of the ions are not spherical. For an ion to be spherical all the orbitals of each sub-set must be equally occupied. For the d-block ions this condition is realised only for d^0, d^5 and d^{10} configurations, owing to the operation of ligand-field effects. In many crystal lattices the metal ions occupy octahedral sites so that the d-orbitals are split into the t_{2g} and e_g sub-sets, with electrons occupying preferentially the t_{2g} set. These orbitals are those which are directed away from the ligands (in this case, these are the surrounding anions); the ligands will thus be less shielded from the nuclear charge than if the d-electrons were equally distributed between the t_{2g}- and e_g-orbitals. The greater the number of t_{2g}-electrons the greater this effect will be. Thus, if a smooth curve is drawn through the points for the spherical d^0, d^5, and d^{10} ions (Ca^{2+}, Mn^{2+}, and Zn^{2+}), the radii for d^1, d^2, and d^3 ions will lie progressively further below this curve. For the d^4 case, one electron is present in the e_g orbital and will exert some shielding; the radius will still be less than the interpolated value but lies closer to the curve. This case is further complicated by the Jahn–Teller effect discussed above. The d^5 ion is spherical, but the pattern is repeated in the second half of the series. Similar effects are seen for the tripositive ions, when Sc^{3+}, Fe^{3+} and Ga^{3+} have the d^0, d^5 and d^{10} configurations, and Mn^{3+} has the irregular environment.

Fig. 4.15   Ionic radii (Shannon and Prewitt) for M^{2+} and M^{3+}. Note that the two scales are displaced

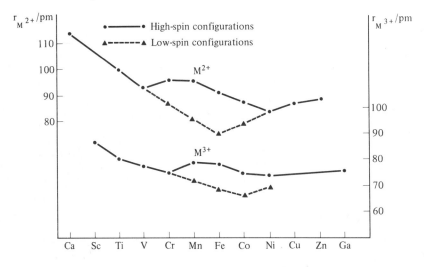

For low-spin complexes, the radii would be expected to decrease until the t_{2g} subset is full, i.e. at Fe^{2+} or Co^{3+}, and then to rise again for the d^7 configuration, and this trend is also found in practice (Fig. 4.15).

4.6.3   Ligand-field stabilisation energies

The distribution of electrons between the t_{2g} and e_g orbitals also gives rise to thermodynamic effects. In a manner analogous to the discussion on radii above, the behaviour of the metal ion may be compared to that of the hypothetical spherical ion in which the d-electrons are distributed equally between the five d-orbitals. That is, instead of each electron having an energy corresponding to the baricentre of the splitting pattern, each t_{2g} electron in an octahedral complex has an energy which is lower by $0.4\Delta_o$. Similarly, each e_g electron is relatively destabilised by $0.6\Delta_o$. Clearly, for a high-spin d^5 or a d^{10} configuration the net energy is unaffected, but in all other cases the actual ion will be more stable than the hypothetical ion. This difference in energy is known as the **ligand-field stabilisation energy (LFSE)**. The magnitude of the LFSE for the various electronic configurations in octahedral complexes is shown in Table 4.3. Similar calculations may be made for other geometries. Some of the effects of LFSE will now be surveyed.

Table 4.3   Electronic configurations and ligand-field stabilisation energies

d-configuration		1	2	3	4	5	6	7	8	9	10
Hypothetical	e_g	0.4	0.8	1.2	1.6	2.0	2.4	2.8	3.2	3.6	4.0
spherical ion	t_{2g}	0.6	1.2	1.8	2.4	3.0	3.6	4.2	4.8	5.4	6.0
Actual ion	e_g	0	0	0	1	2	2	2	2	3	4
(high-spin)	t_{2g}	1	2	3	3	3	4	5	6	6	6
	LFSE/Δ_o	0.4	0.8	1.2	0.6†	0	0.4	0.8	1.2	0.6†	0
Actual ion	e_g					0	0	0	1		
(low-spin)	t_{2g}					4	5	6	6		
	LFSE/Δ_o					1.6	2.0	2.4	1.8†		

† subject to additional Jahn–Teller stabilisation

The total LFSE is $1.0\Delta_o$ for each electron transferred from the e_g-orbital of the hypothetical ion to the t_{2g}-orbital of the actual ion. Alternatively, working entirely from the observed configurations, LFSE is $-0.6\Delta_o$ for each e_g electron and $+0.4\Delta_o$ for each t_{2g} electron (note – stabilisation energies are always positive, although they decrease the enthalpy of the complex).

(*a*) *Direct thermodynamic effects*   If the enthalpies of hydration of the divalent metal ions, or the lattice energies of their compounds, are plotted against atomic number, double-humped curves are obtained (Fig. 4.16). If the deviations from the smooth curve through the points for Ca^{2+}, Mn^{2+} and Zn^{2+} are due to ligand-field effects, it should be possible to adjust the data by calculating the LFSE, since Δ_o can be obtained from the visible spectra. In Table 4.4 and Fig. 4.16 this is shown for the enthalpies of hydration. The adjusted values all lie close to the interpolated curve, suggesting that the deviations are indeed due to the ligand field. It should be noted that in this, and other cases, the LFSE is only a small component of the total energy (less than 10%). The appearance of double-humped curves like that in Fig. 4.16 is usually indicative of ligand-field effects.

Table 4.4   Hydration energies (kJ mol^{-1})

Ion	ΔH^0_{hydr}	Δ_o	LFSE	$\Delta H'_{hydr}$
Ca^{2+}	−1577	0	0	−1577
V^{2+}	−1869	156	187	−1682
Cr^{2+}	−1904	172	103	−1801
Mn^{2+}	−1841	97	0	−1841
Fe^{2+}	−1946	129	52	−1894
Co^{2+}	−1996	115	92	−1904
Ni^{2+}	−2105	105	126	−1979
Cu^{2+}	−2100	156	94	−2006
Zn^{2+}	−2046	0	0	−2046

Fig. 4.16   Enthalpies of hydration of dispositive metal ions before and after correction for LFSE

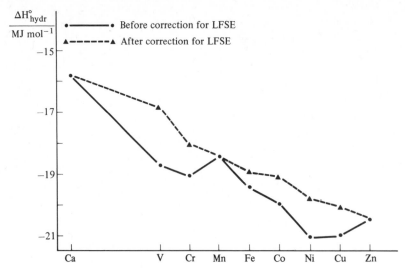

(*b*) *Stability of complexes*   The formation of a complex in aqueous solution involves displacement of coordinated water by the new ligand. The equilibrium constant (K) for this reaction is a measure of the stability of the complex, and is frequently called the **stability constant**; its logarithm is directly proportional to the free energy of the formation reaction. This free energy represents mainly the difference in bond energy between the aquo complex and the new complex (solvation enthalpies of the complexes and ligands are also involved, and in some cases the entropy contributions can be large). These bond energy differences would be expected to vary smoothly along the transition series. However, there will also be a contribution from LFSE, since the enthalpy of the reaction must also reflect the difference in LFSE between the two complexes. A plot of log K against atomic number for a series of complexes of a given ligand would therefore show the characteristic double-humped shape, and corrections may again be applied (Fig. 4.17). This result

Fig. 4.17   Enthalpies for the reaction $M_{aq}^{2+} + 3en \rightarrow Men_3^{2+}$ before and after correction for LFSE
    (en = $H_2N.CH_2.CH_2.NH_2$)

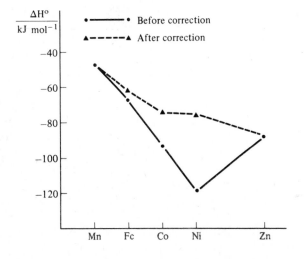

has been generalized in the Irving–Williams series, in which the dipositive ions of the $3d$-metals are ranked in order of stability constant:

$$Mn < Fe < Co < Ni < Cu > Zn.$$

This series applies for all ligands except where Jahn–Teller effects, spin-state changes, or other complications arise.

(c) Octahedral vs tetrahedral coordination   For metals in moderate oxidation states (+2, +3), tetrahedral complexes are relatively rare and usually occur only with large or highly polarizable ligands (see p. 81). However, the factors other than LFSE contributing to the formation of tetrahedral complexes may again be expected to vary smoothly along the series of metals, increasing from Mn^{2+} to Zn^{2+}, and major differences between one metal and the next may be attributed to ligand-field effects. Experimentally it is found that cobalt(II) forms tetrahedral complexes relatively readily, whereas nickel(II) does not [cf. the experiment in which an aqueous solution of cobalt(II) is turned from pale pink to deep blue by the addition of concentrated hydrochloric acid, representing the formation of a small percentage of a highly coloured tetrahedral complex; similar addition of the acid to a nickel(II) solution does not noticeably affect the colour, although tetrahedral nickel(II) complexes are equally intensely coloured (and can be obtained in non-aqueous media)]. The differences in LFSE are shown in Table 4.5, from which it is seen that the octahedral arrangement always gives the larger LFSE, but that cobalt(II) (d^7) and iron(II) (d^6) are least penalised by adopting the tetrahedral configuration, while nickel(II) (d^8) is heavily discriminated against.

Table 4.5   Site preference energies

Configuration	LFSE(oct)	LFSE(tet)	LFSE(oct)–LFSE(tet)†
d^1, d^6	$0.4\Delta_o$	$0.6\Delta_t$	$0.1\Delta_o$
d^2, d^7	$0.8\Delta_o$	$1.2\Delta_t$	$0.2\Delta_o$
d^3, d^8	$1.2\Delta_o$	$0.8\Delta_t$	$0.8\Delta_o$
d^4, d^9	$0.6\Delta_o$	$0.4\Delta_t$	$0.4\Delta_o$

† assuming $\Delta_t = \frac{1}{2}\Delta_o$

These effects can be seen more directly in the structures of mixed oxides of spinel structure, an important class of oxides which contain both di- and tri-positive metal ions, $M^{II}(M^{III})_2O_4$. The structure has been discussed in detail on p. 71 but the relevant feature is that two basic types may exist. In the normal spinel the tripositive ions are situated on octahedral sites, maximising the electrostatic lattice energy; other things being equal, this is the structure which is expected. In some cases, however, ligand-field effects appear to be responsible for the adoption of the inverse spinel structure, in which the dipositive ions are on octahedral sites and the tripositive ions occupy both types of site. Since the LFSE is always greater for octahedral than tetrahedral coordination (Table 4.5), a dipositive ion for which this difference (the site-preference energy, see Table 4.6 and 7) is large may be able to force a change of structure type. Thus, in Table 4.8, it is seen that the nickel(II) spinels are nearly all inverted, the exception being $NiCr_2O_4$ in which the site-preference energy for Cr^{3+} is considerably larger than that for Ni^{2+}. The structures of the oxides M_3O_4 have been similarly explained; only Fe_3O_4 is inverted, in agreement with the site-preference energy of Fe^{2+} being larger than that of Fe^{3+}, while those of Mn^{2+} and Co^{2+} are less than those of the respective tripositive ions. It is clear, however, that this may be something of an oversimplification since, although Fe^{3+} has no LFSE and might therefore be displaced relatively readily from the octahedral

Table 4.6 Ligand-field stabilisation energies in normal and inverse spinels

	Ion distribution	LFSE
Normal	$(M_{tet}^{2+})(M_{oct}^{3+})_2O_4$	$LFSE(M_{tet}^{2+}) + 2LFSE(M_{oct}^{3+})$
Inverse	$(M_{tet}^{3+})(M_{oct}^{2+})(M_{oct}^{3+})O_4$	$LFSE(M_{tet}^{3+}) + LFSE(M_{oct}^{2+})$ $+ LFSE(M_{oct}^{3+})$
Difference	LFSE(norm) − LFSE(inv)	$[LFSE(M_{oct}^{3+}) - LFSE(M_{tet}^{3+})]$ $-[LFSE(M_{oct}^{2+}) - LFSE(M_{tet}^{2+})]$

Table 4.7 Site-preference energies (kJ mol^{-1})

	LFSE(oct)	LFSE(tet)	SPE
Mn^{2+}	0	0	0
Fe^{2+}	49·8	33·1	16·7
Co^{2+}	92·9	61·9	31·0
Ni^{2+}	122·2	36·0	86·2
Cu^{2+}	90·4	26·8	62·4
Cr^{3+}	224·7	66·9	157·8
Mn^{3+}	135·6	40·2	95·4
Fe^{3+}	0	0	0
Co^{3+}			> 150

The data are estimates based on the spectra of hydrates and oxides (after J. D. Dunitz and L. E. Orgel, *Adv. Inorg. Chem. Radiochem.*, **2**, 30 (1960)).

Table 4.8 Cation distribution in spinels (δ)

M^{3+} \ M^{2+}	Mg^{2+}	Mn^{2+}	Fe^{2+}	Co^{2+}	Ni^{2+}	Cu^{2+}	Zn^{2+}
Al^{3+}	0	0	0	0	0·76		0
Cr^{3+}	0	0	0	0	0	0·1	0
Mn^{3+}	0	0	0·67?	0·67?	1	0	0
Fe^{3+}	0·9	0·2	1	1	1	1	0
Co^{3+}				0			0

$\delta = 0$ for a normal spinel
$\delta = 1$ for an inverse spinel
$\delta = 0.67$ for completely random distribution of cations between tetrahedral and octahedral sites
(after Dunitz and Orgel, *loc. cit.*)

site, it is curious that all the ferrites (except $ZnFe_2O_4$) should be inverted when the corresponding aluminates are normal. This difference may be partly due to the smaller size of Al^{3+}, which would magnify the lattice-energy effects. It is also likely that magnetic coupling between iron(III) ions in the two types of site stabilises the inverse arrangement ($ZnFe_2O_4$ is not ferromagnetic). The manganites $FeMn_2O_4$ and $CoMn_2O_4$ appear to have random distributions of cations despite the large site-preference energy of Mn^{3+}, but it is not clear what oxidation states are involved for each metal; Fe^{3+}, Mn^{2+} is a more likely combination than Fe^{2+}, Mn^{3+}, and Co^{3+}, Mn^{2+} is quite likely in view of the high LFSE of Co^{3+}.

(d) *Reaction mechanism* There is a great deal of evidence to show that octahedral complexes undergo substitution reactions by a dissociative mechanism; the loss of the departing ligand is the slow, rate-determining step of the reaction, and the entry of the substituent is rapid. Even when similar complexes are studied, e.g. hexa-aquo ions, a wide variety of reaction rates is found, e.g. $V(OH_2)_6^{2+}$ and $Cr(OH_2)_6^{2+}$ undergo exchange with solvent water with rate constants of about 10^2 s^{-1} and 4×10^8 s^{-1} respectively. This enormous difference in rates of reaction (corresponding to about 38 kJ mol^{-1} difference in activation energies) is due, at least in part, to ligand-field effects.

The rate of reaction is governed by the activation energy which, in this case, represents the energy of forming the five-coordinate transition state. One factor (of many) contributing to this energy is the difference in LFSE between the intermediate and the starting complex. As shown in Table 4.9, this difference sometimes increases the activation energy and sometimes decreases it, and there is rather good agreement between the predictions of this model and the qualitative reactivities of the complexes. Thus, metal ions of d^4 configuration (e.g. Cr^{2+}) are expected to be labile while a d^3 configuration (e.g. V^{2+}, Cr^{3+}) confers inertness. Among the tripositive metals, chromium(III) (d^3) and cobalt(III) (low spin d^6) are found to undergo substitution reactions very slowly. The tenacity with which the low-spin iron(II) ion (d^6) in oxy-haemoglobin holds the coordinated oxygen has been referred to above (p. 99).

Table 4.9 LFSE-contributions to activation energies for ligand-substitution

Configuration	LFSE(oct) Δ_o	LFSE(spy) Δ_o	Contribution to ΔH Δ_o
High-spin			
d^1, d^6	0·400	0·457	−0·057
d^2, d^7	0·800	0·914	−0·114
d^3, d^8	1·200	1·000	+0·200
d^4, d^9	0·600	0·914	−0·314
High-spin			
d^4	1·600	1·457	+0·143
d^5	2·000	1·914	+0·086
d^6	2·400	2·000	+0·400
d^7	1·800	1·914	−0·114

The crystal-field energies of the d-orbitals in a square-pyramidal complex (in units of Δ_o) are: $d_{xy,yz}$, −0·457; d_{xy}, −0·086; $d_{x^2-y^2}$, +0·086; d_{z^2}, +0·914.
(After F. Basolo and R. G. Pearson, *Mechanisms of Inorganic Reactions*, Wiley, New York, 1967)

4.6.4 The eighteen-electron rule

Many compounds of the d-block metals, notably the carbonyls and organometallic derivatives, follow the 'eighteen-electron' or 'nine-orbital' rule, i.e. the total number of electrons associated with the metal atom is eighteen. This number is made up of the 'non-bonding' d-electrons plus the electrons donated by the ligands (normally two per ligand). Thus, $Cr(CO)_6$ is an 18-electron compound since the chromium (0) atom has a d^6 configuration and the CO-groups donate a further 12 electrons. The occurrence of these compounds, rather than those with other numbers of electrons, invited comparison with other 'closed-shell' systems, where the electron configuration resembles that of the following rare gas atom. It is, however, very noticeable that there are many more exceptions than adherents to this rule. Nevertheless, it is possible to classify complexes in the following way:

(a) complexes which appear to have no restriction on the electron-number, typically high-spin complexes of the $3d$-metals;

(b) complexes which have up to, but never more than eighteen electrons, typically low-spin complexes, especially those of the $4d$- and $5d$-metals;

(c) complexes containing strong π-acceptor ligands, typically the carbonyls, which adhere rigorously to the rule.

These types of complexes are best related to the molecular orbital diagrams, Figs. 4.5 and 4.7. In terms of octahedral complexes, the 18-electron complex is one in which the t_{2g}-orbitals are completely filled (d^6) and has no e_g^*-electrons, the class (b) complex will have up to six t_{2g}-electrons and again no e_g^*-electrons. The class (a) complex may have electrons in t_{2g}, or t_{2g}- and e_g-orbitals.

For non-π-bonding ligands, the t_{2g}-orbitals are non-bonding; the number of electrons in those orbitals has therefore no direct effect on the bond-energy of the complex. The e_g^*-orbitals, however, are anti-bonding, and become more so the greater the bond-energy of the metal–ligand bonds (since the stabilisation of the bonding orbitals and the destabilisation of the anti-bonding orbitals are complementary). For high-spin complexes, with relatively small values of Δ_0 the e_g^*-orbitals are only slightly anti-bonding and electrons may be accommodated in them with very little loss of bond energy and, of course, a gain in exchange energy. In this case there will be no restriction on the electron number, and examples may readily be found of complexes with any number of electrons from 12 [d^0, e.g. $Ti(C_2O_4)_3^{2-}$] to 22 [d^{10}, e.g. $Zn(OH_2)_6^{2+}$].

In low-spin complexes, class (b), Δ_0 is large; the e_g^*-orbitals have become strongly anti-bonding and must remain empty. The t_{2g}-orbitals are still non-bonding and may accommodate up to six electrons, giving complexes with up to, but not more than, 18 electrons.

For strongly π-accepting ligands, the e_g^*-orbitals are still very anti-bonding, but now the t_{2g}-orbitals are bonding, by interation with the ligand π-system. It is therefore important to have as many electrons as possible in these orbitals, to maximise the bond-energy.

For other coordination numbers similar arguments apply. The s- and p-orbitals and some of the d-orbitals (the total number of orbitals corresponding to the coordination number) are involved in σ-bonding, giving a set of σ-anti-bonding orbitals of relatively low energy corresponding to the e_g^*-orbitals. The remaining d-orbitals are either non-bonding or may be involved in π-bonding, corresponding to the t_{2g}-orbitals. The same division into classes (a), (b) and (c) can still be made.

Bibliography

CW, 19–21, 24; **ES**, 15–6, 18–9; **H**, 8–9; **HJ**, 6, 28; **L**, 17–8; **MM**, 12; **PW**, 24–5, 28–9.

F. Basolo and R. Johnson, *Coordination Chemistry*, Benjamin, 1964. Excellent, readable, introductory presentation of several aspects of coordination chemistry.

A. Earnshaw and T. Harrington, *The Chemistry of the Transition Elements*, Oxford University Press, 1973. A good introductory text.

M. M. Jones, *Elementary Coordination Chemistry*, Prentice-Hall, 1964. A good survey.

J. Lewis and R. G. Wilkins, *Modern Coordination Chemistry*, Wiley, 1960. Detailed reviews of selected topics.

D. Nicholls, *Complexes and First-Row Transition Elements*, Macmillan, 1975. Good coverage of coordination chemistry.

L. E. Orgel, *Introduction to Transition Metal Chemistry: Ligand-Field Theory*, 2nd ed., Methuen, 1966. A clear account of ligand-field theory and its applications.

J. D. Dunitz and L. E. Orgel, *Adv. Inorg. Chem. Radiochem.*, **2**, 1 (1960). Good, critical consideration of the ionic model and crystal-field effects.

P. George and D. S. McClure, *Prog. Inorg. Chem.*, **1**, 381 (1959). A survey of the effects of LFSE.

F. Basolo and R. G. Pearson, *Mechanisms of Inorganic Reactions*, 2nd edn, Wiley, 1967. Good review of crystal- and ligand-field theories and a very detailed treatment of the mechanisms of substitution and oxidation-reduction reactions.

D. Benson, *Mechanisms of Inorganic Reactions in Solution, An Introduction*, McGraw Hill, 1968. Useful introduction.

P. R. Mitchell and R. V. Parish, *J. Chem. Educ.*, **46**, 811 (1969). An explanation of the 'eighteen-electron rule'–when and why it is obeyed.

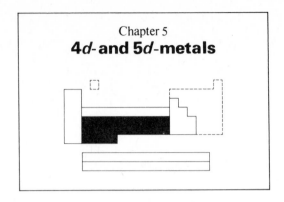

Chapter 5
4d- and 5d-metals

The metals of the 4d- and 5d-series form a strong contrast with those of the 3d-series. The metals themselves are generally very hard, high-melting and unreactive, and are often used for these properties. In their compounds a wide range of oxidation states is shown, but all are characterised by the formation of bonds of high covalent character, and there are no simple ionic compounds. Only in a few cases are even the simple aquated cations known, other ligands, often anions, being bound in preference to water.

Within each Group, the 4d- and 5d-metals are often closely similar, especially in the earlier Groups, and this gives rise to difficulties in separation and identification. It is, for example, not easy to obtain samples of hafnium or zirconium uncontaminated by the other. These similarities are the result of the 'lanthanide contraction'. In Group III, yttrium and lanthanum show the differences in their chemistry which would be anticipated from the difference in ionic radii, ionisation energies, etc., but the interpolation of the fourteen lanthanide elements between lanthanum and zirconium, with the resultant increase in effective nuclear charge, reduces the radii and increases the ionisation energies to values close to those for hafnium. These effects are seen to build up through the 4f-series (see Ch. 6) and to extend across the sixth Period into the p-block (Ch. 8).

The metals of Group VIII (Ru, Os, Rh, Ir, Pd, Pt) are often grouped together as the *platinum metals* and they, together with silver and gold are often known as the *noble metals* on account of their chemical inertness (in the elemental state).

5.1 Occurrence, extraction, and uses

The 4d- and 5d-metals are all of low natural abundance (cf. Table 5.1) and one, technetium, is not found at all in nature, being radioactive (all the isotopes are β-emitters, the longest half-life being *ca.* 10^5 years). In many cases there are no economically workable concentrated deposits, and molybdenum, rhenium, silver, and cadmium are obtained almost entirely as by-products from the extraction of copper and zinc. Gold is also recovered from copper and nickel ores but may be found native, as may the platinum metals; the latter often occur alloyed together, in addition to forming a range of mixed sulphides and arsenides. Zirconium and niobium are always associated with hafnium and tantalum respectively, and their separation was very difficult and costly before the use of ion-exchange and solvent-extraction methods.

Various extraction processes are used most of which involve several stages, and often each source of a given metal requires different treatment. The most common methods are summarised in Table 5.1 and Fig. 5.1.

In all cases, production of the elemental metal greatly exceeds that of the compounds. The early metals are widely used as additives in steels, giving improved strength (Zr, Nb, Mo), corrosion

Fig. 5.1 Extraction of the platinum metals (data from International Nickel Co.)

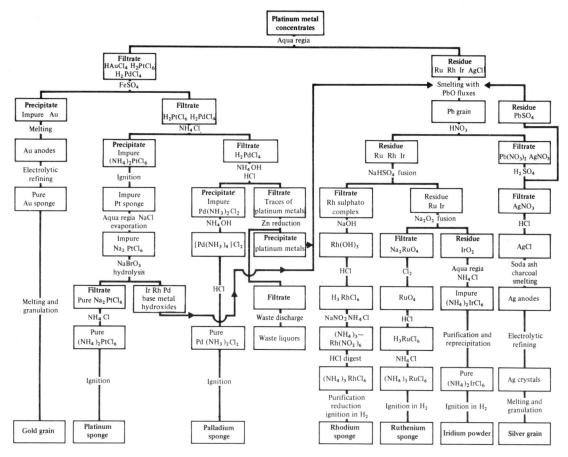

resistance (Nb, Mo) and temperature- and wear-resistance (W), and these alloys are employed in tools, bearings, turbines, jet engines and various stainless steels. The carbides of niobium, tantalum, and tungsten are very hard and resistant to wear, and are used in dies and cutting tools and as abrasives. Zirconium and niobium, having low neutron cross-sections, are used in fuel-element cladding (e.g. in the Dounreay reactors), but must be carefully purified from hafnium and tantalum which have high cross-sections. Their resistance to corrosion by a wide variety of reagents, including liquid metals, offsets the relatively high production costs. Tantalum, cadmium, gold, and the platinum metals are also used for their corrosion resistance, either on their own (Ta, Mo, Re, Pt, alloys of Pt with Ru, Os, Rh, Ir) or plated on other metals (Cd, Au), and the good electrical conductivity also shown by these metals leads to their widespread application in electronic components. The resistance to tarnishing and chemical attack which characterises the noble metals led, of course, to their long-standing use in jewelry and coinage, although in the latter application they have been largely superseded by the cupro-nickel alloys. Many of the metals also have high catalytic activity, and are used in petroleum refining (Mo, W, Pt), hydrogenation and dehydrogenation (W, Pd), oxidation of ammonia for HNO_3- and H_2SO_4-manufacture (Rh – Pd) and sulphur dioxide for H_2SO_4-manufacture (Pt, now superseded by V_2O_5), and compounds of rhodium, palladium and platinum catalyse many reactions of alkenes.

Table 5.1 Occurrence and isolation of 4d- and 5d-metals

	Abundance ppm	Principal Ores	Occurrence	Isolation	Purification
Zr	200	Zircon, $ZrSiO_4$	USA, Australia,	C-arc furnace $ZrC \xrightarrow{O_2} ZrO_2$; $ZrC \xrightarrow{Cl_2} ZrCl_4 \xrightarrow[1150°]{Mg} Zr$	Zone refining
Hf		Baddeleyite, ZrO_2	Brazil	Separate by cation exchange, solvent extraction.	van Arkel–de Boer
Nb Ta		Pyrochlore, $NaCaNb_2O_6F$ Columbite, (Fe, Mn) (Nb, Ta)$_2O_6$	Canada, Brazil, Norway, Nigeria, Congo, Australia	HF or alkali dissolution or C-red^n to carbide or ferrometal. Solvent extraction on HF solution.	Zone refining, electron-beam melting
Mo	1·5	Molybdenite, MoS_2 Copper ores	USA, Canada, Chile, USSR	Roast, $MoO_3 \xrightarrow{NH_4OH} (NH_4)_2MoO_4 \xrightarrow{ht} MoO_3 \xrightarrow[500°]{H_2} Mo$	consumable-electrode melting
W	1·6	Scheelite, $CaWO_4$ Wolframite, (Fe, Mn)WO_4	China, N. Korea, USA, Portugal	hot $NaOH \rightarrow Na_2WO_4 \xrightarrow{HCl} WO_3 \xrightarrow{H_2 \text{ or } C} W$	
Tc	0	Nuclear fuel elements		Solvent-extraction of fission products.	
Re	3×10^{-3}	Molybdenum, copper ores		$\xrightarrow{Roast} Re_2O_7$. Ion exchange or solvent extraction. $NH_4ReO_4 \xrightarrow{H_2} Re$	Electrolysis
Ru Os Rh Ir Pd Pt	10^{-1}	Elemental Sperryite, $PtAs_2$ Stibiopalladite, Pd_3Sb Laurite, RuS_2 Braggite, (Pt, Pd, Ni)S	S. Africa Canada S. Africa S. Africa S. Africa	See flow sheet Fig. 5.1	
Ag	0·1	copper, lead, zinc ores		Electrol. slime extracted H_2SO_4, smelt, electrolyse.	Electrolysis
Au	0·25	Elemental Copper, nickel ores	S. Africa, USA, USSR	$KCN/O_2 \rightarrow KAu(CN)_2 \xrightarrow{Zn} Au$	Electrolysis
Cd	0·2	Zinc ores		Extract residues H_2SO_4, reduce with $Zn \rightarrow Cd$	Electrolysis
Hg	0·5	Cinnabar, HgS	Spain, Italy, Yugoslavia	Roast. Hg distils out	

5.2 Elemental metals

The metals of the early Groups (IV–VIII) are hard and high-melting with large enthalpies of atomisation, reflecting the high strength of interatomic binding resulting from the efficient overlap of $4d$- and $5d$-orbitals and the number of bonding electrons available. The noble metals have more modest melting points and atomisation enthalpies, and are generally soft and easily worked, and the series ends with mercury which is, of course, the only metal liquid at room temperature. With increasing nobility along the series, the metals become easier to reduce; very mild reducing agents (e.g. formic acid) liberate metallic gold from solutions of its salts, and compounds of the platinum metals are also decomposed quite readily. In contrast, quite vigorous conditions are required to obtain the early metals in the elemental state (e.g. carbon- or hydrogen-reduction at high temperatures).

These metals are the least reactive of all (see Table 5.2). Unless finely divided, they are all unaffected by air or water at room temperature (often owing to the formation of a protective film of oxide), although technetium and rhenium are slowly tarnished by moist air (the oxide, M_2O_7, is not protective in these cases). Only cadmium is attacked readily by mineral acids but most of the

Table 5.2   Properties of the elemental metals

	MP **°C**	**Reacts with**
Zr	1 855	Oxidising acids, HF. Hot air and X_2, F_2.
Hf	2 150	Oxidising acids, HF. Hot air and X_2, F_2.
Nb	2 468	Oxidising acids, HF. Cold F_2, hot X_2, O_2.
Ta	2 980	Oxidising acids, HF. Hot X_2, F_2.
Mo	2 620	Molten oxidising alkali. Cold F_2, hot X_2, O_2.
W	3 420	Hot oxidising acids, molten oxidising alkali. Cold F_2, hot X_2, O_2.
Tc	2 250	Oxidising acids, H_2O_2. Hot O_2, X_2. Tarnished by moist air.
Re	3 180	Oxidising acids, H_2O_2. Hot O_2, X_2. Tarnished by moist air.
Ru	2 427	Oxidising acids, molten alkali. Hot O_2, X_2.
Os	2 697	Molten oxidising alkali. Hot O_2, X_2.
Rh	1 967	Hot oxidising acids, molten $KHSO_4$. Hot X_2.
Ir	2 454	Hot oxidising acids. Hot O_2, X_2.
Pd	1 555	Oxidising acids. Hot X_2.
Pt	1 769	Hot oxidising acids. Hot X_2.
Ag	961	Oxidising acids. Hot F_2.
Au	1 063	Hot oxidising acids. Hot F_2. KCNaq/O_2.
Cd	321	Mineral acids. Hot O_2, X_2.
Hg	−39	Oxidising acids. Hot O_2, X_2.

Reagents considered are mineral acids, oxidising acids, aqueous alkali, molten oxidising alkali, O_2, F_2 and the other halogens (X_2). Reagents not listed under a given metal do not attack.

metals will dissolve in strongly oxidising acids (e.g. nitric acid, aqua regia), although rhodium and iridium, especially, require heating. Zirconium, hafnium, niobium and tantalum are attacked by hydrofluoric acid; these metals form very stable complexes with fluoride ion, which is able to displace oxo–ligands. Niobium and tantalum are also soluble in aqueous alkali, but the other early metals react only with molten alkalis under oxidising conditions.

Table 5.3   Uses of the 4*d*- and 5*d*-metals

Zr	Fuel element cladding. Steel additive (strength). $ZrOCl_2.8H_2O$, pigments, water repellents. ZrO_2, refractories.
Nb	Steel additive (strength, temperature). Fuel element cladding. Carbide, cutting tools.
Ta	Corrosion-resistant equipment.
Mo	Steel additive (strength, toughness, wear-resistance). Heaters. MoS_2, lubricant. MoO_3, redox catalysts. Molybdates, pigments.
W	Steel additive (heat resistance, strength, high-speed tools). Lamp filaments. Carbide, abrasives, dies.
Re	Lamp filaments, furnace windings, special crucibles, catalysts.
Ru	Pd, Pt alloys (hardness pivots, pen nibs). Catalysts.
Os	Pt alloys (hardness needles, pivots, pen nibs)
Rh	Pt alloys (hardness). Catalysts.
Ir	Pt alloys (hardness). Special crucibles.
Pd	Jewelry. H_2-extraction. Catalysts.
Pt	Electrical contacts, electrodes, windings, temperature-measurement. Jewelry (with Ir, Ru). Crucibles. Corrosion-resistant plating. Catalysts.
Ag	Photography (nitrate, halides). Electrical contacts, jewelry (with Cu, Au), solders, catalysts.
Au	Jewelry, dentistry, electronic components, corrosion-resistant plating.
Cd	Plating on Fe (corrosion resistance), solders, low-melting alloys. Nuclear-reactor control rods. Sulphides, pigments, phosphors.
Hg	Electrical apparatus, chlorine-cells. HgO, germi- and fungi-cides, pharmaceuticals.

5.3   Halides

The halides reported for the 4*d*- and 5*d*-metals are shown in Table 5.4 and some of their properties are summarised in Table 5.5. It is probable that several more technetium halides could be prepared; the chemistry of this element has been much less well studied than for the other members of the series. The characterisation of higher halides has been complicated by the ease with which they hydrolyse and react with oxygen or the metal oxide, and it is difficult to obtain samples uncontaminated by oxyhalide. Much of the early data refers to impure products. It should also be noted that several of the lower halides do not have simple stoicheiometries.

In comparison with the 3*d*-metal halides, two features are noticeable: (a) with each halogen higher oxidation states are usually obtained for the 4*d*- and 5*d*-metals, except in Groups IV, IB, and IIB, and (b) many lower oxidation states are either not represented or are unstable to oxidation or disproportionation: this is particularly true of the fluorides, and it is probable that many of the unknown lower fluorides are unstable to disproportionation. However, in terms of the general distribution of compounds throughout the series, the patterns are roughly similar to those of the 3*d*-block. The highest oxidation states are found for the fluorides of the central metals, and although the early metals form the Group oxidation state readily, the later metals are oxidised beyond the trivalent state only with difficulty.

The chemistry of many of the halides has not been extensively investigated; this is especially true of the higher halides, all of which are very sensitive to hydrolysis. The penta- and hexa-halides are extensively hydrolysed and, in the case of the later metals, reduced by aqueous acids, although niobium(V) and tantalum(V) can be crystallised from hydrofluoric acid as salts of the anions $NbOF_6^{3-}$, NbF_7^{2-} or TaF_7^{2-} (this was the basis of an early separation process). The tetrahalides are usually soluble in aqueous hydrohalic acids forming halogeno- or oxyhalogeno-complexes and hydrolysis usually does not proceed beyond the introduction of one oxo-ligand. Many of the lower halides have complex structures and dissolve in water or dilute acids to give polymeric species; much of the interest taken in these halides and their coordination chemistry in recent years has

Table 5.4.a Halides of the 4d-metals

Zr	Nb	Mo	Tc	Ru	Rh	Pd	Ag	Cd
		MoF_6	TcF_6	RuF_6	RhF_6			
	NbF_5	MoF_5	TcF_5	RuF_5	RhF_5			
ZrF_4	NbF_4	MoF_4		RuF_4	RhF_4	PdF_4		
ZrF_3		MoF_3		RuF_3	RhF_3	PdF_3		
ZrF_2	$NbF_{2.5}$					PdF_2	AgF_2	CdF_2
							AgF	

Zr	Nb	Mo	Tc	Ru	Rh	Pd	Ag	Cd
			$TcCl_6$					
	$NbCl_5$	$MoCl_5$						
$ZrCl_4$	$NbCl_4$	$MoCl_4$	$TcCl_4$	$RuCl_4$				
$ZrCl_3$	$NbCl_{2.67-3.13}$	$MoCl_3$		$RuCl_3$	$RhCl_3$			
$ZrCl_2$		$MoCl_2$				$PdCl_2$		$CdCl_2$
							$AgCl$	

Zr	Nb	Mo	Tc	Ru	Rh	Pd	Ag	Cd
	$NbBr_5$							
$ZrBr_4$	$NbBr_4$	$MoBr_4$						
$ZrBr_3$	$NbBr_{2.67-3.3}$	$MoBr_3$		$RuBr_3$	$RhBr_3$			
$ZrBr_2$		$MoBr_2$				$PdBr_2$		$CdBr_2$
							$AgBr$	

Zr	Nb	Mo	Tc	Ru	Rh	Pd	Ag	Cd
	NbI_5							
ZrI_4	NbI_4							
ZrI_3	$NbI_{2.67-3.0}$	MoI_3		RuI_3				
ZrI_2	$NbI_{1.83}$	MoI_2				PdI_2		CdI_2
							AgI	

stemmed from the elucidation of these structures, which involve tightly-bound clusters of metal atoms (see below).

Two **heptafluorides** are known, ReF_7 and OsF_7. Repeated attempts have been made to prepare TcF_7 without success. The osmium compound is stable only under a high pressure of fluorine, decomposing above $-100\,°C$ in its absence, but ReF_7 is thermally stable. The latter and all the **hexafluorides** (Mo–Rh, W–Pt) are low-melting, volatile compounds, presumably monomeric covalent molecules. Thermal stability decreases along each series and PtF_6 is sometimes used as a (very vigorous) fluorinating agent, e.g. in the preparation of the first genuine compounds of xenon. Very few other **hexahalides** are known (WCl_6, WBr_6, $TcCl_6$, $ReCl_6$). Technetium hexachloride and

Table 5.4b   Halides of the 5d-metals

Hf	Ta	W	Re	Os	Ir	Pt	Au	Hg	Hg₂
			ReF_7						
		WF_6	ReF_6	OsF_6	IrF_6	PtF_6			
	TaF_5		ReF_5	OsF_5	IrF_5	PtF_5	AuF_5		
HfF_4		WF_4	ReF_4	OsF_4		PtF_4			
					IrF_3		AuF_3		
						PtF_2		HgF_2	
									Hg_2F_2

Hf	Ta	W	Re	Os	Ir	Pt	Au	Hg	Hg₂
		WCl_6	$ReCl_6$						
	$TaCl_5$	WCl_5	$ReCl_5$						
$HfCl_4$	$TaCl_4$	WCl_4	$ReCl_4$	$OsCl_4$		$PtCl_4$			
$HfCl_3$	$TaCl_{2.9-3.1}$	WCl_3	$ReCl_3$	$OsCl_3$	$IrCl_3$	$PtCl_3$	$AuCl_3$		
$HfCl_2$	$TaCl_{2.67}$	WCl_2				$PtCl_2$		$HgCl_2$	
	$TaCl_{2.33}$						$AuCl$		Hg_2Cl_2

Hf	Ta	W	Re	Os	Ir	Pt	Au	Hg	Hg₂
		WBr_6							
	$TaBr_5$	WBr_5	$ReBr_5$						
$HfBr_4$	$TaBr_4$	WBr_4	$ReBr_4$	$OsBr_4$		$PtBr_4$			
$HfBr_3$	$TaBr_{2.9-3.1}$	WBr_3	$ReBr_3$	$OsBr_3$	$IrBr_3$	$PtBr_3$	$AuBr_3$		
$HfBr_2$	$TaBr_{2.5}$	WBr_2				$PtBr_2$		$HgBr_2$	
	$TaBr_{2.33}$						$AuBr$		Hg_2Br_2

Hf	Ta	W	Re	Os	Ir	Pt	Au	Hg	Hg₂
	TaI_5								
HfI_4	TaI_4		ReI_4			PtI_4			
HfI_3		WI_3	ReI_3	OsI_3	IrI_3	PtI_3			
	$TaI_{2.33}$	WI_2	ReI_2	OsI_2		PtI_2		HgI_2	
			ReI	OsI			AuI		Hg_2I_2

WBr_6 are thermally unstable, the former losing chlorine even at room temperature to give $TcCl_4$. All appear to be monomeric (low-melting and soluble in organic solvents) but WCl_6 is much less volatile than expected.

The **pentafluorides** (Nb-Rh, Ta-Au) are also low-melting solids, but they form viscous, associated liquids. In the solid state all, with the possible exception of TcF_5, have the tetrameric

Table 5.5a Properties of the 4*d*-metal halides

	Colour	MP/°C	$\frac{\Delta H_f^0}{\text{kJ mol}^{-1}}$	Structure	Preparation	Properties
ZrF_4	white	932	−1 912	8-coord.	$Zr/F_2/400°$	Hydrolysed by H_2O.
$ZrCl_4$	white	438	−981		Zr/Cl_2, ZrO_2/CCl_4	Instantly hydrolysed by H_2O ($ZrOCl_2.H_2O$).
$ZrBr_4$	white	450	−760	cubic	$ZrO_2/C/Br_2/560°$	Hydrolyses rapidly.
ZrI_4	orange	500	−485		$ZrO_2/AlI_3/400°/\text{s.t.}$	
ZrF_3	blue	dec		ReO_3	$ZrH_3/HF/H_2/750°$	$\xrightarrow{300°}$ $Zr + ZrF_4$.
$ZrCl_3$	blue	dec	−720	BiI_3	$ZrCl_4/Al$, H_2 or Zr	$\xrightarrow{400°}$ $ZrCl_2 + ZrCl_4$. Dissolves in H_2O with liberation of H_2.
$ZrBr_3$	blue	dec	−632	hexag	$ZrBr_4/Al$, H_2 or Zr	$\xrightarrow{300°}$ $ZrBr_2 + ZrBr_4$.
ZrI_3	blue		−431	hexag	$ZrI_4/Zr/400°$	$\xrightarrow{350°}$ $ZrI_2 + ZrI_4$.
ZrF_2	black		−937		Zr/atomic $F/350°$	$\xrightarrow{800°}$ $Zr + ZrF_4$. Ignites in air on warming.
$ZrCl_2$	black		−520		$ZrCl_3/500°$, $ZrCl_4/Zr/675°$	$\xrightarrow{600°}$ $Zr + ZrCl_4$. Dissolves in hot acids, liberating H_2.
$ZrBr_2$	blue		−418		$ZrBr_3/350°$	$\xrightarrow{400°}$ $Zr + ZrBr_4$
ZrI_2	blue		−285		$ZrI_3/400°$	
NbF_5	white	79	−1 814	MoF_5	$Nb/F_2/300°$	Highly associated liquid. Hydrolysed by moist air.
$NbCl_5$	yellow	204	−797	Nb_2Cl_{10}	$Nb/Cl_2300°$	Dimeric. Hydrolysed rapidly. Soluble organic solvents.
$NbBr_5$	orange	255	−565		$Nb/Br_2/300°$	Readily hydrolysed.
NbI_5	golden		−427		$Nb/I_2/270°/\text{s.t.}$	$\xrightarrow{250°}$ NbI_4. Readily hydrolysed.
NbF_4	black			SnF_4	$NbF_5/Nb/350°$	$\xrightarrow{400°}$ $NbF_{2.5} + NbF_5$ $\xrightarrow{\text{air}}$ NbO_2F. Hydrolyses rapidly.
$NbCl_4$	black	dec	−695		$NbCl_5/Nb/380°$	$\xrightarrow{450°}$ $NbCl_3 + NbCl_5$. Diamagnetic chain structure with Nb_2 pairs.
$NbBr_4$	black				$NbBr_5/Nb/410–350°/\text{s.t.}$	$\xrightarrow{450°}$ $NbBr_3 + NbBr_5$. Diamagnetic. Oxidised by air.
NbI_4	grey			chain	$NbI_5/270°/\text{s.t.}$	$\xrightarrow{550°}$ Nb_3I_8. Diamagnetic chain structure (α) with Nb_2 pairs.
$NbCl_{2.67}$	black		−538	hexag	$NbCl_4/500°$	Trinuclear cluster, $Nb_3Cl_4Cl_{6/2}Cl_{3/3}$. $\mu_{eff} = 1.68\mu_B$ per Nb_3-unit Composition range up to $NbCl_{3.13}$.
$NbBr_{2.67}$	black				$NbBr_4/400°$	Non-stoicheiometric, $NbBr_{2.67–3.13}$.
$NbI_{2.67}$	black				$NbI_4/550°$	Non-stoicheiometric, $NbI_{2.67–3.13}$.
$NbF_{2.5}$				cubic	$NbF_5/Nb/700°$	Hexanuclear cluster, $[Nb_6F_{12}]F_{6/2}$.
$NbCl_{2.33}$	green		−475		$NbCl_5/Cd/300°$	Hexanuclear cluster, $Nb_6Cl_{12}Cl_{4/2}$. Stable to H_2O.
$NbBr_{2.33}$	green				$NbBr_5/Nb/300°$	Hexanuclear cluster, $[Nb_6Br_{12}]Br_{4/2}$.
$NbI_{1.87}$					$NbI_5/600°$	Hexanuclear cluster, $[Nb_6I_8]I_{6/2}$
MoF_6	col'less	17	−1 626		$Mo/F_2/200°$	BP 34 °C
MoF_5		64			$MoF_6/Mo/300°$	Tetrameric. $\xrightarrow{165°}$ $MoF_4 + MoF_6$. Associated liquid.
$MoCl_5$	black	19	−530	$NbCl_5$	$Mo/Cl_2/400°$	Dimeric. Hydrolyses very readily. $\xrightarrow{O_2}$ $MoOCl_4$.
MoF_4	green				$MoF_5/200°$	Readily hydrolysed.
$MoCl_4$			−477		$MoCl_5/C_6H_6/80°$	Layer lattice (hcp).
$MoBr_4$			−321		$Mo/Br_2/900°$	$\xrightarrow{400°}$ $MoBr_3$.
MoF_3	pink			ReO_3	$MoF_5/Mo/400°$	Readily hydrolyses.
$MoCl_3$	red		−		$MoCl_5/300°$	Layer lattice with Mo_2 pairs.
$MoBr_3$	green				$Mo/Br_2/Et_2O$	Chain structure (?), antiferromagnetic.
MoI_3					$Mo/I_2/300°/\text{s.t.}$	Chain structure (?), antiferromagnetic.
$MoCl_2$	yellow		−289		$MoCl_3/340°$	$\xrightarrow{530°}$ $Mo + MoCl_4$. Hexameric cluster, $[Mo_6Cl_8]Cl_{4/2}$.
$MoBr_2$			−261		$Mo/Br_2/N_2/650°$	$\xrightarrow{900°}$ $Mo + MoBr_4$. Hexameric cluster, $[Mo_6Br_8]Br_{4/2}$.
MoI_2			−105		$MoI_3/100°/\text{vac.}$	Hexameric cluster, $[Mo_6I_8]I_{4/2}$.

continued

Table 5.5a   Properties of the 4d-metal halides (continued)

	Colour	MP/°C	$\frac{\Delta H_f^0}{kJ\ mol^{-1}}$	Structure	Preparation	Properties
TcF_6	yellow	37			$Tc/F_2/400°$	Associated liquid.
$TcCl_6$	green	*ca.* 25			Tc/Cl_2 (minor product)	Decs. at room temp, even under Cl_2, to $TcCl_4$. Rapidly hydrolysed.
TcF_5	yellow	50			$Tc/F_2/400°$	Decs. at 60°. Readily hydrolysed.
$TcCl_4$	red-brown				Tc/Cl_2 (major product)	Chain structure. Incompletely hydrolysed by H_2O.
RuF_6	brown-red	*ca.* 54			$Ru/F_2/$quench vapour	Very reactive (attacks glass). Dissociates readily to $ReF_5 + F_2$.
RuF_5	green	86	−893	MoF_5	$Ru/F_2/300°$	Tetrameric. Very reactive (attacks glass >100°).
RuF_4	yellow				$RuF_5/I_2/IF_5$	Readily hydrolysed. Attacks glass >300°.
RuF_3	brown				$RuF_5/I_2/250°$	
$RuCl_3$	brown		−253		Ru/Cl_2	
$RuBr_3$	brown		−184		$Ru/Br_2/550°$	Insoluble in H_2O. Dissociates on heating.
RuI_3	black		−160		$Ru/I_2/350°$	Dissociates on heating.
RhF_6	black	*ca.* 70			$Rh/F_2/$quench	
RhF_5	dk. red	95		MoF_4	$Rh/F_2/400°/6$ atm	Dec. at room temp. to $RhF_5 + F_2$. Attacks glass.
RhF_4	purple				$RhBr_3/BrF_3$	Tetrameric. Powerful oxidant. Hydrolyses violently.
RhF_3	red				$RhX_3/F_2/400°$	Readily hydrolysed.
$RhCl_3$	red		−299	$AlCl_3$	$Rh/Cl_2/400°$	Insol. in H_2O.
$RhBr_3$	red				Rh/Br_2	
PdF_4	red			UCl_4	$PdF_3/F_2/300°$	Readily reduced. Violent reaction with H_2O.
PdF_3	black				$PdX_2/F_2/200°$	$Pd^{II}Pd^{IV}F_6$. Paramagnetic. Hydrolyses rapidly.
PdF_2	violet			TiO_2	$PdF_3/SeF_4/$reflux	Paramagnetic, $\mu_{eff} = 1·84\mu_B$
$PdCl_2$	red	678	−172	chain	$Pd/Cl_2/300°$	Chain structure and hexanuclear structure Pd_6Cl_{12}.
$PdBr_2$	red		−104	$PdCl_2$	Pd/Br_2	
PdI_2	black		−64		H_2PdCl_4/KI	Insol. in H_2O.
AgF_2	brown	*ca.* 690	−353		$Ag/F_2/250°$	Instantly hydrolysed by moist air. Good fluorinating agent.
AgF	yellow		−203	$NaCl$	$Ag_2CO_3/HF/$evap	V. sol. in H_2O. Mild fluorinating agent.
$AgCl$	white		−126	$NaCl$	Ag^+/Cl^-	Light-sensitive ($\rightarrow$ Ag).
$AgBr$	cream		−115	Nace	Ag^+/Br^-	Light-sensitive ($\rightarrow$ Ag).
AgI	yellow	555	−64	wurtzite	Ag^+/I^-	Light-sensitive ($\rightarrow$ Ag). Many crystal phases.
Ag_2F	yellow			CdI_2	$AgF/$electrol	$\xrightarrow{200°} Ag + AgF$.
CdF_2	white	1 110	−700	CaF_2	Cd/F_2	
$CdCl_2$	white	868	−391	$CdCl_2$	Cd/Cl_2	
$CdBr_2$	white	568	−316	$CdCl_2$	Cd/Br_2	
CdI_2	white	387	−203	CdI_2	Cd/I_2	

Table 5.5b   Properties of the 5d-metal halides

	Colour	MP/°C	$\frac{\Delta H_f^0}{kJ\ mol^{-1}}$	Structure	Preparation	Properties
HfF_4	white		−1 930	ZrF_4	$Hf/F_2/400°$	Hydrolyses readily.
$HfCl_4$	white	434	−992		Hf/Cl_2	Readily hydrolysed.
$HfBr_4$	white	425	−836	cubic	$HfO_2/C/Br_2/750°$	Hydrolyses.
HfI_4	orange	449		cubic	Hf/I_2	
$HfCl_3$	black	dec	−778		$HfCl_4/Hf/600°$	$\xrightarrow{400°} HfCl_2 + HfCl_4$.
$HfBr_3$	black		−647		$HfBr_4/H_2$, Hf or Al	$\xrightarrow{350°} HfBr_2 + HfBr_4$.

Table 5.5b Properties of the 5*d*-metal halides

	Colour	MP/°C	ΔH_f^0 kJ mol^{-1}	Structure	Preparation	Properties
HfI$_3$	black		−473	hexag.	HfI$_4$/Hf or Al	
HfCl$_2$	black		−544		HfCl$_3$/500°	
HfBr$_2$	black		−452		HfBr$_3$/350°	$\xrightarrow{400°}$ Hf + HfBr$_4$.
TaF$_5$	white	97	−1 904	MoF$_5$	Ta/F$_2$/300°	Associated liquid. Hydrolyses in air.
TaCl$_5$	white	216	−858	monoclin	Ta/Cl$_2$/300°	Dimeric. Readily hydrolysed.
TaBr$_5$	orange	270	−686		Ta/Br$_2$/350°	Readily hydrolysed.
TaI$_5$	brown	496	−490		Ta/I$_2$/350°/s.t.	Readily hydrolysed. $\xrightarrow[\text{RT}]{O_2}$ Ta$_2$O$_5$.
TaCl$_4$	black		−707		TaCl$_5$/Ta/630°	$\xrightarrow{450°}$ TaCl$_3$ + TaCl$_5$. Diamagnetic.
TaBr$_4$	black				TaBr$_5$/Ta/630– 300°/s.t.	$\xrightarrow{450°}$ TaBr$_3$ + TaBr$_5$. Diamagnetic. Oxidised by air.
TaI$_4$	black				TaI$_5$/Al/500– 350°/s.t.	
TaF$_3$	blue			ReO$_3$		May be an oxyfluoride.
TaBr$_{2.83}$					TaBr$_4$/435°	
TaCl$_{2.67}$					TaCl$_5$/Al/350–400°/s.t.	$\xrightarrow{340°}$ TaCl$_{2.33}$ + TaCl$_5$. Trinuclear cluster, [Ta$_3$Cl$_4$]Cl$_{6/2}$Cl
TaCl$_{2.5}$			−474		TaCl$_5$/Ta/470– 630°/s.t.	Hexanuclear cluster.
TaBr$_{2.5}$					TaBr$_4$/250°	Hexanuclear cluster, [Ta$_6$Br$_{12}$]Br$_{6/2}$.
TaCl$_{2.33}$	green				TaCl$_5$/Na, Hg/500°	Hexanuclear cluster, [Ta$_6$Cl$_{12}$]Cl$_{4/2}$.
TaBr$_{2.33}$	green				TaBr$_5$/Ta/640°	Hexanuclear cluster, [Ta$_6$Br$_{12}$]Br$_{4/2}$.
TaI$_{2.23}$	green				TaI$_5$/Ta/585–530°/s.t.	Hexanuclear, [Ta$_6$I$_{12}$]I$_{4/2}$.
WF$_6$	col'less	2	−1 748	orthorhomb.	W/F$_2$/200°	BP 17°.
WCl$_6$	blue	280	−682		W/Cl$_2$/600°	Readily hydrolysed.
WBr$_6$	blue	309	−349		W/Br$_2$/N$_2$/200°	$\xrightarrow{200°}$ WBr$_5$ $\xrightarrow[\text{RT}]{O_2}$ WO$_2$Br$_2$ + WO$_4$Br$_4$. Readily hydrolysed.
WCl$_5$	black	244	−513	NbCl$_5$	WCl$_6$/P	Dimeric. Extremely air and moisture sensitive WOCl$_3$.
WBr$_5$	black		−314		W/Br$_2$/500°	Very readily hydrolysed.
WF$_4$	brown				WF$_6$/C$_6$H$_6$	Hydrolyses readily.
WCl$_4$	black		−469	NbCl$_4$	WCl$_6$/Al/475– 225°/s.t.	$\xrightarrow{400°}$ WCl$_2$ + WCl$_5$. Diamagnetic.
WBr$_4$	black				WBr$_5$/Al/475–225°/s.t.	
WCl$_3$	red				WCl$_2$/Cl$_2$/100°	Hexanuclear [W$_6$Cl$_{12}$]Cl$_6$.
WBr$_3$	black				WBr$_2$/Br$_2$/50°	$\xrightarrow{80°}$ WBr$_2$ + Br$_2$. Hexanuclear.
WI$_3$					W(CO)$_6$/I$_2$/120°/s.t.	
WBr$_{2.67}$					WBr$_2$/Br$_2$	Hexanuclear [W$_6$Br$_8$]Br$_4$(Br$_4$)$_{2/2}$.
WCl$_2$	yellow		−256		WCl$_4$/400°	Hexanuclear, [W$_6$Cl$_8$]Cl$_2$Cl$_{4/2}$
WBr$_2$	yellow				WBr$_4$/450°	Hexanuclear, W$_6$Br$_8$]Br$_2$Br$_{4/2}$. $\xrightarrow{Br_2}{150}$ [W$_6$Br$_8$]$^{6+}$-species.
WI$_2$	red				WCl$_2$/KI/LiI/540°	
ReF$_7$	yellow			IF$_7$	Re/F$_2$/400° (minor prod)	BP 48. ReF$_6$ always formed too. Instantly hydrolysed by H$_2$O.
ReF$_6$	yellow	187		cubic	Re/F$_2$/120° (major prod)	BP 34. Very readily hydrolysed with disproportionation to Re^{VII} + Re^{IV}.
ReCl$_6$	red-green	29			Re/Cl$_2$/600° (minor prod)	$\xrightarrow{300°}$ ReCl$_5$. Readily hydrolysed. $\xrightarrow{O_2}$ ReO$_3$Cl
ReF$_5$	green	48			ReF$_6$/W(CO)$_6$	$\xrightarrow{140°}$ ReF$_6$ + ReF$_4$. Rapidly hydrolysed by moist air. Associated liquid.
ReCl$_5$	red– brown	261	−372	MoCl$_5$	Re/Cl$_2$/600° (major prod)	$\xrightarrow{300°}$ ReCl$_3$. Dimeric. Very moisture-sensitive.
ReBr$_5$	blue	*ca* 30			Re/Br$_2$/650° (major prod)	$\xrightarrow{300°}$ ReBr$_3$.
ReF$_4$	blue				ReF$_5$/150°	Hydrolyses to ReO$_2$.

continued

Table 5.5b   Properties of the 5*d*-metal halides (continued)

	Colour	MP°/C	$\dfrac{\Delta H_f^0}{kJ\ mol^{-1}}$	Structure	Preparation	Properties
$ReCl_4$	black				$ReCl_5/ReCl_3/300°/s.t.$	Chain structure (β), $Re_2Cl_7Cl_{2/2}$. Extremely moisture-sensitive.
$ReBr_4$	dk. red				ReI_4/HBr	
ReI_4	black				$HReO_4/HI$	$\xrightarrow{RT} ReI_3$. Hydrolyses to ReO_2.
$ReCl_3$	red		−264		$ReCl_5/300°$	Trinuclear, $[Re_3Cl_3]Cl_3Cl_{6/2}. \xrightarrow{O_2} ReO_3Cl$. Hydrolysed slowly by H_2O, stable in acid.
$ReBr_3$	red-brown		−167		$ReBr_5/300°$	Trinuclear, $[Re_3Br_3]Br_3Br_{6/2}$.
ReI_3	black				$HReO_4/HI/EtOH$	Trinuclear, $[Re_3I_3]I_3I_{6/2}$. Loses I_2 in vacuum at RT.
ReI_2	black			cubic	$ReI_3/350°/s.t.$	Probably polymeric.
ReI				cubic	$ReI_4/200°$	$\xrightarrow[200°]{I_2} ReI_3$.
OsF_7	col'less				$Os/F_2/550°/350\ atm$	$\xrightarrow{-100°} OsF_6$.
OsF_6	yellow	33		cubic	$Os/F_2/250°$	Instantly hydrolysed by moisture to OsO_4.
OsF_5	blue	70		MoF_5	$OsF_6/Cr(CO)_6/0°$	$\xrightarrow{180°} OsF_6+OsF_4$. Tetrameric. Very readily hydrolysed.
OsF_4	yellow				$OsF_5/200°$	
$OsCl_4$	black		−255		$Os/Cl_2/600°$	$\xrightarrow{350°} OsCl_3$. Rapidly hydrolysed by alkali.
$OsBr_4$	black				$Os/Br_2/450–20/s.t.$	$\xrightarrow{350°} OsBr_3$. Rapidly hydrolysed by alkali.
$OsCl_3$	grey		−190		$OsCl_4/470°$	Hydrolysed by alkali.
$OsBr_3$	black				$Os/Br_2/350°$	
OsI_3	black				$OsO_4/HI_{aq}/dehydrate$	
IrF_6	yellow	44	−580	cubic	$Ir/F_2/350°$	
IrF_5	yellow–green	105		MoF_5	$Ir/F_2/350°$	Tetrameric. Readily hydrolysed.
IrF_3	black			RhF_3	IrF_5/Ir	$\xrightarrow{250°} Ir+F_2$.
$IrCl_3$	green		−244	$\alpha\text{-}AlCl_3$	$Ir/Cl_2/700°$	$\xrightarrow{775°} Ir+Cl_2$.
$IrBr_3$	yellow				$Ir/Br_2/600°$	
IrI_3	black					
PtF_6	dk. red	61			$Pt/F_2 600°/quench$	BP 69°. $\xrightarrow{200°} PtF_5 \longrightarrow PtF_4+PtF_6$. Vigorous oxidant.
PtF_5	red	80		MoF_4	$PtCl_2/F_2/350°$	Tetrameric. Readily disproportionates to PtF_6+PtF_4.
PtF_4	yellow–brown			UCl_4	$PtCl_2/BrF_3/200°$	$\xrightarrow{100°, H_2} Pt$. Hydrolysed slowly by H_2O.
$PtCl_4$	red		−236	cubic	$Pt/Cl_2/300°$	$\xrightarrow{350°} PtCl_2$. Soluble in H_2O.
$PtBr_4$	dk. red		−159		$Pt/Br_2/HBr/150°$	$\xrightarrow{180°} PtBr_2$.
PtI_4	brown		−73		$Pt/I_2/200°$	$\xrightarrow{80°} PtI_3$. Chain structure.
$PtCl_3$	green		−174			Hexanuclear Pt_6Cl_{12} plus chains $PtCl_2Cl_{4/2}$.
$PtBr_3$	green		−129			
PtI_3	black			cubic	$H_2PtCl_6/KI/200°$	$\xrightarrow{250°} PtI_2$.
$PtCl_2$	green		−111		$Pt/Cl_2/500°$	Hexanuclear cluster, Pt_6Cl_{12}.
$PtBr_2$	brown		−97		Pt/Br_2	
PtI_2	black				$Pt/I_2/270°$	$\xrightarrow{500°} Pt+I_2$
AuF_5	red	75–8			$AuF_6/150°/vac$	Polymeric
AuF_3	yellow		−364	hexag.	$AuCl_3/F_2/200°$	$\xrightarrow{500°} Au+F_2$. Vigorous fluorinating agent. Chain structure.
$AuCl_3$	red		−118		$Au/Cl_2/200°$	$\xrightarrow{150°} AuCl$. Dimeric.

continued

Table 5.5b Properties of the 5*d*-metal halides (continued)

	Colour	MP/°C	$\dfrac{\Delta H_f^0}{kJ\ mol^{-1}}$	Structure	Preparation	Properties
$AuBr_3$	red		−53		$AuBr_2/150°$	Dimeric
$AuCl$	yellow		−35		$AuCl_3/150°$	
$AuBr$	orange		−14		$AuBr_3/150°$	
AuI	orange		0		$Au/I_2/120°$	
HgF_2	white	645 dec	−423	CaF_2	Hg/F_2	
$HgCl_2$	white	280	−230			Hydrolysed by water.
$HgBr_2$	orange	238	−169			
HgI_2	red	257	−105			Phase change to yellow form at 126°.
HgF			−242			$\xrightarrow{H_2O}$ Hg + HgO + HF. Dimeric molecule, Hg_2F_2.
$HgCl$			−132			Dimeric molecule, Hg_2Cl_2. Insoluble in H_2O.
$HgBr$			−102			Dimeric molecule, Hg_2Br_2. Insoluble in H_2O.
HgI			−51			Dimeric molecule, Hg_2I_2. Insoluble in H_2O.

structure first established for MoF$_5$ (Figure 5.2) although the structure of the recently discovered AuF$_5$ is not known. As with the hexafluorides, stability to reduction decreases along the series; RhF$_5$ and PtF$_5$ are vigorous fluorinating agents and oxidants. Other **pentahalides** are found only for Groups V–VII. All are very readily hydrolysed and many react with oxygen, forming oxyhalides or the metal oxide. In their preparation care must be taken to remove oxygen and it is often advisable to reduce the metal before treating with the halogen. Most of the pentahalides can be purified by sublimation. Structures are known only for the chlorides which, apart possibly from WCl$_5$, are dimeric in the solid state (Fig. 5.3). This difference from the fluorides is found in other systems; fluorine-bridges are linear while the other halogens give bent linkages. This presumably reflects the

Fig. 5.2   The MoF$_5$-structure

Fig. 5.3   The NbCl$_5$-structure

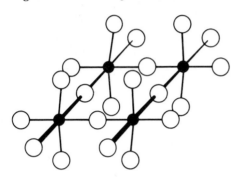

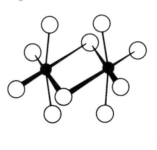

shortness and lower covalency of the M–F bonds and greater positive charge on the metal atoms, leading to greater repulsion.

The **tetrafluorides** are not well-characterised. Structure determinations have been made only for ZrF$_4$ and NbF$_4$. The latter has the SnF$_4$-structure, being polymeric with six-coordinate niobium atoms (see p. 185). Zirconium tetrafluoride is also polymeric, but in this case all the fluorine atoms act as bridging groups so that eight of them are bound to each zirconium atom in a square-antiprismatic array. In contrast to the 3d-metals (and to GeCl$_4$ and SnCl$_4$), all the other **tetrahalides** are solids and it is probable that all have polymeric structures with six-coordinate metal atoms. In ZrCl$_4$, TaCl$_4$ and TcCl$_4$, octahedral MCl$_6$ units share *cis* edges to form zig-zag chains, while in NbI$_4$ and probably the tetrahalides of niobium, tantalum, molybdenum and tungsten, the chains are linear, *trans* edges of the octahedra being shared. In α-NbI$_4$, the distances between adjacent metal atoms along the chain are alternately long and short, indicating the formation of metal–metal bonds (Fig. 5.4). The formation of these bonds is responsible for the diamagnetism observed for many of these compounds. The thermal stability of the tetrahalides decreases along each series and with increasing atomic number of the halogen.

Very few of the **lower halides** have conventional pseudo-ionic structures. In some cases (ZrCl$_3$, MoF$_3$, MoCl$_3$, PdF$_2$, AgF, AgCl, Ag$_2$F, CdCl$_2$, CdBr$_2$, CdI$_2$) the metal ions appear to

Fig. 5.4   The α-NbI$_4$-structure

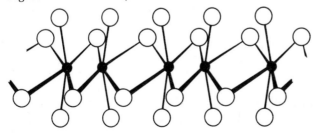

occupy octahedral sites in regular, close-packed anion lattices, although in the zirconium and molybdenum compounds there may be metal–metal bonds formed between adjacent pairs of ions. Silver iodide has the wurtzite structure (tetrahedral coordination) and CdF_2 the fluorite structure (eight-coordination). The remaining lower halides for which structural data are available show a fascinating variety of structures unlike those found anywhere else in the Periodic Table, and are best discussed individually.

The gold monohalides, AuX, are linear polymers containing chains –Au–X–Au–X–. Linear two-coordination is characteristic of Au^+ (and is often shown by Ag^+ and sometimes by Cu^+). The gold trihalides and one form (α) of $PdCl_2$ all show the square planar coordination typical of $4d$- and $5d$-metal ions with d^8 electron configurations. In AuF_3 the squares are linked by *cis* bridges (i.e. linearly bridging fluoride ions), whereas in the other trihalides bent bridges give dimeric units (Figs. 5.5 and 5.6), and in α-$PdCl_2$ all the chloride ions are bridging, giving infinite linear chains (Fig. 5.7).

Fig. 5.5 The AuF_3-structure

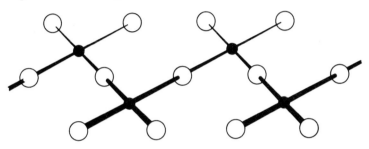

Fig. 5.6 The $AuCl_3$-structure

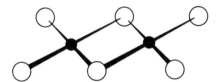

Fig. 5.7 The α-$PdCl_2$-structure

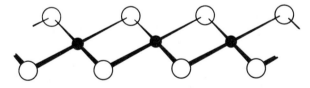

Square coordination of the metal ion is retained in β-$PdCl_2$, and in β-$PtCl_2$, but six units are linked in a cubic cluster, M_6Cl_{12}, with the chloride ions forming bridges across the edges of the M_6-octahedra. The same unit is found in the niobium and tantalum halides, $MX_{2.33}$, which should therefore be formulated M_6X_{14} or, better still, $[M_6X_{12}]X_{4/2}$, where the notation $X_{4/2}$ signifies four doubly-bridging halide ions which link the $M_6X_{12}^{2+}$-units into infinite, planar sheets (note that, in this instance, geometric constraints give rise to linear inter-cluster bridges with all halides). There is a slight difference from the platinum cluster in that the niobium and tantalum atoms are slightly sunk in the cube faces, presumably to allow the formation of stronger metal–metal bonds. These hexameric units, which have a beautiful emerald-green colour, are very stable and act as integral units like very large, single ions, forming octahedral complexes with anions or neutral ligands and undergoing one-electron oxidations. Thus, when the halides are dissolved in water or fused with alkali halides, the cluster structure is retained giving products in which water molecules or halide ions are coordinated to the metal atoms in the sites above the cube faces, e.g. $[Ta_6Cl_{12}]Cl_2.4H_2O$ (in the heptahydrate), or $K_4\{[Nb_6Cl_{12}]Cl_6\}$. In aqueous solution the clusters undergo one- or two-electron oxidations, forming $M_6X_{12}^{3+}$ and $M_6X_{12}^{4+}$ cluster-ions.

Fig. 5.8   The Pt_6Cl_{12}-structure

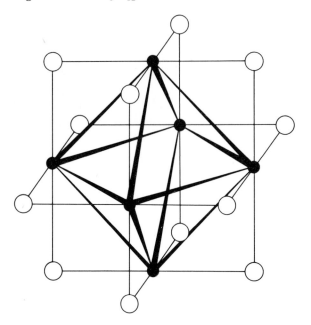

Hexameric units are also found in the molybdenum and tungsten dihalides, but of different stoicheiometry and structure. In these cases eight halide ions bridge the faces of the octahedral M_6-units. In the anhydrous halides, the clusters are again linked into planes by linearly bridging halide ions, and two terminal halide ions are coordinated to the two remaining *trans* metal ions, $[M_6X_8]X_2X_{4/2}$ (Fig. 5.9). The bridges can be broken by neutral ligands, as in the dihydrates, and anionic species can also be obtained e.g. $\{[Mo_6Cl_8]Cl_6\}^{2-}$. Tungsten dibromide reacts with bromine to give W_6Br_{14}, W_6Br_{16}, and W_6Br_{18} ($\equiv WBr_3$), all of which contain the $W_6Br_8^{6+}$-unit, i.e. only a two-electron oxidation has occurred; the additional bromine is incorporated as polybromide ions.

In two cases the structure types are transposed. Oxidation of W_6Cl_{12} with chlorine gives $[W_6Cl_{12}]Cl_6$, with a structure similar to that of the niobium-tantalum species, while niobium has an iodide Nb_6I_{11} which contains $Nb_6I_8^{3+}$-units.

The remaining niobium halides are non-stoicheiometric, with compositions varying smoothly through the range $NbX_{2.67}$ to about $NbX_{3.1}$. At the niobium-rich end of this range, niobium ions occupy octahedral sites in a roughly hcp lattice of anions, forming triangular Nb_3-units with a bridging chloride ion below each edge of the triangle and a triply-bridging chloride ion above the triangle (Fig. 5.10). Each niobium ion is also linked to three other chloride ions which form bridges to other triangles, $[Nb_3Cl_4]Cl_{6/2}Cl_{3/3}$. As the niobium-content falls, Nb_3-units are converted to Nb_2-units similar to those found in $NbCl_4$.

Trinuclear clusters are also found in the deep red rhenium trihalides. In $ReCl_3$ equilateral triangular $Re_3X_3^{6+}$-units are linked by two bridging chloride ions on each rhenium ion which also

Fig. 5.9 The M_6X_8-cluster

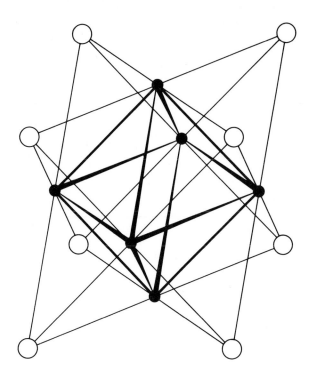

Fig. 5.10 The Nb_3Cl_8-structure

Upper layer

Lower layer

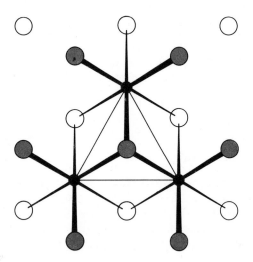

bears one terminal chloride ligand, $[Re_3Cl_3]Cl_{6/2}Cl_3$ (Fig. 5.11). From solutions in hydrohalic acid the ions $Re_3X_{12}^{3-}$ can be isolated, and corresponding complexes with other ligands are known, e.g. $Re_3X_9L_3$. It does not seem to be possible to oxidise this cluster without disrupting it.

Fig. 5.11   The Re_3Cl_9-structure

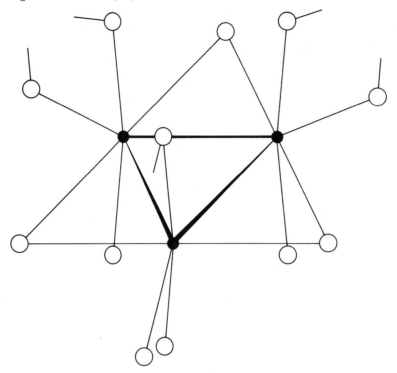

In some cases apparently simple explanations of the bonding can be given, e.g. Mo^{2+}, W^{2+} and Re^{3+} are d^4-systems and could thus form four single bonds (as in $M_6X_8^{4+}$) or two double bonds ($Re_3X_3^{6+}$) to neighbouring metal atoms. However, in the majority of cases, there are insufficient electrons available to formulate two-electron bonds between all adjacent pairs of metal atoms, and elaborate molecular-orbital schemes are needed.

Nevertheless, the isolation of this fascinating range of halides, containing single, double, triple or sextuple sets of metal atoms, often with intense and attractive colours, has stimulated much preparative and theoretical work and provided interesting problems in the characterisation of these unusual compounds.

5.4   Oxides

The known oxides and some of their properties are summarised in Tables 5.6 and 5.7. With the exception of rhenium, each metal forms only a small number of oxides (although some of the systems are not well-characterised and other compounds may be discovered). It is particularly striking that low oxidation states (+2, +3) appear only for the heaviest members of each series; in these respects oxides resemble fluorides.

Table 5.6 Oxides of the 4*d*- and 5*d*-metals

				RuO_4				
			Tc_2O_7					
		MoO_3						
	Nb_2O_5	Mo_2O_5						
ZrO_2	NbO_2	MoO_2	TcO_2	RuO_2	RhO_2			
		Mo_2O_3			Rh_2O_3			
	NbO					PdO	AgO	CdO
							Ag_2O	

				OsO_4				
			Re_2O_7					
		WO_3	ReO_3					
	Ta_2O_5		Re_2O_5					
HfO_2		WO_2	ReO_2	OsO_2	IrO_2	PtO_2		
					Ir_2O_3	Pt_3O_4	Au_2O_3	
						PtO		HgO

Table 5.7 Properties of the oxides

Oxide	Colour	MP/°C	$\dfrac{\Delta H_f^0}{\text{kJ mol}^{-1}}$	Structure	Preparation	Properties
ZrO_2	white	2 400	−1 097		Zr/O_2	Many polymorphs. Unreactive.
Nb_2O_5	white	*ca.* 1 500	−1 897		Acid ppt[n]. Ignite	Insol. acids, except HF. Non-stoicheiometric (block structures).
NbO_2	blue–black		−794		$Nb_2O_5/H_2/900°$	Non-stoicheiometric.
NbO	black		−407			Diamagnetic. Chain structure with alternating Nb–Nb distances (280, 320 pm). Non-stoicheiometric, $NbO_{0.94–1.1}$.
MoO_3	white	795		layer	Ht Mo cpds in air	Insol. acids, sol. alkali. Non-stoicheiometric (shear phases).
Mo_2O_5	violet				$MoO_3/Mo/750°$	Sol. warm acids.
MoO_2	violet		−588	TiO_2, d	$MoO_3/H_2/450°$	Insol. acids and bases (non-oxidising). $\xrightarrow{1100°}$ Mo + MoO_3. Diamagnetic. Alternating Mo–Mo distances (250, 310 pm).
Mo_2O_3					Mo^{3+}/OH^-/dehydrate	Sol. acids. Hydrated by H_2O.
Tc_2O_7	yellow	119	−1 113	molecular	$Tc/O_2/400°$	BP 311°. $\xrightarrow{H_2O}$ $HTcO_4$. Mild oxidant.
TcO_2				TiO_2, d	$NH_4TcO_4/700°$.	Probably metal–metal bonded.

continued

Table 5.7   Properties of the oxides (continued)

Oxide	Colour	MP/°C	ΔH_f^0 kJ mol^{-1}	Structure	Preparation	Properties
RuO_4	yellow	25	−239	molecular	Ru soln/MnO_4^-/distl.	BP 40°. Very toxic. Powerful oxidant. Explodes above 180°.
RuO_2	blue–black		−305		Ru/O_2/1 000°	Often O-deficient. Unreactive to cold acids. Probably Ru–Ru bonded.
RhO_2	black			TiO_2	Rh_2O_3aq/O_2/500°	
Rh_2O_3	brown		−343	α–Al_2O_3	Rh^{3+}/OH^-/dehydrate	
PdO	black		−85		Pd/O_2	Insol. all acids. $\xrightarrow{875°}$ Pd
AgO	black		−12		Ag_2O/OH^-/$S_2O_8^{2-}$	Diamagnetic ($Ag^I Ag^{III} O_2$). Powerful oxidant. $\xrightarrow{H^+} Ag^+ + O_2$.
Ag_2O	brown-black		−31	Cu_2O	Ag^+/OH^-	$\xrightarrow{160°} Ag + O_2$. Always impure. Sol. alkali.
CdO	yellow		−258	NaCl	Cd/O_2	Black forms are O-deficient.
HfO_2	white	*ca.* 2 800	−1 145		Hf/O_2	Very unreactive.
Ta_2O_5	white	1 785	−2 046		acid ppt$_n$/ignition	Insol. acids except HF. Non-stoichiometric (block structures) $TaO_{2.0–2.5}$.
WO_3	yellow	1 470	−843	ReO_3	W cpd/ignite	Sol. alkali. Non-stoicheiometric (shear phases).
WO_2	brown	*ca.* 1 500		TiO_2, d	WO_3/H_2/$H_2O^{(g)}$/800°	Diamagnetic. Alternating W–W distances (249, 308 pm).
Re_2O_7	yellow	220	−1 240		Re/O_2/150°	Readily volatile. Structure has 4- and 6-coord Re. $\xrightarrow{H_2O} HReO_4$.
ReO_3	red		−605	ReO_3	Re_2O_7/CO/300°	Insol. non-oxidising acids, alkalis. $\xrightarrow{300°} ReO_2 + Re_2O_7$. Conc. alkali $\longrightarrow ReO_2 + ReO_4$.
Re_2O_5	blue				ReO_4^-/H_2SO_4/electrol.	$\xrightarrow{200°} ReO_2$.
ReO_2	dk. blue		−987	MoO_2	Re_2O_7/H_2/300°	$\xrightarrow{700°} Re_2O_7 + Re$. Sol. HX. Probably Re–Re bonded.
OsO_4	yellow	40	−394	molecular	Os/air	BP 101°. $\xrightarrow{H_2O} OsO_4(OH)_2^{2-}$. Strong oxidant. Very toxic.
OsO_2	red			TiO_2	OsO_4/Os/600°	Readily oxidised by warm air to OsO_4.
IrO_2	black		−274		Ir/O_2	$\xrightarrow{HCl} IrCl_6^{2-}$. Insol alkali.
Ir_2O_3	brown			TiO_2	K_3IrCl_6/K_2CO_3/300°	$\xrightarrow{400°} IrO_2 + Ir$. Never pure (contains alkali).
PtO_2	brown				$PtCl_6^{2-}$/OH^-/dehydrt.	Decomposes 650°. Cannot be dehydrated completely without losing O_2.
Pt_3O_4			−163	cubic	Pt/O_2	
PtO	grey–black			PdO	$PtCl_4^{2-}$/OH^-dehydrt.	Never obtained pure.
Au_2O_3	brown		−81		$AuCl_4^-$/OH^-/dehydrt.	$\xrightarrow{160°} Au + O_2$. Sol. conc. min. acids, alkali.
HgO	red		−91	chain	$Hg(NO_3)_2$/200°.	Sol. acids, insol. alkali. Also a yellow form.

In the **tetroxides**, RuO_4 and OsO_4, the highest known oxidation state for any metal is attained. As might be expected, these compounds are strong oxidants, and OsO_4 is occasionally used for this purpose (to oxidise alkenes to *gem*-diols). The same property makes these compounds highly toxic. The ruthenium compound is the less stable, and has been known to explode violently on heating to

$180\,°C$, forming oxygen and RuO_2. Both tetroxides have simple tetrahedral molecular structures and are low-melting and readily volatile. Both are soluble in water and alkalis; RuO_4 suffers reduction but OsO_4 give $OsO_4(OH)_2^{2-}$.

The two **heptoxides**, Tc_2O_7 and Re_2O_7, are also water-soluble, forming the acids $HTcO_4$ and $HReO_4$, and are mild oxidants. Both are readily volatile and the vapours consist of discrete dimeric molecules, as does solid Tc_2O_7. The solid rhenium compound has a curious structure containing both four- and six-coordinate metal atoms (Fig. 5.12). The dihydrate, obtained by evaporating aqueous solutions, has a similar structure, $O_3Re-O-ReO_3(OH_2)_2$.

Fig. 5.12   The Re_2O_7-structure

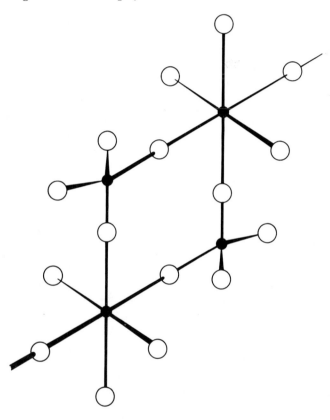

The **trioxides** (MoO_3, WO_3, ReO_3; TcO_3 has not been definitely established) form a sharp contrast with CrO_3. All are solids; MoO_3 sublimes slowly at about $300\,°C$ at which temperature ReO_3 disproportionates into ReO_2 and Re_2O_7. None shows any oxidising properties, although ReO_3 is readily reduced to ReO_2. All are insoluble in water but dissolve in alkali to give anionic species (ReO_3 requires concentrated alkali); again, rhenium(VI) disproportionates, giving insoluble ReO_2 and ReO_4^-. In the solids the metal ions are all six-coordinate. The structure of ReO_3 (Fig. 5.13) is adopted by a wide variety of materials, and may be described as an incomplete fcc array of oxide ions with rhenium ions in one-quarter of the octahedral sites. Tungsten trioxide adopts a slightly distorted version of this structure but MoO_3 has an unusual layer structure. Molybdenum and tungsten both form homologous series of non-stoicheiometric oxides, M_nO_{3n-1}, in which a small proportion of pentavalent metal ions are accommodated by omission of oxide ions along regularly spaced planes in the lattice (see Ch. 10).

Fig. 5.13   The ReO$_3$-structure (after D. M. Adams (1974) *Inorganic Solids*, John Wiley & Sons)

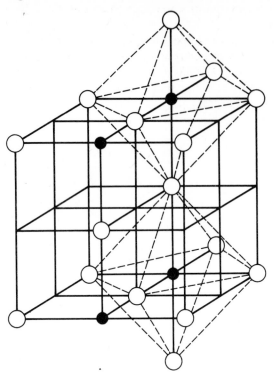

The **pentoxides** of niobium and tantalum are non-stoicheiometric in a similar way, and even the stoicheiometric compounds are known in several different crystal forms. In all cases the metal ions are octahedrally coordinated in the crystal lattice. These oxides are insoluble in water and acids, except HF which gives fluoro-complexes, but when freshly precipitated (by acidification of niobate(V) or tantalate(V) solutions) are soluble in alkali. After dehydration they require fusion with a base or carbonate before solution can be effected. Both are resistant to reduction.

A much wider range of metals forms **dioxides** (Zr-Rh, Hf, W-Pt). With the exception of ZrO$_2$ and HfO$_2$, all those studied have structures similar to that of rutile. In several cases the structure is distorted to allow formation of bonds between pairs of metal ions, and this is reflected in their magnetic properties. The monoclinic forms of ZrO$_2$ and HfO$_2$ have curious structures in which the metal ions are seven-coordinate; such coordination in a binary compound is unique. The dioxides of the earlier metals of the series are readily oxidised (except, of course, ZrO$_2$ and HfO$_2$), while PtO$_2$ loses oxygen on heating, and WO$_2$ and ReO$_2$ disproportionate when heated in vacuum (to W+WO$_3$ or Re+Re$_2$O$_7$). All are very insoluble in water but the majority will react with acids. Zirconium and hafnium dioxides are so unreactive, especially after heating and sintering, that they are used as refractories and for special crucibles.

Sesquioxides, M$_2$O$_3$, have been established only for three metals (Rh, Ir, Au); this contrasts sharply with the 3d-metals, where the sesquioxide is one of the most important oxides, being found from scandium to cobalt (note the later 3d-metals do not form sesquioxides, whereas in the 4d- and 5d-series they are found only for the later metals). The iridium compound has never been obtained completely pure; it is precipitated by alkali from aqueous iridium(III) solutions, but always carries some alkali down with it and dehydration is complicated by the facile disproportionation. Presumably the sesquioxides of the earlier metals are also unstable to disproportionation.

Gold(III) oxide is the only oxide known for this metal, and dissociates readily (160 °C). It is soluble in alkali and in concentrated mineral acids, forming four-coordinate anionic complexes.

The **monoxides** are also sparse and many are unstable. Palladium(II) and mercury(II) oxides are readily reduced, the former becoming incandescent when exposed to hydrogen (the elemental metal is able to dissolve hydrogen). Silver monoxide is a vigorous oxidising agent and its structure and diamagnetism indicate that it contains the metal in both the +1 and the +3 oxidation states. The Ag^{3+} ions have square planar coordination ($4d^8$ configuration) while the Ag^+ ions are two-coordinate as in the lower oxide Ag_2O and many silver(I) complexes. The Hg^{2+} ions in HgO are also linearly coordinated in a chain structure. Cadmium oxide is the only one of the series displaying the NaCl-structure which characterises the monoxides of the $3d$-metals.

Thus, in comparison with the $3d$-metals, the heavy transition metals clearly form higher oxides more readily and are more resistant to reduction. Relatively low oxidation states (+2, +3) are found only for the later metals. There are also considerable structural differences between the series. In particular, the penta- and hexa-positive heavy metals are six-coordinate when the corresponding $3d$-metals show lower coordination.

5.5 Aqueous chemistry

Study of the aquo-, hydroxo-, and oxo-complexes (Table 5.8) of the $4d$- and $5d$-metals is complicated by two factors. Firstly, when the metals are in relatively low oxidation states a great many ligands, including most simple anions, are able to displace water from the coordination sphere. In order to avoid hydrolysis it is usually necessary to work with acidic solutions, so that an excess of anions is present. The metal is usually found in anionic complexes which may or may not contain coordinated water, or hydroxo- or oxo-groups. Consequently, most redox-potential data refer to complexes rather than to aquated species, and the values vary with the anion present. In a few cases special care has been taken to use acids whose anions coordinate very weakly (ClO_4^-, NO_3^-), and simple aquated cations have been observed for Mo^{3+}, Ru^{2+}, Ru^{3+}, Rh^{3+}, Pd^{2+}, Ag^+, Au^{3+}, Cd^{2+} and Hg^{2+}. Rhodium(II) and mercury(I) form binuclear aquated cations, Rh_2^{4+} and Hg_2^{2+}. The second complicating factor is that, for the higher oxidation states in alkaline solution, polymeric species are formed which coexist over wide pH-ranges in complex series of slowly-attained equilibria. It is difficult to establish the nature of the species present and, as discussed on pp. 77–8, the species which can be isolated in solid salts may bear no relation to those present in solution.

However, it is possible to make broad comparisons with the $3d$-series. In general, the lower oxidation states (<4) are more prone to oxidation and the higher oxidation states more resistant to reduction. The highest oxidation state observed is +8 in $OsO_4(OH)_2^{2-}$, formed by treating aqueous OsO_4 with alkali. It is rather readily reduced to the osmate(VI), $OsO_2(OH)_4^{2-}$, which has a *trans*-octahedral configuration, in contrast to the tetrahedral ruthenate(VI), RuO_4^{2-}. The latter ion is formed by treating RuO_4 with alkali or by alkaline oxidation of ruthenium metal (e.g. with fused KOH/KNO_3). A ruthenate(VII), RuO_4^-, can also be obtained by the alkaline oxidation route but it is not stable in strong alkali, being reduced to RuO_4^{2-}. Although RuO_4 can be distilled from oxidised solutions of ruthenium (e.g with $KMnO_4$) there are no reports of ruthenate(VIII) species, which would presumably have unfavourable stereochemistry and coordination number. The TcO_4^- and ReO_4^- ions are both tetrahedral and are stable over wide pH ranges, and $HTcO_4$ and $HReO_4$ both function as strong monobasic acids. The pertechnetate and per-rhenate ions are mild oxidants, but much weaker than permanganate.

Table 5.8 Species found in aqueous solution

Species	Colour	Conditions	Species	Colour	Conditions
$Zr_4(OH)_8^{8+}$	col'less				
$Nb_6O_{19}^{8-}$	col'less		$Ta_6O_{19}^{8-}$	col'less	Not protonated
$HNb_6O_{19}^{7-}$	col'less				
$H_2Nb_6O_{19}^{6-}$	col'less				
MoO_4^{2-}	col'less	pH > 8	WO_4^{2-}	col'less	pH > 6
$Mo_7O_{24}^{6-}$	yellow	pH ~ 6	$HW_6O_{21}^{5-}$	yellow	pH ~ 6
$Mo_8O_{26}^{4-}$	yellow	pH ~ 5	$W_{12}O_{42}^{12-}$	yellow	pH ~ 6
			$H_2W_{12}O_{40}^{6-}$	yellow	pH 4
$Mo(OH_2)_6^{3+}$	red				
TcO_4^-	col'less		ReO_4^-	col'less	wide pH range
TcO_4^{2-}	rose	disprop. $TcO_4^- + TcO_2$			
RuO_4^-	yellow –green	reduced by OH^- to RuO_4^{2-}	$OsO_4(OH)_2^{2-}$	dp. red	reduced by OH^- to $OsO_2(OH)_4^{2-}$
RuO_4^{2-}	orange	stable in alkali	$OsO_2(OH)_4^{2-}$	pink	*trans*, diamag.
$Ru(OH_2)_6^{3+}$	col'less	not isolated			
$Ru(OH_2)_6^{2+}$	yellow				
$Rh(OH_2)_6^{3+}$					
Rh_2^{4+}	green				
$Pd(OH_2)_4^{2+}$	yellow	low pH only	$Pt(OH)_6^{2-}$	orange	high pH only
$Ag(OH_2)_2^{2+}$	col'less	pH < 7	$Au(OH_2)_4^{3+}$	yellow	absence ligands
$Ag(OH)_2^-$	col'less	conc. alkali	$Au(OH)_4^-$		conc. alkali

In alkaline solution, molybdenum(VI) and tungsten(VI) also give simple tetrahedral oxo-anions, MO_4^{2-}, but on lowering the pH condensation occurs and polymeric units are formed, containing octahedrally coordinated metal ions. The two molybdenum species $Mo_7O_{24}^{6-}$ and $Mo_8O_{26}^{4-}$ are well-characterised and have been isolated in crystalline salts. It is likely that the structures of the anions in solution are similar to those found in the crystal, illustrated in Fig. 5.14. The tungstate system is more difficult to study because equilibria are attained only slowly and there may be more species involved than for molybdenum. The two dodecatungstates (metatungstate, $H_2W_{12}O_{40}^{6-}$, and paratungstate-Z, $W_{12}O_{42}^{12-}$) have related structures in which four groups of three WO_6-octahedra are linked in a tetrahedral array (Fig. 5.15). If condensation occurs in the presence of other ions, these may be incorporated into the structure, occupying the tetrahedral cavity in the centre of the metatungstate structure. Such heteropolytungstates are formed with a wide variety of hetero-ions, both non-metallic (e.g. Si^{4+}, P^{5+}) and metallic (e.g. Fe^{2+}, Co^{2+}, V^{5+}); similar species are found for molybdenum. These materials are useful in gravimetric analysis and as cation exchangers (the cation which exchanges is the counter-ion, not that in the centre of the polyanion).

In the niobate(V) and tantalate(V) systems, only hexameric species have been detected, $M_6O_{19}^{8-}$, although for niobium two protonated species are also formed. The anion in $K_6Ta_6O_{19} \cdot 16H_2O$ and similar materials is an octahedron of octahedra (Fig. 5.14), and the structure

Fig. 5.14 The structures of edge-shared isopolyanions showing their relation to the $M_{10}O_{28}$-structure: (*a*) M = V; (*b*) M = Mo; (*c*) M = Mo; (*d*) M = Nb, Ta (reprinted with permission from D. L. Kepert, *Inorg. Chem.* **8**, 1556 (1969). Copyright by the American Chemical Society)

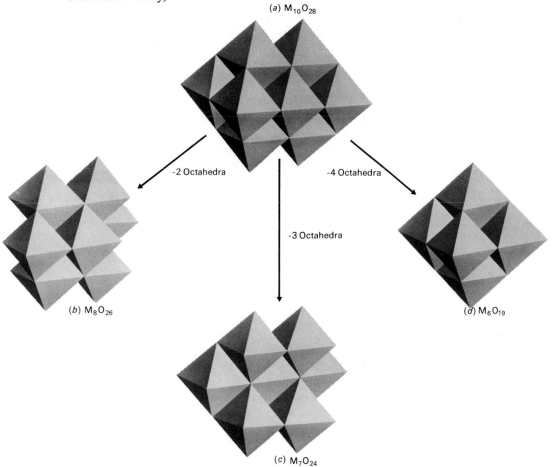

(*a*) $M_{10}O_{28}$

−2 Octahedra   −4 Octahedra

−3 Octahedra

(*b*) M_8O_{26} (*d*) M_6O_{19}

(*c*) M_7O_{24}

in solution is almost certainly very similar. In these cases, no simple monomeric species are known in solution, although solid mixed-oxide phases can be obtained. For these metals, and for molybdenum(VI) and tungsten(VI), acidification of the solutions leads eventually to precipitation of the hydrous oxides which do not dissolve in excess of the acid unless complexing ions are present (e.g. F^-).

With a tetrapositive metal, zirconium(IV) (and presumably hafnium(IV)), polymeric species are also formed, but in acidic solution. Addition of alkali precipitates 'zirconium hydroxide', probably also a complex polymer, which is insoluble in excess alkali. The most important species in acidic solution is the tetrameric cation, $Zr_4(OH)_8^{8+}$, which is found coordinated by sixteen water molecules in $ZrOCl_2 \cdot 8H_2O$. The cation contains eight-coordinate zirconium ions (Fig. 5.16) and similar structures are found in a variety of other basic salts. There is again no evidence for mononuclear species, and the 'zirconyl' ion, ZrO^{2+}, seems definitely to have been disproved.

The lower oxidation states (+2, +3) of the early metals are very readily oxidised, e.g. Zr^{3+} liberates hydrogen from water. However, as each series is traversed high oxidation states become more difficult to attain and the lower states become more stable (to oxidation). At the end of the

Fig. 5.15   The probable structure of the paratungstate-Z ion, $W_{12}O_{42}^{12-}$ (reprinted with permission from W. N. Lipscomb, *Inorg. Chem.* **4**, 133 (1965). Copyright by the American Chemical Society)

Fig. 5.16   Structure of $[Zr_4(OH)_8.16H_2O]^{8+}$ (after J. H. Canterford and R. Colton, (1968) *Halides of the Second and Third Row Transition Elements* John Wiley & Sons)

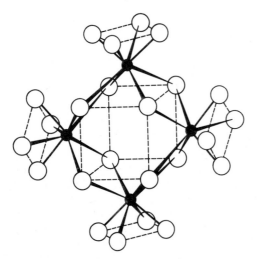

series, even these states are readily reduced. Thus, both Ag^+ and Au^{3+} (usually obtained as $AuCl_4^-$) are mild oxidants, and Ag^{2+} is a vigorous oxidant.

The Hg_2^{2+} ion deserves some comment as one of the early examples of a simple system containing a metal–metal bond. In the absence of ligands stronger than water, the mercurous ion is stable to disproportionation

$$Hg_2^{2+} \rightleftharpoons Hg(l) + Hg^{2+}$$

$$\Delta G^0 = +12 \cdot 7 \text{ kJ mol}^{-1}; \qquad K = \frac{[Hg^{2+}]}{[Hg_2^{2+}]} = 6 \cdot 0 \times 10^{-3}$$

The vast majority of coordinating anions and other ligands bind more strongly to Hg^{2+} than to Hg_2^{2+}, so that the disproportionation reaction occurs readily in the presence of OH^-, I^-, CN^-, NH_3, etc. Consequently, the only mercury(I) salts which can be isolated are those, such as the nitrate or perchlorate, in which the anions do not coordinate and those which are protected by their insolubility, e.g. the halides. The soluble fluoride decomposes in water giving HF, Hg and HgO (by disproportionation of '$Hg_2(OH)_2$').

5.6   Resumé

It is clear from the above descriptions that the chemistry of the $4d$- and $5d$-metals is much more complex than that of the $3d$-metals and, indeed, of most of the other metals in the Periodic Table. The rather brief survey given barely does justice to these elements, and the reader may wish to consult the more detailed treatments listed in the bibliography at the end of this chapter.

All the compounds show considerable covalency, and descriptions in terms of the ionic model are likely to be rather inaccurate. This covalency is perhaps most plainly demonstrated by the behaviour of the metals in aqueous solution, when even halide ions are tightly coordinated. This observation is complicated by the low rates at which ligand-exchange occurs, but it does seem that most ligands, especially the 'soft' ligands, are bound in preference to water.

However, in the oxides and halides the same general trends are found as for the $3d$-metals, i.e. in the early Groups low oxidation states are very unstable to oxidation and high oxidation states are readily obtained, but these latter states become less stable again in the latter half of each series. This trend is more marked in the $4d$- and $5d$-series because many of the low oxidation states of the early metals are extremely reducing or, in some systems, not even known, while the higher states are easier to obtain, are more stable to reduction, and occur more widely. Thus, the highest oxidation state attainable in the $3d$-series is +7 in Mn_2O_7, which is a very unstable compound. The technetium and rhenium analogues are much more robust compounds, and in the next Group an even higher oxidation state is reached, in RuO_4 and OsO_4 (cf. Fe_2O_3 and the strongly oxidising FeO_4^{2-} as the highest attainable states for iron). Oxidation states of +2 and +3 are normal at the end of all three d-series, but in the early Groups the heavier metals seem to form these states only in compounds in which there is significant metal–metal bonding. Such bonding also occurs in the $3d$-series, but mainly in very low oxidation states (zero or negative) as in the carbonyls and their derivatives. For the $4d$- and $5d$-metals, metal–metal bonding occurs much more frequently and is known even in the tetrahalides.

A further contrast is the higher degree of polymeric-anion formation found for the $4d$- and $5d$-metals and the greater prevalence of six- (and higher) coordination. In the $3d$-series, only the vanadates(V) show any marked degree of polymerisation while the chromates(VI) give only di- and possibly tri-mers. With the heavier metals extensive polymerisation occurs amongst the niobates(V), tantalates(V), molybdates(VI) and tungstates(VI) and, in cationic species, with zirconium(IV).

Some of the possible underlying reasons for these differences may now be examined.

Despite the covalency of the compounds, the best available guide to the oxidation-state behaviour is the enthalpy of formation of the ions. Data are given in Table 5.9 and comparison with

Table 5.9   Enthalpies of formation of gas-phase ions, $M^{n+}(g)$ (kJ mol^{-1})

n	0	1	2	3	4	5	6	7
Zr	611	1 285	2 553	4 770	8 083	16 074		
Nb	774	1 438	2 819	5 235	8 935	13 705	23 663	
Mo	659	1 344	2 902	5 520	9 424	14 821	21 766	33 815
Tc	649	1 352	2 824	5 674	9 820	15 510	22 832	31 890
Ru	669	1 380	2 997	5 743	10 220	16 287	24 111	33 776
Rh	577	1 297	3 041	6 037	10 430	16 892	25 093	35 218
Pd	381	1 185	3 059	6 236	10 943	17 303	25 964	36 549
Ag	286	1 017	3 089	6 449	11 461	18 197	26 774	37 945
Cd	111	987	2 617	6 232				
Hf	703	1 463	2 903	5 153	8 363	16 354		
Ta	781	1 541	3 101	5 256	8 448	12 961		
W	837	1 607	3 317	5 639	9 049	13 672	19 550	
Re	791	1 550	3 150	5 660	9 292	14 208	20 379	27 994
Os	728	1 568	3 208	5 618	9 467	14 655	21 224	29 215
Ir	690	1 569	3 217	5 819	9 585	15 066	22 011	30 505
Pt	339	1 209	3 000	5 745	9 703	15 017	22 255	31 125
Au	368	1 257	3 237	6 132	10 324	15 930	22 959	32 206
Hg	62	1 069	2 878	6 178				

the *3d*-metals is made in Fig. 5.17. It is immediately apparent that in each Group the formation of M^+ and M^{2+} becomes more endothermic as the Group is descended but that the higher degrees of ionisation become easier to achieve. The latter trend, together with the larger radii (and hence lower polarising of power) of the heavier elements is responsible for the relative stabilisation of the higher oxidation states. The *4d*- and *5d*-orbitals are more diffuse and extensive, relative to the atomic cores, than the *3d*-orbital, so that the effective nuclear charges acting on the *4d*- and *5d*-electrons are relatively low, resulting in easier ionisation, cf. Fig. 5.18. The greater size of the *4d*- and *5d*-orbitals also reduces the importance of exchange energies, so that the breaks in the ionisation energy trends at the d^5 configurations are less marked.

The differences in enthalpies of formation of the mono- and di-positive cations are due to two factors. Firstly, the first ionisation energy increases on descending each Group and in many cases the second ionisation energy increases also. This difference from the higher ionisation energies is due to the electrons which are removed being *s*-electrons rather than *d*-electrons. The *s*-electrons penetrate the core and are greatly influenced by the increasing nuclear charge. This effect is somewhat offset by the additional shielding of the *4d*-electrons, but that of the *5d*-electrons is compensated by the low shielding of the *4f*-electrons and the increase of nuclear charge across the lanthanide series. Thus, in each Group, the first ionisation energy increases uniformly with increasing atomic number, and the removal of two *s*-electrons is considerably more endothermic for the *5d*-elements than for the *4d*- or *3d*-elements (Fig. 5.18).

The second factor which augments the enthalpies of formation of the gaseous cations is the enthalpy of atomisation. Except for the heaviest metals, the ΔH^0_{at}-values increase markedly down each Group. As discussed in Chapter 9, the *d*-electrons play a large part in determining the binding energies of the metallic lattices, and the interaction (overlap) between *d*-orbitals increases with increasing size and spatial extension of the orbitals, i.e. with increasing principal quantum number.

Fig. 5.17   Proportional enthalpies of formation of gaseous *d*-block cations

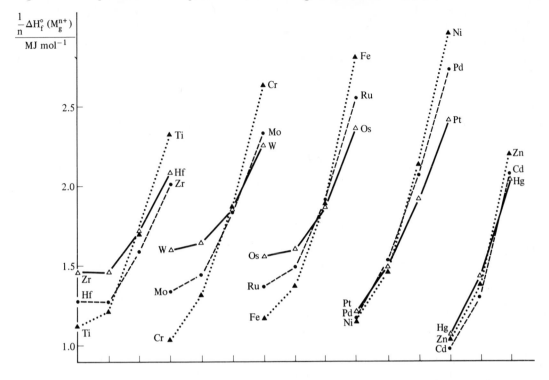

Fig. 5.18   The energy required for the removal of the two *s* electrons from the configuration $d^{n-2}s^2$ as *n* goes from 2 to 12 in the three transition series. (Note that these are not necessarily the ground-state configurations of the ions) (after C. S. Phillips and R. J. P. Williams, (1965) *Inorganic Chemistry*, **2**, OUP)

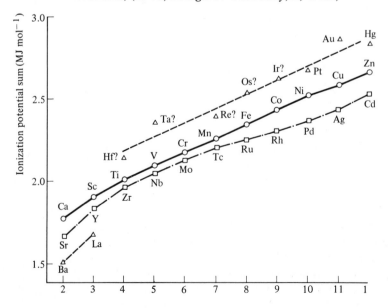

The enthalpy of atomisation contributes directly to the formation-enthalpy of the ions, but is much more important for the lower degrees of ionisation, where the sum of the ionisation energies is relatively small. A large enthalpy of atomisation therefore destabilises low oxidation states more than the higher ones for which, in any case, the effect of its increase down the Group has been more than offset by the reduction in ionisation energies.

The operation of these factors is illustrated in Table 5.10 which presents calculations of the enthalpies of formation of $CrCl_2$ and WCl_2 based on the ionic model. The value obtained for $CrCl_2$ is close to the experimentally determined value, but that for WCl_2 is positive, i.e. on this basis WCl_2 would be expected to be unstable to disproportionation into the metal and a higher chloride. The large difference between the two calculated values is due primarily to the endothermic terms, the ionisation energies and enthalpies of atomisation, all of which are significantly greater for tungsten than for chromium, so that enthalpy of formation of W^{2+} is 676 kJ mol^{-1} greater than that of Cr^{2+}. The major part of this difference arises from the enthalpies of atomisation.

Tungsten dichloride is actually a reasonably stable compound, rather susceptible to oxidation, but certainly showing no tendency to disproportionate, and it is certainly not endothermic as the calculation suggests. The lattice energy assumed is probably too low, since some allowance should be made for covalency, but there is a more serious defect in the calculation, viz. that WCl_2 is observed to be a hexameric 'cluster' compound, and in no way resembles a simple ionic material. The structure retains considerable metal–metal bonding within the cluster, so that any notional energy cycle involving breaking down of the metal lattice should also include a term to take account of the formation of the metal–metal bonds. An alternative view would be that the lattice need be broken only into W_6-units rather than separate atoms.

Similar considerations apply to the other metals in this region of the Periodic Table. It is very noticeable that most of the known compounds involving the metals of the earlier Groups in low oxidation states have structures involving some form of metal–metal bonding. Such bonding will be favoured when the d-orbitals are able to overlap and interact well, which requires a low positive charge on the metal atom. Thus, most metal–metal bonded systems involve low oxidation states and non-metal groups (or other ligands) of low electronegativity. The formation of metal–metal bonds is quite rare among fluorides and not common in oxides. For the 4d- and 5d-metals lower fluorides and oxides are often unknown, presumably being unstable to disproportionation.

Table 5.10   Ionic Born–Haber terms for the formation of $CrCl_2$ and WCl_2 (kJ mol^{-1})

	ΔH^0_{at}	I_1	I_2	$2\Delta H^0_f(Cl^-)$	$U(MCl_2)$	ΔH^0_f	$\Delta H^0_f(obs)$
$CrCl_2$	397	652	1 592	−467	−2 510	−336	−397
WCl_2	837	770	1 710	−467	−2 420	+430	−151

The formation of polymeric species in aqueous solution was discussed in Chapter 3 (p. 79), where it was shown that a delicate balance exists between the formation of oxo-, hydroxo-, and aquo-species, and monomeric and polymeric systems. The availability of orbitals with suitable overlap and energy to allow multiple M–O bonding (the formation of π-donor bonds) is undoubtedly important, but not easy to analyse. The polarising nature of the metal ion also exerts a great influence. In the 4d- and 5d-series the ions have larger radii than the corresponding 3d-ions and are therefore less polarising. As a consequence, higher coordination numbers are formed with ions of high formal charge, e.g. in MoO_3, WO_3, TcO_3 and ReO_3 the metals occupy octahedral sites, whereas in CrO_3 the metal is four-coordinate. Rhenium(VII) shows intermediate behaviour in Re_2O_7, which has both six- and four-coordination in contrast to Mn_2O_7 in which both metal atoms are tetrahedrally coordinated. Molybdenum(VI) and tungsten(VI) are also six-coordinate in the extensive series of polyanions. The degree of polymerisation is presumably related to the lower polarising power of the metal ions and the lower cation–cation repulsion energies resulting from the greater metal–metal distances. Low polarising power and large size also assist the formation of even higher coordination numbers, e.g. in the polymeric cation $Zr_4(OH)_8^{8+}$ zirconium(IV) is eight-coordinate, a coordination number which is not uncommon for this metal.

Bibliography

BENT, 28–9, 33, 35–6, 38–9, 43; **CW**, 26; **H**, 12; **HJ**, 32–5, 39–41; **MM**, 14; **PW**, 26.

S. A. Cotton and F. A. Hart, *The Heavy Transition Metals*, MacMillan, 1975. Useful, detailed account of systematic chemistry, with some coordination chemistry.

J. H. Canterford and R. Colton, *Halides of the Second and Third Row Transition Metals*, Wiley, 1968. Comprehensive, detailed account of preparations, structures and properties.

R. A. Walton, *Prog. Inorg. Chem.*, **16**, 1 (1972). Review of preparation, properties and structures of halides and oxyhalides of the metals of Groups IV–VI and rhenium.

A. Carrington and M. C. R. Symons, *Chem. Rev.*, **63**, 443 (1963). Structure and reactivity of the oxyanions of transition metals.

J. Selbin, *J. Chem. Educ.*, **41**, 86 (1964). Metal oxocations.

E. M. Larsen, *Adv. Inorg. Chem. Radiochem.*, **13**, 1 (1970). Comprehensive review of the chemistry of zirconium and hafnium.

F. Fairbrother, *The Chemistry of Niobium and Tantalum*, Elsevier, 1967.

R. V. Parish, *Adv. Inorg. Chem. Radiochem.*, **9**, 315 (1966). Review of the chemistry of tungsten.

R. Colton, *The Chemistry of Rhenium and Technetium*, Wiley Interscience, 1965.

W. P. Griffiths, *The Chemistry of the Rare Platinum Metals*, Wiley Interscience, 1967.

C. A. McAuliffe (Ed.), *The Chemistry of Mercury*, MacMillan, 1976. A collection of reviews.

H. L. Roberts, *Adv. Inorg. Chem. Radiochem.*, **11**, 309 (1968). The chemistry of mercury.

F. A. Cotton, *Acc. Chem. Res.*, **2**, 240 (1969); *Quart. Rev.*, **20**, 389 (1966); *Rev. Pure Appl. Chem.*, **17**, 25 (1967). Excellent reviews of metal–metal bonding and cluster compounds.

D. L. Kepert and K. Vrieze, 'Compounds of the Transition Metals Involving Metal–Metal Bonds', **BENT**, 47.

R. B. King, *Prog. Inorg. Chem.*, **15**, 287 (1971). Metal-cluster compounds.

D. L. Kepert, 'Isopolyanions and Heteropolyanions', **BENT**, 51. Good review of the condensation process, polymerisation, and structures of polyanions. See also Kepert, *Prog. Inorg. Chem.*, **4**, 199 (1962), and **ES**, 10.

R. M. Diamond and D. G. Tuck, *Prog. Inorg. Chem.*, **2**, 109 (1960). Wide-ranging survey of solvent-extraction equilibria.

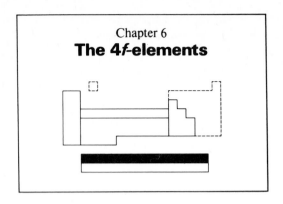

Chapter 6
The 4*f*-elements

The *f*-block consists of two series of elements in which the 4*f*- and 5*f*-orbitals are filled. However, the chemistry and properties of these two series are so very different that, as with the *d*-block, it is more convenient to treat them separately. The 4*f*-elements are therefore considered in this Chapter, and the 5*f*-elements in the next.

The 4*f*-elements (alias lanthanons, lanthanides or lanthanoids) have a very simple chemistry since with but few exceptions only one oxidation state is displayed, viz. +3. In this respect they resemble the *s*-block elements, and indeed there are pronounced similarities to calcium, which often occurs in lanthanide minerals, and to strontium and barium, particularly in the complicated solid-state structures found.

6.1 Occurrence, isolation, and uses

Although the old and still widely used name for these elements (or, strictly, their oxides) is the 'rare earths', they are in fact considerably more abundant than some 'common' metals (see Table 6.1). The major exception is promethium, which occurs in only minute quantities as a product of the spontaneous fission of uranium-238; even the longest-lived isotope has a half-life of only 2·64 years.

The two major mineral sources of the lanthanides are monazite (MPO_4) and bastnasite ($MFCO_3$), both of which contain several of the elements (see Table 6.2). Because of the similarity in ionic radii, solubilities of salts, etc., adjacent elements are very similar in properties and tend to occur together. There is some differentiation from one end of the series to the other, and most minerals contain either the earlier metals (the 'cerium group', lanthanum to about gadolinium) or the later metals plus, usually, yttrium (the 'yttrium group', gadolinium to lutetium, and yttrium; the ionic radius of Y^{3+} (88 pm) is very similar to those of Ho^{3+} and Er^{3+}). No commercial uses have yet been found for the yttrium group, although some workable deposits are known.

Of the two major cerium-group minerals, bastnasite is used only on a relatively small scale, when it is desired to avoid the complications of handling the radioactive thorium which occurs in monazite ($r_{Th^{4+}} = 90$ pm). Monazite is a very hard mineral, resistant to weathering, and it therefore accumulates on beaches and in alluvial deposits along with other dense minerals such as ilmenite, zircon, gold, or cassiterite. The monazite forms only 1–5 per cent of such deposits and is usually recovered as a by-product from the separation of e.g. zircon or cassiterite (SnO_2). Similarly, the lanthanides were originally recovered as by-products from the processing of monazite for thorium for use in incadescent gas mantles. Processing is still usually carried out in two stages, firstly to recover thorium and secondly to separate the lanthanides.

Table 6.1   Abundances and ionic radii of lanthanide elements

Element	Z	Abundance (ppm)	$r_{M^{3+}}$ (pm)
La	57	18	104
Ce	58	46	103
Pr	59	5·5	101
Nd	60	24	99·5
Pm	61	$4·5 \times 10^{-20}$	97·9
Sm	62	6·5	96·4
Eu	63	1·0	95·0
Gd	64	6·4	93·8
Tb	65	0·91	92·3
Dy	66	4·5	90·8
Ho	67	1·2	89·4
Er	68	3·0	88·1
Tm	69	0·3	86·9
Yb	70	2·7	85·8
Lu	71	0·8	84·8
Sc	21	5	68
Y	39	28	88
Th	90	12	90 (Th^{4+})

Table 6.2   Mineral sources of the lanthanides

Mineral	Composition†	Location
Monazite MPO_4	La 15, Ce 28, Pr 5 Nd 14, Sm 2 Y-group 1 Th 10	S. India, Brazil, Australia, Malaysia
Bastnasite $MFCO_3$	Ce-group 42‡ Y-group 1 Th 0·03	California Scandinavia

† expressed as percentage M_2O_3
‡ distribution of elements probably similar to that in monazite

Pure monazite is obtained by a combination of flotation, magnetic and electrostatic separation procedures, and is then treated either with strong alkali or strong acid. The action of boiling concentrated sodium hydroxide solution (55–75% NaOH, 140–170 °C) gives the hydroxides which are filtered off and added to hydrochloric acid to give a final pH of about 3·5, at which thorium phosphate is insoluble but the lanthanides pass into solution. The caustic soda solution is concentrated and filtered to remove sodium phosphate and then recycled. Alternatively, the ore is treated with concentrated sulphuric acid (98%, 200–300 °C), giving the anhydrous sulphates which are extracted with water. The lanthanides are crystallised as double sulphates (with sodium), either leaving thorium in solution or after its removal as phosphate, depending on the acidity and sulphate concentration. The sulphates are usually converted to chlorides by dissolution, precipitation as hydroxides, treatment with hydrochloric acid and neutralisation with lanthanide carbonate. Thorium can also be removed by solvent extraction using tributyl phosphate (TBP) and nitrate solutions [thorium dissolves in the organic phase as the complex $Th(NO_3)_4(TBP)_2$]. Cerium is rather readily oxidised to the +4-state and must either be kept in the lower oxidation state or recovered from the organic solvent by treatment with sodium nitrite solution.

The great similarity between the lanthanide elements makes their separation from each other difficult. As indicated above, cerium (alone in the series) can be oxidised [using permanganate or hypochlorite (bleaching powder)] and extracted, or precipitated by hydrolysis, being considerably less basic than the trivalent lanthanides. After removal of cerium, lanthanum can be recovered by fractional precipitation of hydroxides or double sulphates, but the other metals cannot easily be separated by this technique. Frequently, separation was not attempted, and the mixed product was sold as a 'didymium' salt. The most general separation process, which is now used on a large scale, is ion exchange. The lanthanide solution is passed down a column of a cation-exchange resin which binds the M^{3+} ions tightly and quantitatively. These ions are then removed as anions by complexation with ethylenediaminetetra-acetate ion ($EDTA^{4-}$), applied to the column as a solution of the copper complex $Cu(EDTA)^{2-}$ (the free acid is not very soluble under the conditions used). The lanthanides from the complex ions $M(EDTA)^-$ and an equilibrium is set up between the solution and the resin. The metal which forms the most stable complex is eluted first and, since the stability of the complex is inversely related to the radius of the metal cation, the metals appear in reverse order of atomic weight. By this method clean separations can be obtained quite simply, in marked contrast to the 'classical' fractional crystalisation procedures which required many hundreds of stages.

Although the lanthanides represent one-sixth of known elements, they have very little commercial application (Table 6.3). This is mainly for economic reasons, in that they have several

Table 6.3   Major products derived from the lanthanides

Product†	Application
$Ce(45)Cl_3.6H_2O$	Production of mischmetal
$Ce(45)F_3.\frac{1}{2}H_2O$	Component of carbon arc rods
$Ce(45)_2O_3–CeO_2$	Polishing and decolourising glass
$Ce(45)(OH)_4$	
$(NH_4)_2Ce(NO_3)_6$	Oxidants
$(NH_4)_4Ce(SO_4)_4.2H_2O$	
Mischmetal	Lighter flints, additive to non-ferrous alloys
$Y(Eu)VO_4$	Red phosphor (colour TV)
Pr_2O_3	Ceramic glazing pigment (yellow)

† Ce(45) indicates that a mixture of Ce-group lanthanides is present, of which 45 per cent is cerium.

useful properties but are usually more expensive than less effective substitutes. Cerium is produced in the largest bulk, partly because it is the most abundant, but also because it is relatively easy to separate. Frequently, complete separation is unnecessary, and Ce45 products are used, i.e. material in which 45 per cent of the lanthanide content is cerium, the remainder being in the proportions found in monazite. Ce45 chloride is produced in relatively large quantities, mainly for electrolysis in an alkali-chloride melt to give 'mischmetal', a solid solution of the elemental metals. When finely divided this alloy is pyrophoric, which property is only slightly modified by alloying with iron, in which form it is used as lighter flints. Mischmetal is also finding increasing application as an additive to non-ferrous alloys. Small additions (0·05–0·1%) give marked improvements in the corrosion resistance and strength of magnesium (jet engines), aluminium (electric cables), copper (conductors) and nickel-cobalt (marine turbine) alloys. Alloys with cobalt, MCo_5 (M = Sm, Ce, Y, Pr) are ferromagnetic and show great promise for the miniaturisation of magnet systems. Ce45 fluoride is an important component of carbon-arc rods for projection lamps; the mixture of lanthanides gives emission lines covering almost the whole of the visible spectrum, improving the colour-balance. Cerium oxide is the best abrasive for glass polishing, being rather better than zirconium oxide and considerably better than the oxides of aluminium, iron, titanium or tin. Its use, however, is restricted to the production of quality glass such as spectacle lenses and mirrors. Chemical uses of the lanthanides are confined to the application of cerium(IV) as an oxidant, e.g. as 'ceric sulphate' or as an additive in glass-making to oxidize iron and thus improve the colour of the glass.

6.2   The elemental metals

Although individual metals can be obtained by electrolysis of fused salts, careful control of conditions is required, and the reduction of a halide with an s-block metal is a better method. The anhydrous fluorides (used in preference to the cheaper chlorides, because the latter are very hygroscopic) are heated at about 1 000 °C with calcium or magnesium and excess of the reductant is distilled from the resulting alloy under vacuum. Under these conditions, samarium, europium and gadolinium are reduced only to the divalent state; these metals can be obtained by reduction of their oxides with lanthanum, followed by vacuum distillation.

   The metals are silvery-white and fairly reactive. In air, the lighter metals tarnish rapidly but the heavier ones are affected only slowly. Europium oxidises most rapidly and may even ignite (cf. its anomalous structure, see below). In every case the oxide, M_2O_3, or its hydrate is formed. Reaction with water is slow at room temperature but acids attack the lanthanides very rapidly. In appearance and reactivity the metals resemble calcium and strontium. Europium and ytterbium are soluble in liquid ammonia, like the s-block metals, giving blue solutions containing the bivalent cations and 'solvated electrons'.

   The metals are denser and higher-melting than the s-block metals, and have higher heats of atomisation (cf. Table 6.4). These and related properties vary smoothly throughout the series, but europium and ytterbium are anomalous in having different structures, lower melting points, densities and heats of atomisation than their congeners. In these two cases, the metallic lattice can be regarded as being composed of M^{2+} ions with two electrons donated to the conduction band, whereas with the other metals all three valence electrons appear to be in the conduction bands (see Ch. 9).

6.3   Halides

Direct reactions of the metals with halogens gives the trihalides in all cases except cerium, which with fluorine forms CeF_4. Tetrafluorides are also known for praseodymium and terbium, and double fluorides (with alkali fluorides) containing neodymium(IV) and dysprosium(IV) have been described. Some dihalides are known, obtained either by reduction (e.g. with hydrogen) or thermal decomposition of the trihalides. Thermal decomposition becomes easier as the halide becomes larger, Cl < Br < I, and di-iodides of several of the lanthanides are known (Table 6.5). Europium dihalides can also be obtained from aqueous solution (e.g. by zinc-reduction), but the dipositive cations of the other metals are oxidised by water. Only in the cases of samarium, neodymium, europium, dysprosium, thulium, and ytterbium do the dihalides appear to be ionic solids involving the M^{2+} ions. Those of the other metals are electrical conductors and have higher melting points

Table 6.4　Properties of the elemental lanthanides

Metal	Crystal structure	M.P. (°C)	$\dfrac{r_M}{pm}$	$\dfrac{\Delta H^0_{at}}{kJ\ mol^{-1}}$
La	hcp	920	187·7	431
Ce	hcp	798	182·4	468
Pr	bcc	935	182·8	373
Nd	double hexag	1 016	182·2	328
Pm	double hexag	1 168	(181)	—
Sm	hcp	1 072	180·2	203
Eu	bcc	826	204·2	180
Gd	hcp	1 312	180·2	397
Tb	hcp	1 356	178·2	394
Dy	hcp	1 407	177·3	298
Ho	hcp	1 470	176·6	296
Er	hcp	1 522	175·7	343
Tm	hcp	1 545	174·6	248
Yb	fcc	816	194·0	153
Lu	hcp	1 675	173·4	428
Sc	hcp	1 539	164	326
Y	hcp	1 500	182	410
Th	fcc	1 750	179·5	—

Table 6.5　Colours and melting points (°C) of lanthanide trihalides

	Fluorides		Chlorides		Bromides		Iodides	
Sc	white		white	960	white	560	white	945
La	white	1 493	white	862	white	789	grey	772
Ce	white	1 430	white	817	white	733	yellow	766
Pr	green	1 395	green	786	green	691		737
Nd	violet	1 374	mauve	758	violet	682	green	784
Pm	mauve		blue					(797)
Sm	white	1 306	yellow	682	yellow	640	orange	850dec
Eu	white	1 276	yellow	dec	grey	dec		dec
Gd	white	1 231	white	602	white	770	yellow	925
Tb	white	1 172	white	582	white	828		957
Dy	green	1 154	white	647	white	879	green	978
Ho	pink	1 143	yellow	720	yellow	919	yellow	994
Er	pink	1 140	violet	776	violet	923	violet	1 015
Tm	white	1 158	yellow	824	white	954	yellow	1 021
Yb	white	1 157	white	865	white	dec	white	dec
Lu	white	1 182	white	925	white	1 025	brown	1 050

Also
SmF_2, yellow; EuF_2
$NdCl_2$, green, 841; $SmCl_2$, brown, 848; $EuCl_2$, white, 731;
$DyCl_2$, black, 721dec; $TmCl_2$; $YbCl_2$, green, 702.
$SmBr_2$, brown, 669; $EuBr_2$, white, 683; $YbBr_2$, green, 613;
$TmBr_2$, 619.
LaI₂, block, 820; CeI_2, bronze, 808; *PrI₂*, bronze, 758;
NdI₂, violet, 562; *GdI₂*, bronze, 831; SmI_2, green, 520;
EuI_2, green, 580; TmI_2, black, 756; YbI_2, black, 772.
CeF_4, white; PrF_4, white; TbF_4, white.
Dihalides shown in italics are metallic conductors.

Table 6.6 Properties of lanthanide oxides

Oxide	Colour	$\Delta H_f^0/kJ\ mol^{-1}$	Lattice type†
La_2O_3	white	-1 794	A
Ce_2O_3	white	-1 803	A
Pr_2O_3	green	-1 823	A
Nd_2O_3	mauve	-1 809	A
Pm_2O_3			A
Sm_2O_3	yellow	-1 815	B
Eu_2O_3	pink	-1 641	B
Gd_2O_3	white	-1 815	B
Tb_2O_3	white	-1 864	C
Dy_2O_3	white	-1 869	C
Ho_2O_3	yellow	-1 881	C
Er_2O_3	pink	-1 898	C
Tm_2O_3	green	-1 889	C
Yb_2O_3	white	-1 815	C
Lu_2O_3	white	-1 878	C
Sc_2O_3	white	-1 906	C
Y_2O_3	white	-1 905	C

† see text.

than their congeners; they probably contain M^{3+} ions, with the extra electron contributing to a conduction band.

Europium difluoride has the same crystal structure as SrF_2 (the fluorite structure) and the chloride and $SmCl_2$ have the $PbCl_2$-structure like $BaCl_2$. The ytterbium dihalides (Cl, Br, I) all have the CdI_2-structure. The smallest metal ion thus has the smallest coordination number. A similar trend is seen in the structures of the trichlorides: those of lanthanum to gadolinium have the UCl_3-structure, in which the metal ions are nine-coordinate, while dysprosium to lutetium adopt the $AlCl_3$-structure with six-coordination. The tribromides of lanthanum, cerium and praseodymium also have the UCl_3-structure and LaI_3 is isostructural with UI_3 (eight-coordination). The trifluorides also display two types of structure. In the LaF_3-structure (La to Eu), the metal ions are nine-coordinate with M–F distances in the range 242–264 pm (for LaF_3), whereas in the YF_3-structure (Sm to Lu) there are eight close neighbours (225–232 pm in YF_3) and one slightly more distant (260 pm).

The trifluorides are insoluble in water and may be precipitated even from acid solution. The other trihalides are readily soluble and are often hygroscopic or deliquescent. The hydrates obtained from these solutions (with some difficulty, as they are very soluble) cannot safely be dehydrated by heating except for the lighter elements. Formation of the oxyhalides, MOX, occurs more readily as the cation becomes smaller, as might be expected. Dehydration is therefore best effected in an atmosphere of hydrogen chloride.

The oxyhalides are well-defined compounds and all have structures in which the metal ions are eight-coordinate (cubic). The oxyfluorides have the CaF_2-structure and, although fluoride and oxide ions have almost identical radii, the anions are arranged in regular patterns, there being either four of each type associated with each metal ion or alternate sets of six and two. The four-four arrangement is found for the other oxyhalides (PbFCl-structure). Both of these structures have similarities with those of the oxides (see below).

The enthalpies of formation of the trihalides, where known, become less negative as the radius of the halide increases, as in other series, e.g. $\Delta H_f^0(PrX_3) = -1\ 053(Cl)$, $-940(Br)$,

$-635(I)$ kJ mol^{-1}. Along the series of metals, however, the enthalpies become less negative with increasing atomic number of the lanthanide (Fig. 6.1). Since the ionic radii are decreasing, the resultant rise in lattice energy must be insufficient to offset the increasing ionisation energies, an effect seen also in the d-block. Few data are available for dihalides, but estimates have been made which confirm that most dihalides are unstable to disproportionation (Fig. 6.1).

Fig. 6.1 ΔH_f^0-values for lanthanide di- and tri-chlorides (data from D. A. Johnson, *J. Chem. Soc.* (*A*), 2579 (1969); ▲ denotes experimentally determined values, ○ denotes an estimated value). Note the much greater variation in $\Delta H_f^0(MCl_2)$ than $\Delta H_f^0(MCl_3)$. Stable dichlorides are known for Nd, Sm, Er, Dy, Tm and Tb

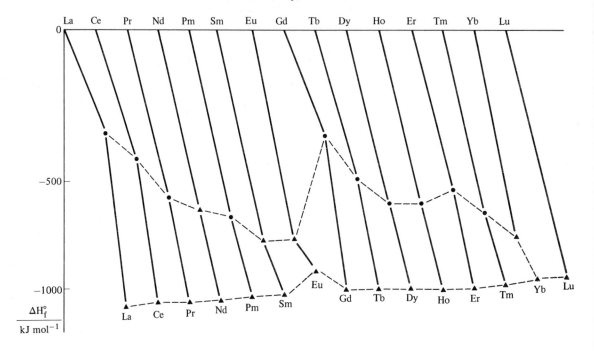

6.4   Oxides

The oxides M_2O_3 are obtained by the direct reaction of the metal with air or oxygen (except for cerium, praseodymium, and terbium which oxidise further), or by the direct reaction of the metal with air or oxygen, or by the action of heat on the hydroxides or on a salt of almost any oxo-anion (e.g. nitrate or carbonate). For cerium, praseodymium and terbium, dehydration of the hydroxide or pyrolysis of a salt *in vacuo* may be used. All these oxides are quite strongly basic and most will absorb carbon dioxide from the atmosphere, which is only completely lost again by heating to high temperatures (above 800 °C). All are insoluble in water, but dissolve readily in acids (even after being ignited) forming the hydrated M^{3+} ions. Addition of alkali to such solutions readily precipitates the hydroxides, $M(OH)_3$; the pH required becomes less as the radius of the cation decreases [e.g. 7·82 for La(OH)$_3$, 6·83 for Gd(OH)$_3$, 6·30 for Lu(OH)$_3$]. The basicity of the oxides and hydroxides is thus decreasing with increasing atomic number, and only those of the last two members, ytterbium and lutetium, show any reaction with alkali; they dissolve in concentrated sodium hydroxide solution at high temperature and pressure, forming Na$_3$M(OH)$_6$.

In the crystalline state, the hydroxides have the UCl_3-structure (nine-coordination). The oxides, however, show three basic structures (A, B, and C) in which the metal ions are either seven- (A, B) or six-coordinate (C). The A-structure is formed by the early metals (La to Sm) and the B-structure by the intermediate members (Pr to Dy). The thermodynamically stable form for all the metals is the C-type structure. This is of interest because it provides a link with the higher-oxidation state oxides formed by cerium, praseodymium and terbium. This structure is similar to the CaF_2-structure but one-quarter of the anions are systematically missing; the metal ion is surrounded by anions positioned at the corners of a cube but only six such sites are occupied. The vacant sites are distributed regularly throughout the lattice. If these sites were occupied, giving a complete fluorite-type lattice, the formula of the oxide would be MO_2 and all the metal ions would have to be M^{4+}. Only the three metals mentioned earlier (Ce, Pr, Tb) form oxides of this type, but all three also give non-stoicheiometric oxides with intermediate formulae, containing both M^{3+} and M^{4+} ions and sufficient oxide-vacancies to ensure electrical neutrality. For example, in $PrO_{1.800}$ (or Pr_5O_9) the average oxidation state of the metal is +3·6, i.e. Pr^{3+} and Pr^{4+} are present in the ratio 2:3, and one-tenth of the anion sites are vacant. At relatively low temperatures (400–500 °C), the vacancies are ordered regularly through the lattice, as they are in M_2O_3, and the system is stable because the extra lattice energy due to the presence of M^{4+} balances the extra ionisation energy. Many of the ordered phases seem to correspond to the general formula M_nO_{2n-2}, and members are known for n = 4, 7, 8, 9, 10, 11, 12, 14. At higher temperatures, the vacancies become randomised as the contribution from entropy becomes significant. Thus, above 685 °C, cerium oxide has the randomised structure throughout the composition range $CeO_{1.72}$–$CeO_{2.00}$, but below this temperature exists as a mixture of appropriate amounts of stoicheiometric CeO_2 and an ordered phase of composition $Ce_{32}O_{58}$. The problem of non-stoicheiometry is more fully described in Chapter 10.

Of these higher oxides, only CeO_2 can be obtained by direct oxidation of the metal (or one of its salts) in air. The other two metals give Pr_6O_{11} and Tb_4O_7 (approximately). Since the radii of the M^{4+} ions decrease in the order $Ce^{4+} > Pr^{4+} > Tb^{4+}$, this clearly indicates that the metals become more difficult to oxidise to the +4-state as the nuclear charge increases. Cerium dioxide is rather inert, but the higher oxides of the other two metals react readily with acids, giving solutions of the M^{3+} ions and oxidising the acid anion (e.g. chloride to chlorine) or water (to oxygen).

In contrast to the halides, the enthalpies of formation of the oxides M_2O_3 become more negative with increasing atomic number, although only by 80 kJ mol^{-1} across the series (Table 6.6). This presumably reflects the higher lattice energy associated with the presence of the doubly-charged anion, which increases more rapidly with the decreasing radius of M^{3+} than the ionisation energies.

Oxides of the divalent metals, MO, have been obtained for samarium, europium and ytterbium, by the reduction of M_2O_3 with the metal or with lanthanum. Despite the large radius of the dipositive cations, these compounds are reported to have the NaCl-structure.

6.5   Aqueous solution chemistry

All the lanthanides form aquated M^{3+} ions, but it is not easy to establish the number of water molecules associated with the cations. There are almost certainly more than six water molecules directly coordinated to the metal ions, and it is probable that the earlier members (La to Nd) are nine-coordinate and the later ones eight-coordinate.

Despite their high charge, the M^{3+} ions are not very polarising because of the large radii. The cations are therefore not subject to hydrolysis and the oxides and hydroxides function as strong bases. Only cerium gives a stable quadrivalent state in solution which is, as would be expected, much more readily hydrolysed forming hydroxo- and oxo-species such as $Ce(OH)^{3+}_{aq}$ and $CeOCe^{6+}_{aq}$. The hydrated oxide is thus much more readily precipitated from solution, allowing cerium to be separated easily from the other lanthanides.

The tripositive ions do not readily form complexes in aqueous solution unless polydentate chelating ligands are used. Cerium(IV), however, complexes much more readily, and complex formation has a pronounced effect on the redox potential $E^0(Ce^{4+}/Ce^{3+})$, which is about 0·3 V lower in sulphuric acid solution (1·44 V for 2M-acid) than in perchloric acid (1·70 V); in hydrochloric acid, the potential is even lower (1·28 V). These figures indicate that complexation of cerium by chloride or sulphate ions stabilises the higher oxidation state more than the lower. All the potentials are higher than the potential of the $O_2, 4H^+/2H_2O$ couple, so that Ce^{4+} should oxidise water; the reaction is slow, however. The dependence of the potential on the anion can be useful: for instance, in perchloric or nitric acid solution the oxidation potential is greater than that of chlorine-chloride (1·36 V), so that chloride ion would be oxidised. In hydrochloric acid solution the potential is so reduced that the anion is not oxidised, and cerium(IV) is one of the few readily available strong oxidants which can be used in this medium. In view of the magnitude of the potential, very strong oxidants are required to obtain cerium(IV) in solution, e.g. persulphate. The conventional cerium(IV) analytical reagents, $(NH_4)_2Ce(NO_3)_6$ or $(NH_4)_4Ce(SO_4)_4.2H_2O$, are obtained by dissolving hydrated cerium(IV) oxide in nitric or sulphuric acid, adding the calculated amount of the appropriate ammonium salt, and evaporating down. A value of about +2·9 V has been estimated for the Pr^{4+}/Pr^{3+} couple; praseodymium(IV) cannot therefore be obtained in aqueous solution.

The potentials $E^0(M^{3+}/M)$ decrease smoothly throughout the series, although the overall change is very small (0·27 V for La to Lu) (Table 6.7). All the potentials are greater in basic solution, demonstrating the cationic nature of the species involved.

Table 6.7 Properties of lanthanide ions in aqueous solution

	Colour, M^{3+}	$E^0(M^{3+}/M)$†	$E^0_b(M(OH)_3/M)$‡	$E^0(M^{3+}/M^{2+})$†	$E^0(M^{4+}/M^{3+})$†
		V	V	V	V
La	colourless	−2·52	−2·07	(−3·8)	
Ce	colourless	−2·48	−2·04	(−3·5)	+1·74 (HClO$_4$, 2M)
Pr	green	−2·46	−2·02	(−3·0)	+2·86
Nd	purple	−2·43	−2·01	(−2·8)	
Pm	pink	−2·42	−2·01	(−2·5)	
Sm	yellow	−2·41	−2·00	−1·15	
Eu	pink	−2·41	−2·00	−0·43	
Gd	colourless	−2·40	−1·99	(−3·6)	
Tb	colourless	−2·39	−1·96	(−3·5)	*ca.* +2·9
Dy	yellow-green	−2·35	−1·95	(−2·6)	
Ho	organge-yellow	−2·32	−1·94	(−2·9)	
Er	red	−2·30	−1·92	(−3·0)	
Tm	green	−2·28	−1·91	(−2·1)	
Yb	colourless	−2·27	−1·90	−1·23	
Lu	colourless	−2·26	−1·89		
Sc	colourless	−2·08	−1·78		
Y	colourless	−2·37	−1·98		

† Acid solution, unit activity of H^+
‡ Alkaline solution, unit activity of OH^-.
  Values in parentheses are estimated (D. A. Johnson, *J. Chem. Soc., Dalton Trans.*, 1671, 1974).

Divalent ions can be obtained in aqueous solution for europium (colourless), samarium (red), and ytterbium (yellow), but all except europium(II) react rapidly with water, liberating hydrogen, as the redox potentials would suggest. The production of samarium(II) and ytterbium(II) requires strong reducing agents, such as sodium amalgam (but care must be taken to avoid reduction to the metal, which readily forms an amalgam; this occurs with all the lanthanides). Europium(II), however, can be obtained with simpler reductants such as zinc. The radius of the Eu^{2+} ion (125 pm) is very similar to that of Sr^{2+}, and the two ions give salts with similar structures and solubilities. Europium can therefore be separated from the other lanthanides by reduction to the divalent state followed by precipitation of the insoluble sulphate. Alternatively, the europium may be left in solution, and the other lanthanides precipitated by addition of (carbonate-free) ammonia solution (giving the trihydroxides).

6.6 Conclusion

Two features are particularly striking in the chemistry of the $4f$-elements, viz. (a) the uniformity of the +3 oxidation state and the small number of other oxidation states, and (b) the irregularity of structures and occurrence of high coordination numbers. In the compounds described here, coordination numbers of six, seven, eight, and nine have been mentioned, and in other compounds ten- and even twelve-coordinate metal ions are found, e.g. in $La_2(SO_4)_3.9H_2O$ and $(NH_4)_2Ce(NO_3)_6$. It is tempting to think that the f-orbitals must be involved in the bonding, since the maximum number of hybrid orbitals which can be constructed from an $s–p–d$-set is nine, and to obtain eight bonding orbitals directed towards the corners of a cube (as in CeO_2) requires at least one f-orbital. There is, however, no evidence to suggest that the f-orbitals are involved at all in the bonding, and even ligand-field effects are extremely small. All the compounds appear to be essentially ionic, with very little covalency involving even the $6s$- or $6p$-orbitals. The curious structures and high coordination numbers are similar to those found with other large cations (e.g. salts of Ba^{2+} or Pb^{2+}) and are presumably a result of the optimisation of electrostatic forces. The large internuclear distances necessitated by the radii of the cations will cause the electrostatic energy per pair of ions to be relatively small, despite the high cationic charge, and many such pairs must be formed to achieve a sufficiently large lattice energy. Similarly, the large radii diminish considerably the polarising effect of the +3 charge which would otherwise be expected to lead to considerable covalency.

If the $4f$-series is considered simply as a group of elements thrust into the third Group of the Periodic Table, the relative constancy of the oxidation state displayed is no more exceptional than that of the other elements of that Group. However, by comparison with the $5d$-elements which follow them, or even with the $5f$-series, such constancy is remarkable. Presumably, most of the compounds of the bipositive metals are unstable to disproportionation and those of the quadripositive metals to dissociation. Such a state of affairs probably arises from a fortuitous balancing of ion-formation energies and lattice (or hydration) energies across the series. For other series of elements it has been possible to analyse these factors, but in this case such an analysis cannot be made directly because the primary data are not available. In particular, very few of the third ionisation energies have been obtained (this is because such values are normally derived from emission ('arc') spectra, but for the f-block elements these spectra are very complex and difficult to analyse). Values have been estimated from other thermochemical data, e.g. the enthalpies of formation of the oxides, M_2O_3, are known (some must be corrected to the value for the C-type structure) and, in the few cases where the third ionisation energy is known, the lattice energies can be calculated. Using the known ionic radii, lattice energies for the oxides of the other metals have been estimated and hence a value for the third ionisation energy obtained. These values have been embodied in Table 6.8 and Figs. 6.2 and 6.3; in using them care must be taken not to enter into circular arguments.

The variation of ionisation energy with atomic number depends on the type of electron being ionised off. In the majority of cases, the first two electrons lost are 6s-electrons (see Table 6.9), and

Table 6.8   Enthalpies of formation (kJ mol^{-1}) of gaseous lanthanide atoms and ions

	M^0	M^+	M^{2+}	M^{3+}
La	431	969	2 036	3 886
Ce	469	1 009	2 056	3 994
Pr	373	894	1 912	3 993
Nd	328	858	1 893	4 022
Pm	296	832	1 883	—
Sm	203	745	1 813	4 099
Eu	180	727	1 812	4 216
Gd	397	992	2 160	4 148
Tb	393	963	2 074	4 167
Dy	297	864	1 990	4 203
Ho	297	871	2 010	4 211
Er	343	924	2 075	4 240
Tm	247	836	1 999	4 272
Yb	153	756	1 930	4 346
Lu	428	941	2 282	4 328

(cf. D. A. Johnson, *J. Chem. Soc.* (*A*), 1525, 1969)

Fig. 6.2   Enthalpies of atomisation and ionisation for lanthanides. Note the maxima in ionisation energies when an f^7-configuration is broken

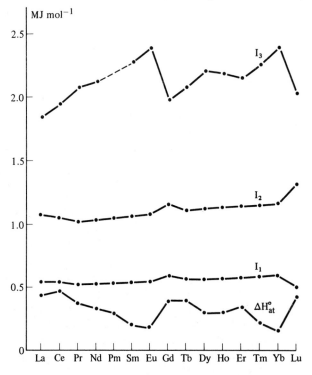

Fig. 6.3 Enthalpies of formation of gaseous lanthanide atoms and ions, $\Delta H_f^0(M^{n+}) = \Delta H_{at}^0 + \sum_{i=1}^{n} I_i$. Note the relatively smooth trend for $n = 3$ compared to the other graphs

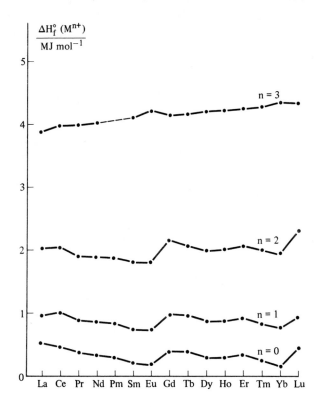

Table 6.9 Electron configurations of gaseous lanthanide atoms and ions

	M^0			M^+			M^{2+}			M^{3+}		
	4f	5d	6s	4f	5d	6s	4f	5d	6s	4f	5d	6s
La	0	1	2	0	2	0	0	1	0	0	0	0
Ce	1	1	2	1	1	1	2	0	0	1	0	0
Pr	3	0	2	3	0	1	3	0	0	2	0	0
Nd	4	0	2	4	0	1	4	0	0	3	0	0
Pm	5	0	2	5	0	1	5	0	0	4	0	0
Sm	6	0	2	6	0	1	6	0	0	5	0	0
Eu	7	0	2	7	0	1	7	0	0	6	0	0
Gd	7	1	2	7	1	1	7	1	0	7	0	0
Tb	9	0	2	9	0	1	9	0	0	8	0	0
Dy	10	0	2	10	0	1	10	0	0	9	0	0
Ho	11	0	2	11	0	1	11	0	0	10	0	0
Er	12	0	2	12	0	1	12	0	0	11	0	0
Tm	13	0	2	13	0	1	13	0	0	12	0	0
Yb	14	0	2	14	0	1	14	0	0	13	0	0
Lu	14	1	2	14	0	2	14	0	1	14	0	0

both ionisation energies increase fairly uniformly across the series, reflecting the increasing nuclear charge (Fig. 6.2). The third electron (and presumably all subsequent electrons) comes from the $4f$-shell and to the regular effect of increasing nuclear charge is added an exchange energy effect similar to that discussed for the $3d$-metals (p. 85). [Exchange energies involving electrons of different sub-shells (e.g. s and f) are very small, and do not upset the regularity of the first and second ionisation energies.] As the first half of the series is traversed, the loss of exchange energy on removal of an electron increases uniformly, augmenting the ionisation energies, but this effect becomes zero again for Gd^{2+} which has a $4f^7 5d^1$ configuration (Gd^{3+} is $4f^7$). A similar effect would be expected in the second half of the series, but is broken by an irregularity around Ho^{2+}. This effect has been explained in terms of an extra stabilisation of ions with large values of the orbital angular momentum (L).†

The enthalpies of formation of M^+ and M^{2+} vary rather irregularly (Fig. 6.3), reflecting principally the irregularities in ΔH_{at}^0. Fortuitously, the unevenness in the third ionisation energy is just sufficient to offset that in $\Delta H_f^0(M^{2+})$, so that $\Delta H_f^0(M^{3+})$ increases fairly regularly across the series. Since lattice and hydration energies vary smoothly with the regularly decreasing radii of the tripositive ions, the enthalpies of formation of the sesquioxides and trihalides and the redox potentials $E^0(M^{3+}/M)$ change quite regularly across the series (note, however, that the values we have been discussing were derived from the enthalpies of formation of the sesquioxides).

The stability of the dipositive state relative to the tripositive depends on the difference between $\Delta H_f^0(M^{3+})$ and $\Delta H_f^0(M^{2+})$ (assuming, reasonably, that lattice and hydration energies involving M^{2+} change smoothly with atomic number). As this difference (i.e. the third ionisation energy) increases, the dipositive state becomes more stable, both absolutely (since $\Delta H_f^0(M^{2+})$ is decreasing) and relative to the tripositive state. The elements which have dipositive states which are stable to disproportionation are thus those close to the maxima in the third ionisation energy, i.e. samarium, europium, dysprosium, thulium, and ytterbium, which accords with experience.

The formation of a tetrapositive state would be expected, if at all, for elements with the lowest fourth ionisation energies. These energies will presumably vary in a similar fashion to the third ionisation energies except that the changes will almost certainly be more dramatic and the minima and maxima will occur for atomic numbers greater by one unit. The smallest fourth ionisation energy will therefore be found for cerium, which is the only member of the series for which the tetrapositive state is at all common. The other two elements which occasionally show this oxidation state are praseodymium, which is adjacent to cerium, and terbium which will be at the central minimum of fourth ionisation energies. In both cases, the ionisation energy will be greater than that for cerium and it must be presumed that the increase in lattice/hydration energies is insufficient to compensate fully, so that praseodymium(IV) and terbium(IV) are obtainable only in oxide and fluoride systems.

A reasonable rationalisation can thus be given for the oxidation states displayed by these elements. The curious cancellation effect of ΔH_{at}^0 and I_3 is one of the quirks of Nature which make chemistry interesting.

---

† The spin and orbital angular momenta of an atom are not completely independent, but interact to an extent expressed by the spin-orbit coupling constant, λ. This constant increases very rapidly with increasing atomic number (roughly as Z^4) and is therefore more important in the second half of the $4f$-series than the first. This phenomenon has the effect of giving extra stability to atoms and ions with large values of the orbital angular momentum, L (*cf* Hund's rules which state that the most stable configuration is that with the largest value for L consistent with the maximum value for S, the total spin momentum). Both Ho^{2+} ($4f^{11}$) and Ho^{3+} ($4f^{10}$) have L = 6 (I-states), whereas for Dy^{2+} ($4f^{10}$) and Dy^{3+} ($4f^9$) the L-values are 6 and 5, i.e. Dy^{2+} is stabilised by this effect relative to Dy^{3+}, and the third ionisation energy is greater than would otherwise be expected. For erbium the situation is reversed (Er^{2+}, L = 5; Er^{3+}, L = 6), the trivalent state is stabilised, and the ionisation energy is lower than expected.

Bibliography

BENT, 44; **CW**, 27; **ES**, 22; **H**, 14; **HJ**, 30; **MM**, 10; **PW**, 21.

K. W. Bagnall (Ed.), *Lanthanides and Actinides*, Butterworth, 1972. (MTP International Review Series). A survey of recent developments.

R. J. Callow, *The Industrial Chemistry of the Lanthanons, Yttrium, Thorium, and Uranium*, Pergamon, 1967. Detailed treatment of occurrence, winning and applications.

T. Moeller, *The Chemistry of the Lanthanides*, Van Nostrand-Reinhold, 1963. A good, simple survey.

D. Brown, *Halides of the Lanthanides and Actinides*, Wiley, 1968. Comprehensive survey of preparations, structures and properties.

L. B. Asprey and B. B. Cunningham, *Prog. Inorg. Chem.*, **2**, 267 (1960). Review of unusual oxidation states of lanthanides and actinides.

D. A. Johnson, *J. Chem. Soc.* (*A*), 1525 (1969) and M. M. Faktor and R. Hanks, *J. Inorg. Nucl. Chem.*, **31**, 1649 (1969). Evaluation of third ionisation energies of lanthanides using Born–Haber cycles.

D. A. Johnson, *J. Chem. Soc.* (*A*), 2578 (1969). Estimation of ΔH_f^0 for lanthanide dihalides and consideration of their stability to disproportionation.

C. E. Myers, *Inorg. Chem.*, **14**, 199 (1975). Thermochemical evidence for covalency in lanthanide trihalides.

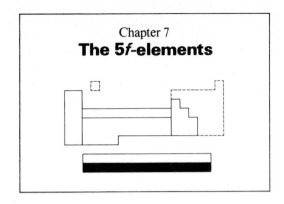

Chapter 7
The 5*f*-elements

In marked contrast to the uniformity of behaviour of the lanthanides, the 5f-elements (actinides) display a considerable variety in their chemistry; e.g., oxidation states between +2 and +7 are found. Being the heaviest elements in the Periodic Table, they are also all radioactive, i.e. their nuclei spontaneously decay by the emission of α- or β^--particles or by fission. The stability of the nuclei decreases rapidly with increasing atomic number so that only two elements, uranium and thorium, can be considered as occurring naturally, i.e. have isotopes with half-lives comparable with or greater than the age of the earth. Four others, actinium, protactinium, neptunium and plutonium, occur in trace amounts in uranium minerals as a result of the radioactivity of the uranium. All the other elements of the series are 'artificial' in the sense that they can only be obtained by the modern alchemy which allows known elements to be transmuted into new ones by reactor- or cyclotron-irradiation. Consequently, most of the actinides have been known only since the 1940s, and it was not until the first trans-uranium elements (neptunium and plutonium) were discovered (synthesised) that it became clear that these elements might form the beginning of a 5f-series.

While uranium and thorium are available in vast quantities, from their ores, and neptunium and plutonium in large amounts from spent uranium fuel elements, the other members can be obtained only in much smaller amounts: americium and curium in gram quantities, californium and berkelium by the milligram, and the rest in microgram or even smaller amounts. Some investigations have been carried out on samples containing only a few dozen atoms of the actinide. In these cases it is obviously not possible to perform conventional chemical reactions nor to isolate and characterise well-defined compounds, and the identification of the species formed and the oxidation states involved relies on techniques such as ion-exchange chromatography. The situation is further complicated by the intense radioactivity of these elements, which generates heat in massive samples and concentrated solutions, and leads to decomposition of solids and ionisation and radical-formation in solution. Clearly, to study the chemistry of such materials is a formidable task, and relatively little is known about the later elements of the series.

7.0   Radioactivity and nuclear reactions

Although the subject of radioactivity is not directly relevant to the study of the chemistry of the metallic (or any other) elements, a brief introduction is of interest at this point as background to the production and spontaneous decay of the actinide elements.

The nucleus may be considered to be composed of protons (equal in number to the atomic number, Z) and neutrons (which make up the rest of the nuclear mass), although these particles themselves are now known to have complex structures. The Coulombic repulsion between the protons in a nucleus is offset by strong, short-range interactions between pairs of nucleons due to exchange of π-mesons (nucleon is the general name for a nuclear particle). Light nuclei have equal numbers of protons and neutrons (hence the empiricism that the atomic mass, A, is roughly twice Z), but as Z increases the Coulombic forces increase and proportionately more neutrons are required to form a stable nucleus: the neutron:proton ratio increases with increasing Z. Above atomic number 83 (bismuth) all known nuclei are unstable and decay in one (or more) of three major ways:

(a) β^--emission, which is the ejection of an electron from the nucleus. The electron arises from the conversion of a neutron into a proton (a neutrino is also formed simultaneously, and carries away some of the energy). Such a mode of decay would therefore be expected of neutron-rich nuclei,

$$n \rightarrow p^+ + \nu^0 + \beta^-$$

such as might be produced by neutron-bombardment of other nuclei, i.e. the products of an (n, γ)-reaction.† This process is important because β^--emission gives a nucleus with a positive charge greater by one unit, and is the chief route to new elements with high Z, e.g.

$$^{238}_{92}U(n, \gamma)^{239}_{92}U \xrightarrow{\beta^-} {}^{239}_{93}Np$$

Some heavy nuclei are stable to β^--emission.

(b) α-emission, which is the ejection of a compound particle composed of two protons and two neutrons (a helium nucleus), which leads to an increase in the neutron:proton ratio. All nuclides above bismuth ($^{209}_{83}Bi$) are α-unstable. A series of α-emissions (and the occasional loss of a β^--particle) should thus eventually lead to a favourable neutron:proton ratio and a stable nucleus, and this form of decay predominates in the four possible decay schemes (Fig. 7.1), which terminate with lead (Z = 82) or bismuth (Z = 83) isotopes. The schemes are named with the α-decay process in mind, since each α-emission lowers the nuclear mass by four units; Z, of course, decreases by only two units.

γ-Radiation may accompany α- and β^--emission, and occurs when the product nucleus is formed in an excited state and drops to one of lower energy. The nucleus has various quantised energy levels allowed to it, corresponding to different arrangements of the nucleons (strictly, to different values of the total angular momentum of the nucleus), just as an atom has various electronic energy levels; transitions between these levels result in the emission (or absorption) of photons.

(c) fission, which is the process in which the nucleus deforms and ultimately splits into two fragments (plus some neutrons) which are themselves unstable to loss of neutrons, being lighter than the parent nucleus. Some nuclei, particularly those of very high Z, are subject to spontaneous fission (e.g. $^{254}_{98}Cf$, $^{256}_{100}Fm$), while others can be induced to undergo fission by neutron bombardment, i.e. a neutron is absorbed and the resulting nucleus is unstable. This is the process utilised in the atomic reactor and the atomic bomb. A fissile nucleus ($^{235}_{92}U$ or $^{239}_{94}Pu$) absorbs a neutron (initially arising from spontaneous fission) and undergoes fission, releasing a large amount of energy and more neutrons. If these neutrons are allowed to interact with more fissile nuclei, the process becomes a self-sustaining chain-reaction which, if not controlled, may become violent. In the atomic reactor the number of neutrons available is controlled by inserting or removing control-rods

---

† The notation used is conventional for nuclear reactions. The first symbol in the bracket represents the bombarding particle (the reagent) and the second the product particle, in this case a γ-ray.

Table 7.1   Longest-lived or most-readily-available isotopes of the actinides

Isotope	Decay-mode	$t_{\frac{1}{2}}$	Production
$^{227}_{89}\mathrm{Ac}$	α	21·6 y	$^{226}_{88}\mathrm{Ra(n,\gamma)}^{227}_{88}\mathrm{Ra} \xrightarrow{\beta^-}$; (natural)
$^{232}_{90}\mathrm{Th}$	α	$1·41\times10^{10}$ y	Natural
$^{231}_{91}\mathrm{Pa}$	α	$3·23\times10^{4}$ y	Fuel-element residues, $^{230}_{90}\mathrm{Th(n,\gamma)}^{231}_{90}\mathrm{Th} \xrightarrow{\beta^-}$
$^{238}_{92}\mathrm{U}$	α	$4·51\times10^{9}$ y	Natural
$^{235}_{92}\mathrm{U}$	α	$7·13\times10^{8}$ y	Natural
$^{237}_{93}\mathrm{Np}$	α	$2·17\times10^{6}$ y	Fuel-elements, $^{235}_{92}\mathrm{U(n,\gamma)(n,\gamma)}^{237}_{92}\mathrm{U} \xrightarrow{\beta^-}$
			$^{238}_{92}\mathrm{U(n^\dagger,2n)}^{237}_{92}\mathrm{U} \xrightarrow{\beta^-}$
$^{239}_{94}\mathrm{Pu}$	α	$2·44\times10^{4}$ y	Fuel-elements, $^{238}_{92}\mathrm{U(n,\gamma)}^{239}_{92}\mathrm{U} \xrightarrow{\beta^-} {}^{239}_{93}\mathrm{Np} \xrightarrow{\beta^-}$
$^{242}_{94}\mathrm{Pu}$	α	$3·79\times10^{5}$ y	$^{241}_{94}\mathrm{Pu(n,\gamma)}$
$^{238}_{94}\mathrm{Pu}$	α	86·4 y	$^{237}_{93}\mathrm{Np(n,\gamma)}^{238}_{93}\mathrm{Np} \xrightarrow{\beta^-}$
$^{241}_{94}\mathrm{Pu}$	β	13 y	$^{240}_{94}\mathrm{Pu(n,\gamma)}$
$^{241}_{95}\mathrm{Am}$	α	458 y	$^{242}_{94}\mathrm{Pu} \xrightarrow{\beta^-}$
$^{243}_{95}\mathrm{Am}$	α	$7·97\times10^{3}$ y	$^{241}_{95}\mathrm{Am(n,\gamma)(n,\gamma)}$
$^{242}_{96}\mathrm{Cm}$	α	162·5 d	$^{241}_{95}\mathrm{Am(n,\gamma)}^{242}_{95}\mathrm{Am} \xrightarrow{\beta^-}$
$^{244}_{96}\mathrm{Cm}$	α	17·6 y	$^{242}_{96}\mathrm{Cm(n,\gamma)(n,\gamma)}$
$^{247}_{97}\mathrm{Bk}$	α	14×10^{3} y	$^{244}_{96}\mathrm{Cm(\alpha,p)}$
$^{249}_{98}\mathrm{Bk}$	α	314 d	$^{239}_{94}\mathrm{Pu[(n,\gamma)/\beta^-]}^{249}_{96}\mathrm{Cm} \xrightarrow{\beta^-}$
$^{249}_{99}\mathrm{Cf}$	α	360 y	$^{249}_{97}\mathrm{Bk} \xrightarrow{\beta^-}$
$^{252}_{98}\mathrm{Cf}$	α	65 y	$^{239}_{94}\mathrm{Pu[(n,\gamma)/\beta^-]}^{252}_{97}\mathrm{Bk}$
$^{254}_{99}\mathrm{Es}$	α	250 d	$^{239}_{94}\mathrm{Pu[(n,\gamma)/\beta^-]}^{253}_{99}\mathrm{Es(n,\gamma)}$
$^{257}_{100}\mathrm{Fm}$	α	*ca.* 85 d	$^{239}_{94}\mathrm{Pu[(n,\gamma)/\beta^-]}^{256}_{100}\mathrm{Fm(n,\gamma)}$
$^{256}_{101}\mathrm{Md}$	E.C.	90 m	$^{253}_{99}\mathrm{Es(\alpha,n)}$
$^{255}_{102}\mathrm{No}$	α	180 s	$^{239}_{94}\mathrm{Pu(n,\gamma)}^7{}^{246}_{94}\mathrm{Pu} \xrightarrow{\beta^-} {}^{246}_{95}\mathrm{Am} \xrightarrow{\beta^-} {}^{246}_{96}\mathrm{Cm}(^{13}_6\mathrm{C,4n})$
$^{256}_{103}\mathrm{Lr}$	α	35 s	$^{243}\mathrm{Am}(^{18}_8\mathrm{O,5n})$
$^{259}_{104}\mathrm{Ku(Rf)}$	α	3 s	$^{249}_{98}\mathrm{Cf}(^{13}_6\mathrm{C,3n})$
$^{261}_{105}\mathrm{Ha}$	α	*ca.* 1 s	$^{243}_{95}\mathrm{Am}(^{22}_{10}\mathrm{Ne,4n})$

$[(n,\gamma)/\beta^-]$ signifies multiple neutron capture and β^--decay processes as shown in Fig. 7.2.
E.C. = electron capture: an orbital electron is absorbed by the nucleus, reducing Z by one unit.
†fast neutrons required.

Fig. 7.1 The four radioactive decay schemes. The 4n+1 scheme originates from a synthetic isotope, the others all involve naturally occurring isotopes. Decay schemes for heavier, artificial isotopes lead to one or other of these four series (see Table 7.2)

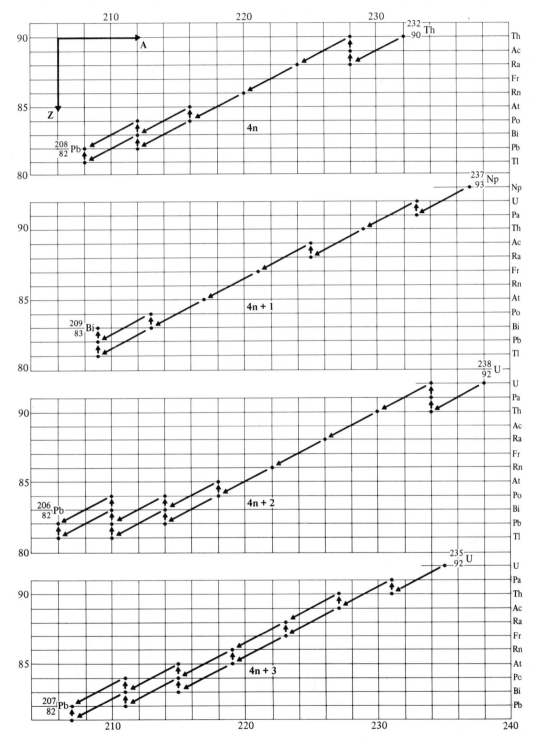

of strongly neutron-absorbing materials (e.g. boron, cadmium). Since low-energy ('thermal') neutrons are captured much more readily than fast neutrons, the reactor also contains large quantities of low-atomic-mass material as moderator (e.g. graphite) to slow down the fast neutrons, which also releases more energy as heat.

The reactor may be used as a source of neutrons, which opens the way to the synthesis of new elements by the (n, γ)-reaction followed by β⁻-decay of the products. A series of such reactions can lead to new nuclei with large Z (similar processes occur also in stars), and actinides up to fermium (Z = 100) are obtained in this way by irradiation of uranium or plutonium (Fig. 7.2). Unfortunately, as Z increases the nuclei become increasingly unstable, both to α-decay and to spontaneous and neutron-induced fission, and even with the highest available neutron-fluxes (including those of a thermonuclear explosion) the losses of nuclei by these routes are so great that elements beyond fermium cannot be obtained in extractable amounts. These elements can only be obtained by bombarding the higher actinides with other nuclei (e.g. those of helium, boron, or carbon atoms) using a cyclotron or linear accelerator. Although the probability that the target nucleus will absorb the projectiles is very small and only a few atoms are formed in one experiment, this does provide a means of obtaining a sudden, relatively large increase in atomic number. At present (1976) the heaviest elements to be produced in this way are 104 and 105 [rutherfordium or kurchatovium (the name is not agreed yet), and hahnium], the first elements beyond the actinide series, members of Groups IV and V.

The major (i.e. longest-lived) isotopes, and their means of production are summarised in Table 7.1. The decay schemes of these isotopes are shown in Table 7.2.

7.1   Occurrence, synthesis, isolation and uses

Only thorium and uranium occur naturally in appreciable quantities. The principal source of thorium is monazite, the treatment of which was discussed in Chapter 6 (p. 143). Thorium can be extracted from a nitric-acid solution with tributylphosphate as the complex $Th(NO_3)_4(TBP)_2$; if the conditions are carefully controlled, separation from cerium and uranium can be effected. Monazite was originally processed almost entirely for its thorium-content which was used, as the dioxide, in the production of incandescent gas mantles. This application has somewhat declined and thoria is now mainly used as a refractory for special crucibles and, more importantly, in the 'breeder' reactor. The naturally occurring isotope of thorium, $^{232}_{90}Th$, when irradiated with low energy ('thermal') neutrons gives a fissionable isotope of uranium:

$$^{232}_{90}Th(n, \gamma)^{233}_{90}Th \xrightarrow{\beta^-} {}^{233}_{91}Pa \xrightarrow{\beta^-} {}^{233}_{92}U$$

By blanketing the reactor with thoria, and absorbing excess neutrons, more fuel can be generated than is consumed.

Uranium occurs in a variety of oxide ores of which pitchblende (approximately U_3O_8) and carnotite $[K_2(UO_2)_2(VO_4)_2 1\text{-}3H_2O]$ are typical. The ore is concentrated if necessary by sedimentation, being dense, and extracted with either sulphuric acid or sodium carbonate solution. The uranium is then either precipitated, by raising the pH (giving an insoluble uranate) or by reduction (giving a uranium(IV) carbonate), or extracted from the solution using an organic solvent or an ion-exchange resin. Although uranium has been known since 1789, it found little application until the development of the nuclear industry, being used on a small scale as a yellow pigment in glass and ceramics.

Table 7.2 Decay-schemes for actinide isotopes

$^{227}_{89}$Ac, [4n+3]

$^{232}_{90}$Th, [4n+2]

$^{231}_{91}$Pa, [4n+3]

$^{238}_{92}$U, [4n+2]

$^{235}_{92}$U, [4n+3]

$^{237}_{93}$Np, [4n+1]

$^{239}_{94}$Pu $\xrightarrow{\alpha}$ $^{235}_{92}$U, [4n+3]

$^{242}_{94}$Pu $\xrightarrow{\alpha}$ $^{238}_{92}$U, [4n+2]

$^{238}_{94}$Pu $\xrightarrow{\alpha}$ $^{234}_{92}$U, [4n+2]

$^{241}_{94}$Pu $\xrightarrow{\beta^-}$ $^{241}_{95}$Am, [4n+1]

$^{241}_{95}$Am $\xrightarrow{\alpha}$ $^{237}_{93}$Np, [4n+1]

$^{243}_{95}$Am $\xrightarrow{\alpha}$ $^{239}_{93}$Np $\xrightarrow{\beta^-}$ $^{239}_{94}$Pu, [4n+3]

$^{242}_{96}$Cm $\xrightarrow{\alpha}$ $^{238}_{94}$Pu, [4n+2]

$^{244}_{96}$Cm $\xrightarrow{\alpha}$ $^{240}_{94}$Pu $\xrightarrow{\alpha}$ $^{236}_{92}$U $\xrightarrow{\alpha}$ $^{232}_{90}$Th, [4n]

$^{247}_{97}$Bk $\xrightarrow{\alpha}$ $^{243}_{95}$Am, [4n+3]

$^{249}_{97}$Bk $\xrightarrow{\beta^-}$ $^{249}_{98}$Cf, [4n+1]

$^{249}_{98}$Cf $\xrightarrow{\alpha}$ $^{245}_{96}$Cm $\xrightarrow{\alpha}$ $^{241}_{94}$Pu, [4n+1]

$^{252}_{98}$Cf $\xrightarrow{\alpha}$ $^{248}_{96}$Cm $\xrightarrow{\alpha}$ $^{244}_{94}$Pu $\xrightarrow{\alpha}$ $^{240}_{92}$U $\xrightarrow{\beta^-}$ $^{240}_{93}$Np $\xrightarrow{\beta^-}$ $^{240}_{94}$Pu $\xrightarrow{\alpha}$ $^{236}_{92}$U $\xrightarrow{\alpha}$ $^{232}_{90}$Th, [4n]

$^{254}_{99}$Es $\xrightarrow{\alpha}$ $^{250}_{97}$Bk $\xrightarrow{\beta^-}$ $^{250}_{98}$Cf $\xrightarrow{\alpha}$ $^{246}_{96}$Cm $\xrightarrow{\alpha}$ $^{242}_{94}$Pu, [4n+2]

$^{257}_{100}$Fm $\xrightarrow{\alpha}$ $^{253}_{98}$Cf $\xrightarrow{\beta^-}$ $^{253}_{99}$Es $\xrightarrow{\alpha}$ $^{249}_{97}$Bk, [4n+1]

$^{256}_{101}$Md $\xrightarrow{EC}$ $^{256}_{100}$Fm – spontaneous fission

$^{255}_{102}$No $\xrightarrow{\alpha}$ $^{251}_{100}$Fm $\xrightarrow{EC}$ $^{251}_{99}$Es $\xrightarrow{EC}$ $^{251}_{98}$Cf $\xrightarrow{\alpha}$ $^{247}_{94}$Cm $\xrightarrow{\alpha}$ $^{243}_{94}$Pu $\xrightarrow{\beta^-}$ $^{243}_{95}$Am, [4n+3]

$^{256}_{103}$Lr $\xrightarrow{\alpha}$ $^{252}_{101}$Md

$^{259}_{104}$Ku $\xrightarrow{\alpha}$ $^{257}_{102}$No $\xrightarrow{\alpha}$ $^{253}_{100}$Fm $\xrightarrow{EC}$ $^{253}_{99}$Es, [4n+1]

$^{261}_{105}$Ha $\xrightarrow{\alpha}$ $^{257}_{103}$Lr $\xrightarrow{\alpha}$ $^{253}_{101}$Md

Actinium and protactinium occur in small quantities in uranium ores, being formed by the decay of $^{235}_{92}$U (in the [4n+3]-series). The half-lives are such that only about 0.2 mg of actinium and 300 mg of protactinium are in equilibrium with a ton of natural uranium ore. The separation of actinium from uranium ore is also difficult because of the similar solubilities of salts of actinium, lanthanum and the earlier lanthanides ($r_{Ac^{3+}} = 111$ pm, $r_{La^{3+}} = 104$ pm), but can now be achieved by ion exchange. Actinium is also obtained in milligram amounts by neutron-irradiation of $^{226}_{88}Ra$, the actinium being separated by solvent extraction or ion exchange. The isolation of protactinium

$$^{226}_{88}Ra(n, \gamma)^{227}_{88}Ra \xrightarrow{\beta^-} {}^{227}_{89}Ac$$

from uranium residues is also difficult because in its most stable oxidation state ($+5$) it is very prone to hydrolysis giving insoluble polymers. Most of the chemical information now available was derived from a single sample (*ca.* 130 g) obtained from the processing of reactor fuel elements, in which it accumulates as the decay product $^{235}_{92}U$:

$$^{235}_{92}U \xrightarrow{\alpha} {}^{231}_{90}Th \xrightarrow{\beta^-} {}^{231}_{91}Pa$$

Neptunium and plutonium are also derived from fuel element residues, by extraction with nitric acid. The addition of nitrite ion reduces the neptunium to the $+5$ state and plutonium to the

$$^{238}_{92}U(n, \gamma)^{239}_{92}U \xrightarrow{\beta^-} {}^{239}_{93}Np \xrightarrow{\beta^-} {}^{239}_{94}Pu$$

$$^{235}_{92}U(n, \gamma)^{236}_{92}U(n, \gamma)^{237}_{92}U \xrightarrow{\beta^-} {}^{237}_{93}Np(n, \gamma)^{238}_{93}Np \xrightarrow{\beta^-} {}^{238}_{94}Pu$$

$+4$ state, leaving uranium as uranium(VI); the metals can then be separated by solvent extraction (e.g. with tributyl phosphate). Plutonium is reduced to the trivalent state with iron(II) sulphamate, when it passes back into the aqueous layer, and this sequence is repeated if necessary to obtain further purification. The separation of plutonium is carried out on a large scale despite the considerable hazards involved, not the least of which is the extreme toxicity of the element; it becomes incorporated into the bones, where its α-activity can do much damage.

The elements americium, curium, berkelium, californium, einsteinium, and fermium are all obtained by prolonged reactor-irradiation of plutonium ($^{239}_{94}Pu$); the sequence of reactions and decays is shown in Fig. 7.2. As mentioned above, the half-lives of the products decrease rapidly

Fig. 7.2   Synthesis of heavy nuclides by neutron bombardment

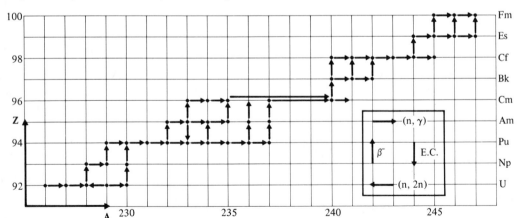

with increasing atomic number (Table 7.1), and for the later elements it is desirable to use high-flux reactors. Separation of the elements from each other and from other elements, particularly the lanthanides which occur as fission products, is best effected by ion exchange methods, two or more stages usually being required.

The remaining elements of the series are obtained by bombardment of one of the earlier actinides with heavy ions in a cyclotron or linear accelerator:

$$^{253}_{99}\text{Es} + ^{4}_{2}\text{He} \rightarrow ^{256}_{101}\text{Md} + ^{1}_{0}\text{n} \quad \text{or} \quad ^{255}_{101}\text{Md} + 2^{1}_{0}\text{n}$$

$$^{241}_{94}\text{Pu} + ^{16}_{8}\text{O} \rightarrow ^{253}_{102}\text{No} + 4^{1}_{0}\text{n}$$

$$^{246}_{96}\text{Cm} + ^{12}_{6}\text{C} \rightarrow ^{254}_{102}\text{No} + 4^{1}_{0}\text{n}$$

$$^{238}_{92}\text{U} + ^{22}_{10}\text{Ne} \rightarrow ^{255}_{102}\text{No} + 5^{1}_{0}\text{n}$$

$$^{252}_{98}\text{Cf} + ^{10}_{5}\text{B} \rightarrow ^{257}_{103}\text{Lr} + 5^{1}_{0}\text{n}$$

$$^{252}_{98}\text{Cf} + ^{11}_{5}\text{B} \rightarrow ^{257}_{103}\text{Lr} + 6^{1}_{0}\text{n}$$

Apart from the nuclear industry and military uses, the actinides are finding increasing application as power sources. All are α-emitters and some (e.g. $^{238}_{94}\text{Pu}$) emit no other radiation and therefore require little shielding. α-Particles have a very short range, being stopped by collision with surrounding atoms, whereupon their kinetic energy appears as heat which can be converted, albeit inefficiently, directly into electrical power with conventional thermopiles. These systems are therefore used where compact, relatively light-weight power sources are required to function undisturbed for long periods, e.g. in satellites and heart 'pace-makers'. The principal isotopes used are $^{238}_{94}\text{Pu}$ ($t_{1/2} = 86 \cdot 4$ y), $^{241}_{95}\text{Am}$ (458 y), $^{242}_{96}\text{Cm}$ (162·5 d) and $^{244}_{96}\text{Cm}$ (17·9 y); the power obtained is, of course, inversely related to the half-life.

7.2   The elemental metals

The most common route to the elemental metals is reduction of an anhydrous fluoride (preferred to the hygroscopic chlorides) with an alkali metal (calcium, barium or magnesium) at a temperature high enough to give the molten metal. If lower temperatures are used, the metal is obtained as a sponge which is highly reactive and difficult to handle. Metallic thorium is usually prepared by calcium-reduction of the oxide (ThO_2). Electrolysis of aqueous solutions cannot be used, as the metals are too electropositive, but fused salts are occasionally employed, e.g. in the refining of scrap plutonium ($PuCl_3$ in a $NaCl/KCl$ melt).

The silvery-white metals are all highly reactive, especially when finely divided, and are often pyrophoric in air. Massive samples oxidise relatively slowly in the atmosphere, but the layer of oxide is usually protective, so that reaction does not proceed very far. Reactivity appears to increase with increasing atomic weight, and elemental plutonium is corroded severely by the atmosphere, so much so that storage of the element is difficult. This is a case where self-heating of the sample is a problem (one gram of plutonium-239 produces about 2 mwatt), so that samples of any size are always appreciably above room temperature. Water (vapour and liquid) reacts with the metals forming mixtures of the oxide and the hydride; the latter is presumably formed from the hydrogen released by oxide-formation.

E.g.
$$3U + 6H_2O \rightarrow 3UO_2 + 6H_2$$
$$4U + 6H_2 \rightarrow 4UH_3$$
$$\overline{7U + 6H_2O \rightarrow 3UO_2 + 4UH_3}$$

The presence of the hydride causes the metal to crumble, further facilitating the reaction. Surprisingly, reaction with most acids is slow or even negligible, except for hydrochloric acid, which attacks all the metals. Presumably, nitric and sulphuric acids give rise to protective oxide layers

Table 7.3   Properties of the elemental actinides.

M	M.P./°C	Crystal structure †	r_M/pm
Ac	1 050	fcc	188
Th	1 750	fcc	179
Pa	1 560	bc tetragonal	163
U	1 132	orthorhombic	156
Np	637	orthorhombic	155
Pu	640	monoclinic	159
Am	994	double hexagonal	173
Cm	1 340	double hexagonal	174
Bk	986	double hexagonal	170
Cf		fcc	

† at room temperature.

(passivation), which can be broken by addition of fluoride ion. None of the metals reacts with alkali unless an oxidant is also present.

The crystal structures of the actinide metals show considerable variety, and all of them except californium are known to crystallise in at least two forms; the extreme example is plutonium which has six different polymorphs, each stable over a considerable temperature range (100–150 °C). Except for the later metals, the structures are not related to those of the lanthanides and this difference also shows up clearly in the metallic radii (Table 7.3). The actinide radii decrease sharply with increasing atomic number and rise again at americium, which is the first element in the series for which a half-filled 5f-shell is likely. In the earlier part of the series it seems that increasing numbers of electrons are involved in the metallic bonding (contrast the lanthanides), and this has been correlated with the range of oxidation states displayed by these metals (see below).

7.3 Halides and oxyhalides

The known halides are listed in Table 7.4. The appearance of some of the gaps in this table reflects the little attention which some of the metals have received, e.g. it is almost certain the trans-einsteinium elements will form trihalides. The pattern of observed oxidation states is very similar to that found for the 4d- and 5d-series; reaction of the elemental metal with halogen gives increasing oxidation states across the series until uranium, followed by a decline to the + 3 state (for fluorides the decline does not begin until americium and only reaches the tetrapositive state; the later metals will probably give trifluorides). Similar patterns are found for the oxyhalides (Table 7.5). A gradual trend from ionic to covalent behaviour with increasing oxidation state is shown both by the structures (decreasing coordination number) and by the chemical and physical properties (decreasing melting and boiling points, increasing susceptibility to hydrolysis).

Only three **dihalides** are known at present, ThI_2, AmI_2 and $CfBr_2$, although it is probable that more could be prepared (especially for mendelevium and nobelium). Of these, AmI_2 and $CfBr_2$ are isomorphous with EuI_2 and $EuBr_2$ and are thus genuinely compounds of the divalent metals, but the thorium compound probably does not contain Th^{2+} ions. The β-form, which is a golden colour, has a very low electrical resistance, suggesting that two electrons are present in a conduction band,

Table 7.4 Actinide halides

formula
colour
coord. no. of M
$\Delta H_f^0/\text{kJ mol}^{-1}$

values in parentheses are estimates

Fluorides

Ac	Th	Pa	U	Np	Pu	Am	Cm	Bk	Cf
			UF$_6$ white 6 −2 188	NpF$_6$ orange 6 (−1 937)	PuF$_6$ brown 6 −1 803				
		PaF$_5$ white 7 (−2 260)	UF$_5$ black 7 −2 059	NpF$_5$ 7 (−1 900)					
	ThF$_4$ white 8 −2 113	PaF$_4$ brown 8 (−1 925)	UF$_4$ green 8 −1 883	NpF$_4$ green 8 (−1 791)	PuF$_4$ brown 8 −1 778	AmF$_4$ tan 8 (−1 674)	CmF$_4$ brown 8	BkF$_4$	CfF$_4$ green
AcF$_3$ white 9 (−1 760)			UF$_3$ black 9 −1 469	NpF$_3$ purple 9 (−1 505)	PuF$_3$ violet 9 −1 552	AmF$_3$ pink 9 (−1 648)	CmF$_3$ white 9	BkF$_3$' yellow 9	CfF$_3$ 8

Chlorides

Ac	Th	Pa	U	Np	Pu	Am	Cm	Bk	Cf	Es
			UCl$_6$ green 6 −1 134							
		PaCl$_5$ yellow 7	UCl$_5$ brown 6 −1 096							
	ThCl$_4$ white 8 −1 192	PaCl$_4$ green-yell. 8 (−1 120)	UCl$_4$ green 8 −1 063	NpCl$_4$ red-brn. 8 −987						
AcCl$_3$ white 9 (−1 090)			UCl$_3$ green 9 −895	NpCl$_3$ green 9 (−904)	PuCl$_3$ green 9 −962	AmCl$_3$ pink 9 −1 046	CmCl$_3$ white 9 (−946)	BkCl$_3$ green 9	CfCl$_3$ green 9	EsCl$_3$

Bromides

Ac	Th	Pa	U	Np	Pu	Am	Cm	Bk	Cf
		PaBr$_5$ red 6	UBr$_5$ 6						
	ThBr$_4$ white 8 −967	PaBr$_4$ brown 8 (−887)	UBr$_4$ brown 8 −799	NpBr$_4$ red 8 −770					
AcBr$_3$ white 9 (−920)			UBr$_3$ red 9 −720	NpBr$_3$ green 9 (−728)	PuBr$_3$ green 8 −787	AmBr$_3$ white 8	CmBr$_3$ white 8	BkBr$_3$ yell.-grn.	CfBr$_3$

continued

Table 7.4 (continued)

Iodides

		PaI$_5$ black							
	ThI$_4$ white 8 −669	PaI$_4$ green (−602)	UI$_4$ black −510						
AcI$_3$ 8 (−707)	ThI$_3$ black· 8	PaI$_3$ black 8	UI$_3$ black 8 −477	NpI$_3$ purple 8 (−502)	PuI$_3$ green 8 (−544)	AmI$_3$ yellow 6 (−611)	CmI$_3$ white 6	BkI$_3$ yellow 6	CfI$_3$ yellow 6

Also known:

	ThI$_2$ golden	Pa$_2$F$_9$ brown 9	U$_2$F$_9$ black 9		Pu$_4$F$_{17}$ red	AmI$_2$			CfBr$_2$ amber
			U$_4$F$_{17}$						

Table 7.5   Actinide oxyhalides

Oxyfluorides

			UO$_2$F$_2$ green 8	NpO$_2$F$_2$ pink 8	PuO$_2$F$_2$ white 8	AmO$_2$F$_2$ brown 8			
		PaO$_2$F white	UO$_2$F	NpO$_2$F green NpOF$_3$ green					
	ThOF$_2$ white 9		UOF$_2$						
AcOF white 8	ThOF 8				PuOF 8				CfOF green 8

Oxychlorides

			UO$_2$Cl$_2$ yellow							
			UO$_2$Cl UOCl$_3$							
	ThOCl$_2$ 9, 8, 7	PaOCl$_2$ 9, 8, 7	UOCl$_2$ 9, 8, 7	NpOCl$_2$ 9, 8, 7						
AcOCl white 8			UOCl 8	NpOCl 8	PuOCl 8	AmOCl 8	CmOCl 8	BkOCl 8	CfOCl 8	EsOCl 8

continued

Table 7.5 (continued)

Oxybromides

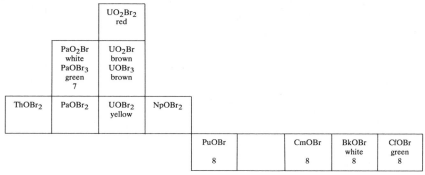

Oxyiodides

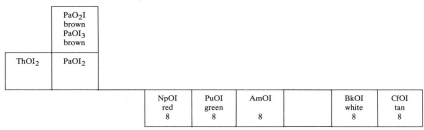

with the lattice composed of Th^{4+} and I^-; the internuclear distances are also shorter than would be expected for Th^{2+}-I^- contacts. This compound (and the tri-iodide, which behaves similarly) is thus comparable to the di–iodides of the early lanthanides.

The structural similarities with the lanthanides are continued in the **trihalides**. The fluorides, except BkF_3, have the LaF_3-structure, involving nine-coordinate metal ions (cf. La to Eu). Berkelium trifluoride has the YF_3-structure, with eight-coordination. Similar changes of coordination number occur in the other trihalides also. Thus the early chlorides (Ac to Cf, La to Gd) and bromides (Ac to Np, La to Pr) have the UCl_3-structure (nine-coordination) while the later members ($CfCl_3$, $PuBr_3$ to $BkBr_3$) show the $PuBr_3$-structure with eight-coordination. In each series, the lower coordination number is found for the smaller ions. The trifluorides are insoluble in water and may readily be precipitated as mono-hydrates. The other trihalides are all hygroscopic and readily soluble in water, from which they crystallise as hexa-hydrates which contain the eight-coordinate cations $[MX_2(H_2O)_6]^+$. They may be dehydrated by heating under vacuum (and can be sublimed at high temperatures), although some oxyhalide is usually formed.

The **tetrahalides** for which X-ray crystallographic studies have been made all have eight-coordinate metal atoms. The fluorides are isostructural with ZrF_4 and HfF_4 and have eight fluoride ions arranged regularly about the metal ion at the corners of a square antiprism. In the chlorides and bromides, the eight halide ions are probably arranged dodecahedrally in two groups of four with different metal-halogen distances (272 and 290 pm in $ThCl_4$), which may represent a compromise situation between ionic bonding (with a high coordination number) and covalent bonding which usually gives a lower coordination. The tetrafluorides (Th, U, Pu) are insoluble in water and can be precipitated as the 2·5-hydrates (Am^{4+} and Cm^{4+} are not stable in aqueous solution). The other tetrahalides are hygroscopic and water-soluble. They are also quite volatile and can be sublimed in vacuum at about 500 °C, although $NpBr_4$ and UI_4 lose halogen at this temperature, forming the corresponding trihalides.

The **pentafluorides** are all polymeric and X-ray powder data suggests seven-coordination for the metal atoms. Protactinium pentachloride has a polymeric chain structure in which each metal atom is linked to three terminal and four bridging chlorine atoms. The pentabromide, and that of uranium (and UCl_5), however, are dimeric, M_2X_{10}, with six-coordinate metal atoms. All are extremely moisture-sensitive and react violently with water giving the hydrated oxides (except uranium, which disproportionates). The uranium fluorides (UF_5, U_2F_9, U_4F_{17}) all disproportionate on heating, to UF_4 and UF_6, and the pentachloride behaves similarly on gentle heating (100 °C); if heated above this temperature however, chlorine is lost giving the tetrachloride (UCl_6 is thermally unstable). Reduction with hydrogen also gives the tetrachlorides.

Of the three **hexafluorides**, UF_6 has been intensely studied because of its importance in the gas-phase centrifugation process for the separation of ^{235}U for use in atomic reactors. Although all three compounds, and UCl_6, are solid at room temperature, they are all readily volatile as expected from their structures which consist of discrete molecules. The thermal stability of these compounds decreases in the order $UF_6 > NpF_6 > PuF_6 \gg UCl_6$, the last losing chlorine above 120 °C to form UCl_4. All four hexahalides are violently hydrolysed by water; under controlled conditions the oxyhalides MO_2X_2 can be obtained.

Relatively little is known about the oxyhalides. As Table 7.5 demonstrates, many expected derivatives are not known; this undoubtedly reflects more a lack of investigation than inherent instability. Thus, many of the oxymonohalides, MOX, have only been obtained accidentally during thermal dehydration of the trihalides. The metal ions in these compounds are eight-coordinate in CaF_2-structures (AcOF, CfOF) or, more commonly, the PbClF-structure, in which the metal ions lie between alternate layers of halide and oxide ions. The oxodihalides, MOX_2, are obtained by heating together stoicheiometric amounts of the tetrahalide and either the metal dioxide or antimony trioxide. On heating in vacuum they disproportionate to Mx_4 and MO_2. The oxodichlorides are isostructural with $PaOCl_2$ which has a crystal built of chains of $Pa_3O_3Cl_6$-units in which the metal atoms have coordination numbers of seven, eight, and nine.

The pentapositive metals show more diversity in the types of oxyhalide formed, although only three metals are involved, protactinium, uranium and neptunium (the latter gives only oxyfluorides). Only for $PaOBr_3$ is the structure known: the metal atom is seven-coordinate, having two terminal bromine atoms with two more and three oxygen atoms bridging to adjacent metal atoms. Little is reported of the chemistry of these compounds, except that most are moisture-sensitive, and all decompose, often by disproportionation, on heating, the temperature required being lower the heavier the halogen.

The oxyhalides of the hexapositive metals are all of the type MO_2X_2 and, apart from the fluorides, are restricted to uranium. Even for this metal, the bromo- and iodo-compounds decompose at room temperature with loss of halogen. The dioxodifluorides, MO_2F_2, have layer structures in which MO_2-units are linked by bridging fluorine atoms forming a puckered hexagon about the metal atom.

7.4 Oxides

The actinide oxide systems are extremely complex owing to the widespread occurrence of non-stoicheiometry. Most of the 'simple' oxides show considerable ranges of composition and there are also many additional intermediate phases. Indeed, the uranium-oxide system is one of the most complex known. The ideal compositions of the known 'simple' oxides are shown in Table 7.6.

Actinium and thorium appear to form only one oxide each, Ac_2O_3 and ThO_2; the latter loses a little oxygen at high temperature or when heated with thorium metal, giving an extreme

Table 7.6 Actinide oxides

Ac	Th	Pa	U	Np	Pu	Am	Cm	Bk	Cf
			UO_3						
			U_3O_8	Np_3O_8					
		Pa_2O_5							
	ThO_2	$Pa\tilde{O}_2$	$U\tilde{O}_2$	$Np\tilde{O}_2$	PuO_2	AmO_2	CmO_2	BkO_2	CfO_2
Ac_2O_3					$\tilde{P}u_2\tilde{O}_3$	$\tilde{A}m_2\tilde{O}_3$	$\tilde{C}m_2\tilde{O}_3$	Bk_2O_3	$\tilde{C}f_2\tilde{O}_3$
	ThO	PaO	UO	NpO	PuO	AmO		BkO	

$\tilde{\ }\ \tilde{\ }$ indicates a region in which ion-stoicheiometric oxides occur. Some of the phases which have been identified are: $PaO_{2, 2\cdot18-2\cdot21,\ 2\cdot33,\ 2\cdot40-2\cdot42,\ 2\cdot42-2\cdot44,\ 2\cdot50}$, $UO_{2-x,2+x}$, U_4O_{9-x}, U_3O_{8-x}, Pu_2O_{3+x}, $PuO_{1\cdot935}$

composition of $ThO_{1\cdot985}$ (at 1 735 °C). Monoxides for all the remaining metals (cubic, NaCl-structure) have been identified only as surface films on the metals and have never been obtained pure; the americium compound is said to have been made by oxidation of the metal with the stoicheiometric amount of oxygen, but it is a metallic material which probably does not contain Am^{2+} ions.

All of the **dioxides** MO_2 have the CaF_2-structure in which each metal ion is surrounded by eight oxide ions at the corners of a cube. For the trans-uranium metals this is the highest oxide formed, but a wide variety of phases of lower oxygen-content (down to $MO_{1\cdot5}$) is known, many of which have cubic structures similar to the fluorite structure but containing anion vacancies (cf. the lanthanide oxides of C–M_2O_3-structure which can take up oxygen, p. 149). In some cases the A–M_2O_3-structure is formed, which appears to be strictly stoicheiometric, presumably because this structure does not lend itself to vacancy-formation. For the earlier metals, protactinium to neptunium, MO_2 appears to be a limiting lower composition limit (a phase UO_{2-x} is stable only above 1200 °C), but further oxidation is possible. In the uranium case this occurs by incorporation of additional oxide ions in the centre of the cubic structure (see Fig. 7.3). If all these sites were

Fig. 7.3 The fluorite structure of MO_2. In oxygen-deficient phases (down to M_2O_3) oxide vacancies occur regularly through the lattice. In oxygen-excess phases, additional oxide ions are incorporated in the interstitial sites (there is an additional interstitial site at the centre of the cube, not shown here) (after R. L. Martin, *J. Chem. Soc. Dalton Trans.*, 1339, (1974))

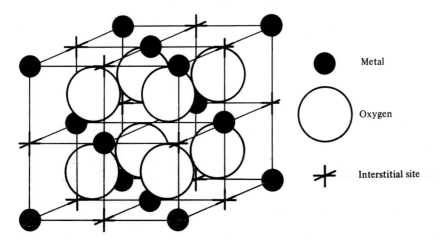

● Metal

○ Oxygen

✛ Interstitial site

occupied the composition would be UO_3, but the actual upper limit appears to be $UO_{2.35}$. Further oxidation results in the appearance of a new phase of limiting composition U_3O_8 (and Np_3O_8) but which may contain less oxygen; under controlled conditions a stoicheiometric material is formed, and this is the most readily obtained uranium oxide. In this phase the metal ions are surrounded by seven oxide ions forming a pentagonal bipyramid. Uranium also forms a **trioxide** which is known to have several crystal modifications the most stable of which (γ-form) contains UO_2-groups joined in chains by four or five bridging oxygen atoms. Uranium trioxide loses oxygen on heating to about 650 °C, forming U_3O_8. Probably the only genuine **pentoxide** of the series is, Pa_2O_5, obtained by heating almost any protactinium compound in air about 650 °C. It appears to be stoicheiometric but can be reduced to PaO_2 with hydrogen at 1 550 °C.

The dioxides are the most important oxides of the actinide elements, being refractory ceramic materials with very high melting points. Thorium dioxide has the highest known melting point of any oxide (3 390 °C), and is used in the manufacture of special crucibles. The uranium and plutonium compounds are used in the manufacture of reactor fuel elements, being chemically inert and well-suited to use in high-temperature reactors. Both are readily soluble in concentrated nitric acid (with the addition of a little fluoride ion for plutonium), which facilitates the processing of 'spent' fuel elements.

The **hydroxides** of the actinides are not well characterised, often being precipitated in gelatinous forms which are difficult to handle. For the early metals (U to Pu), the lower-oxidation state (+3 and +4) hydroxides are also very susceptible to atmospheric oxidation. Protactinium(V) gives, with ammonium hydroxide, what is probably the hydrated oxide, $Pa_2O_5 . xH_2O$, but neptunium(V) and plutonium(V) form $MO_2(OH)$ which almost certainly contain the MO_2^+-unit. All of these materials are basic, dissolving in acids (sometimes with disproportionation, see below) but hardly at all in excess alkali. The hexapositive metals give hydroxides (sometimes formulated as hydrated oxides) of the type $MO_2(OH)_2.xH_2O$, all of which seem to contain MO_2^{2+}-units linked by hydroxo-bridges. These compounds are soluble in acids to form the aquated MO_2^{2+}-cations, but also dissolve in concentrated alkali to form oxo-complexes [e.g. the uranates(VI), probably $UO_2(OH)_4^{2-}$, aq].

7.5 Aqueous solution chemistry

As in the other systems, a variety of oxidation states is known for many of the actinides in aqueous solution (Table 7.7). All except thorium give the +3 state and for californium onwards this is the highest state attainable. This state and the +4 state (Th to Pu, Bk) occur, in acid solution, as the aquated ions M^{3+} and M^{4+}; the coordination numbers are unknown but are almost certainly greater than six, probably nine and eight by analogy with solid compounds. Higher oxidation states occur (in acid solution) as aquated oxo–cations, MO_2^+ and MO_2^{2+}; again, the hydration numbers are

Table 7.7 Species obtainable in aqueous solution

				†NpO_5^{3-}	†PuO_5^{3-}								
			UO_2^{2+}	NpO_2^{2+}	PuO_2^{2+}	AmO_2^{2+}							
		$PaO(OH)_2^+$	UO_2^+	NpO_2^+	PuO_2^+	AmO_2^+							
	Th^{4+}	Pa^{4+}	U^{4+}	Np^{4+}	Pu^{4+}		Bk^{4+}						
Ac^{3+}			U^{3+}	Np^{3+}	Pu^{3+}	Am^{3+}	Cm^{3+}	Bk^{3+}	Cf^{3+}	Es^{3+}	Fm^{3+} Md^{3+} No^{3+} Lr^{3+}		
											Md^{2+} No^{2+}		

† only in alkali.

Most stable states are in bold type.

not known but probably four to six water molecules are coordinated. Neptunium and plutonium are able, in strongly alkaline solution, to undergo oxidation to the $+7$ state, forming the MO_5^{3-} ions.

Oxidation state diagrams constructed from redox potential data are given in Fig. 7.4. However, these are only a rough guide to the relative stabilities of the various oxidation states. For a variety of

Fig. 7.4   Oxidation-state diagrams for actinides in aqueous solution

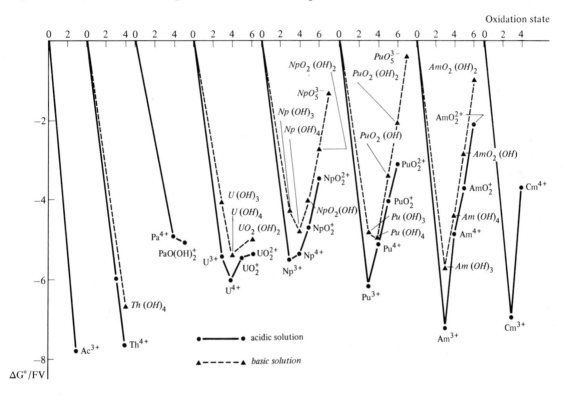

reasons the solution chemistry, particularly of the elements protactinium to americium, is very complicated and is not easy to investigate. Firstly, the oxidation potentials are frequently quite similar, so that various oxidation states can co-exist in appreciable concentrations. For example, for plutonium the following equilibria are important:

$$2PuO_2^+ + 4H^+ \rightleftharpoons PuO_2^{2+} + Pu^{4+} + 2H_2O$$
$$3Pu^{4+} + 2H_2O \rightleftharpoons PuO_2^{2+} + 2Pu^{3+} + 4H^+$$

$$Pu^{4+} + PuO_2^+ \rightleftharpoons Pu^{3+} + PuO_2^{2+}$$

For the final equilibrium the value of the equilibrium constant $[PuO_2^{2+}][Pu^{3+}]/[PuO_2^+][Pu^{4+}]$ is $10 \cdot 7$ (at $25\,^\circ C$, in $0 \cdot 1M$ $HClO_4$), so that all these species will be present simultaneously. Secondly, it is not easy to establish the species which do exist, since all the ions are very susceptible to hydrolysis, forming hydroxo-complexes or polymeric species (see below). This seriously limits the pH-range over which any one species can be studied and, again complex equilibria may be set up. The extent of hydrolysis varies roughly with the overall charge on the ion, $M^{4+} > MO_2^{2+} \geqslant M^{3+} > MO_2^+$ (note that the oxo-ions behave as if the charge on the metal is somewhat higher than the formal charge of the cation would suggest), that is the higher oxidation states (as MO_2-units) are often less hydrolysed than some of the lower ones. There is also an ion-size effect, hydrolysis decreasing in the series $Am > Pu > Np > U$. Coupled with the formation of polymeric species, this results in marked pH-dependence of the relative stabilities of the various oxidation states. Finally, complex-formation is very prevalent, even with common anions such as fluoride, sulphate or carboxylate ions. The stabilities of the complexes do not change regularly with increasing oxidation state, so that the relative stabilities of the oxidation states are quite heavily dependent on the nature and concentration of any complexing agent which may be present. For instance, uranium(V) as UO_2^+ is unstable to disproportionation but is considerably stabilised by fluoride ion which gives UF_6^-.

Despite these gloomy prognostications, reasonably general descriptions of the chemistry of these elements can be given, and these are summarised in Table 7.8. Classification by oxidation states is given below.

The **dipositive state** is known only for mendelevium and nobelium, and only for the latter is it the most stable state. Nobelium is the analogue of the lanthanide ytterbium, and No^{2+} presumably has a $5f^{14}$ configuration.

The **tripositive state** is exhibited by all the elements except thorium and protactinium, for which this state is presumably unstable to disproportionation. For actinium, californium to fermium, and lawrencium it is the only state found in aqueous solution. For the other metals the $+3$ state becomes more stable with increasing atomic number, e.g. U^{3+} is oxidised by water while Am^{3+} is the most stable state of that element and is quite difficult to oxidise. The ions exist as simple aquated (possibly nine-coordinate) cations, not readily hydrolysed. Addition of a strong base, such as ammonium hydroxide, precipitates the trihydroxides, which can be obtained crystalline under suitable conditions.

The **tetrapositive state** is the only one found for thorium, but occurs also for protactinium to plutonium for which it is reasonably stable, being susceptible to oxidation with decreasing ease along the series. Plutonium(IV) disproportionates except at high acidities, but exists in equilibrium with the other states of this metal. Americium(IV) disproportionates at all acidities and curium(IV) would oxidise water; both these states are known in aqueous solution only in the presence of a large excess of fluoride ions, when they form the complex anions MF_6^{2-}.

As would be expected from their charge, the M^{4+} ions (probably eight-coordinate) are the most readily hydrolysed, and function as strong acids, with pKs of $1 \cdot 5 - 1 \cdot 7$. The hydrolysis of thorium(IV) has been the most studied, since it is readily available and there are no complications from other oxidation states, and a large number of deprotonated and polymeric species have been identified. For other elements there is not sufficient data for the species to be fully characterised. At pH greater than 3, thorium-containing species with up to ten thorium atoms have been identified, but the most stable are $Th(OH)^{3+}$, $Th(OH)_2^{2+}$, $Th_2(OH)_2^{6+}$, $Th_4(OH)_8^{8+}$, and $Th_6(OH)_{15}^{9+}$; all of these are, of course, aquated. The dimeric species occurs over a wide pH-range and probably has a doubledehydroxo-bridge between the metal atoms similar to that found in the solid basic nitrate $Th_2(OH)_2(NO_3)_6 \cdot 8H_2O$, since the Th–Th distances are similar.

The other polymers presumably also have hydroxo- or oxo-bridges but nothing is known of their structures. Plutonium(IV) also polymerises extensively, forming some very stable species which do not readily break down again even at acidities which would inhibit their formation. This, together

Table 7.8   Aqueous chemistry of the actinide elements

Ion	Colour	Stability	Preparation
Ac^{3+}	colourless	Stable.	
Th^{4+}	colourless	Stable.	
Pa^{4+}	colourless	Stable in H_2O. Rapid air-oxidation to PaO_2^+.	$PaO_2^+/(Zn/Hg, Cr^{2+}$, or $Ti^{3+}/HCl)$
PaO_2^+	colourless	Stable. Difficult to reduce.	
U^{3+}	red	Oxidised slowly by H_2O, rapidly by air, to U^{4+}.	$UO_2^{2+}/$(electrolysis or Zn/Hg)
U^{4+}	green	Stable in H_2O. Slow air-oxidation to UO_2^{2+}.	U^{3+}/air; $UO_2^{2+}/$(electrolysis or Zn/Hg)
UO_2^+	?	Rapid disprop. to $U^{4+}+UO_2^{2+}$. Least unstable at pH 2.5	$UO_2^{2+}/$(electrolysis or Zn/Hg)
UO_2^{2+}	yellow	Stable. Difficult to reduce.	
Np^{3+}	purple	Stable in H_2O. Rapid air-oxidation to Np^{4+}.	$NpO_2^+/$(electrolysis or H_2/Pt)
Np^{4+}	yellow-green	Stable in H_2O. Slow air oxidation to NpO_2^+.	Np^{3+}/air; $NpO_2^+/(SO_2, Fe^{2+}$ or $I^-)$
NpO_2^+	green	Stable. Disprop. only in strong acid.	$(Np^{3+}$ or $Np^{4+})/(Cl_2$ or $HNO_3)$; $NpO_2^+/(H_2O_2$, Sn^{2+} or $SO_2)$
NpO_2^{2+}	pink	Stable. Readily reduced.	any lower state with $MnO_4^-, Ce^{4+}, Ag^{2+}$
NpO_5^{3-}	green	Stable only in alkali. Reduced by neutral H_2O.	$NpO_2^+/(O_3, S_2O_8^{2-}, ClO^-$, or $BrO_3^-)$ in alkali
Pu^{3+}	violet	Stable to H_2O and air. Oxidised by autoradiol.	any higher state with SO_2 or Zn
Pu^{4+}	tan	Stable in 6M acid. Disprop. in wk. acid to $Pu^{3+}+PuO_2^{2+}$.	$Pu^{3+}/(Ce^{4+}$ or $MnO_4^-)$ in acid; $PuO_2^{2+}/(Fe^{2+}, SO_2, I^-$ or $NO_2^-)$ in acid
PuO_2^+	purple?	Disprop. to $Pu^{4+}+PuO_2^{2+}$. Least unstable at low acidity.	$PuO_2^{2+}/(SO_2, I^-$ or $NH_2OH)$, pH 2
PuO_2^{2+}	orange	Stable. Readily reduces (slowly by autoradiol).	any lower state with MnO_4^-, Ag^{2+}, etc.
PuO_5^{3-}	green	Stable only in alkali. Reduced by neutral H_2O	$PuO_2^{2+}/(O_3, S_2O_8^{2-}$ or $ClO^-)$ in alkali
Am^{3+}	pink	Stable. Difficult to oxidise.	
Am^{4+}	red	Disprop. to $Am^{3+}+AmO_2^+$. Known only as AmF_6^{2-}.	$Am(OH)_4+15M\ NH_4F$
AmO_2^+	yellow	Disprop. in str. acid to $Am^{3+}+AmO_2^{2+}$. Reduced by autoradiol.	$Am^{3+}/(S_2O_8^{2-}$ or $ClO^-)$
AmO_2^{2+}	red	Stable. Reduced by autoradiol.	any lower state with MnO_4^-, Ce^{4+}, etc.
Cm^{3+}	colourless	Stable. Not oxidised chemically.	
Cm^{4+}	yellow	Known only as CmF_6^{2-}. Reduced by H_2O.	$CmF_4+15M\ CsF$
Bk^{3+}		Stable.	
Bk^{4+}		Stable to H_2O. Readily reduced.	$Bk^{3+}/(Cr_2O_7^{2-}$ or $BrO_3^-)$
Cf^{3+}		Stable.	
Es^{3+}		Stable.	
Fm^{3+}		Stable.	
Md^{2+}		Stable in H_2O. Readily oxidised.	$Md^{3+}/(Zn/Hg)$
Md^{3+}		Stable.	
No^{2+}		Stable.	
No^{3+}		Stable in H_2O. Readily reduced.	
Lw^{3+}		Stable.	

with the equilibrium with the other oxidation states, severely complicates the processing of plutonium solutions.

The tetrahydroxides, which precipitate readily, are often gelatinous and contain varying amounts of water; it is not known whether they are genuine hydroxides or hydrated oxides.

The **pentapositive state** is the principal oxidation state of protactinium, for which it is also the highest state attainable. For uranium, plutonium and americium, this state is unstable to disproportionation, but becomes easier to study along that series. Thus, UO_2^+ occurs only as a short-lived species except in the pH-range 2–4 when it is kinetically relatively stable, i.e. the disproportionation reaction if thermodynamically favoured but occurs only slowly. Reactions in which atoms are transferred are usually slower than those involving only electron-exchange. The interconversion of MO_2^+ and M^{4+} is therefore generally slower than those between M^{4+} and M^{3+} and MO_2^+ and MO_2^{2+}. Uranium(V) is considerably stabilised by complexation, e.g. by F^- which gives UF_6^-. Plutonium(V) is known only in equilibrium with other oxidation states; this means, for instance, that the colour of the PuO_2^+ ion has never been observed but had to be deduced from a study of the visible absorption spectra of the equilibrium mixtures. This ion and AmO_2^+ become more stable as the acidity is decreased. In marked contrast, NpO_2^+ is stable to disproportionation and is the major species normally present in aqueous solutions of this element. It becomes less stable with increasing pH.

The marked pH- (and ligand-) dependence of the stability of the MO_2^+ ions is primarily due to the lower charge of this ion than those of the neighbouring ions M^{4+} and MO_2^{2+}; these latter ions are therefore much the more prone to hydrolysis and complexation, so that the relative stabilities of the three oxidation states can change markedly with change of conditions. The equilibria concerned are more complex for plutonium and americium because the +3 state is also involved. Presumably, this accounts for the difference in pH-dependence between these metals and neptunium. The MO_2^+ ions are weakly hydrolysed, functioning as acids of pK 9–10, and protactinium(V) probably exists mainly as $PaO(OH)_2^+$ or $PaO(OH)^{2+}$ even in acid solution. Appreciable hydrolysis occurs only at a pH greater than 8. Addition of ammonium hydroxide to solutions of NpO_2^+ or PuO_2^+ precipitates the oxo-hydroxides $MO_2(OH)$ which are soluble in acids and insoluble in alkali. In strong acid, the MO_2-unit does not apppear to be protonated except possibly for plutonium which gives $PuO(OH)^{2+}$.

The **hexapositive state** is the most important state for uranium, requiring quite vigorous reducing agents. It is also known for neptunium, plutonium and americium, which are considerably easier to reduce, especially the last. With the isotopes of relatively short half-life ($^{238}_{94}Pu$, 86·4 y; $^{241}_{95}Am$, 458 y), α-emission is sufficiently intense for the heat (0·5 and 0·1 watts g^{-1} respectively) and radiolysis products from water ($H^•$, $OH^•$, and H_2O_2) to give slow spontaneous reduction.

The ions MO_2^{2+} aq (and MO_2^+ aq) are unusual in that they contain both M=O and M–OH$_2$ groups but not M–OH. Even in strong acids the oxo–ligand is not protonated and for these ions this ligand cannot be replaced by, e.g. fluoride (contrast MO_2^+). Loss of protons from the coordinated water molecules begins at about pH 3, so that the ions are moderately strong acids. Hydrolysis leads to polymerisation, in which MO_2-units (at least for M = U) are linked by hydroxo bridges. With anions other than perchlorate, complexes are formed and these systems are very complicated. In perchlorate solutions the major species appear to be UO_2^{2+}, $(UO_2)_2(OH)_2^{2+}$ and $(UO_2)_3(OH)_5^+$ while in chloride solutions $(UO_2)_3(OH)_4^{2+}$ is formed (the latter presumably incorporates some Cl^- also).

The **heptapositive state** can be obtained by vigorous oxidation of strongly alkaline solutions of neptunium(VI) or plutonium(VI), yielding the dark green MO_5^{3-} ions, probably more realistically formulated as $MO_2(OH)_6^{3-}$ or $MO_4(OH)_2^{3-}$. Both are strong oxidants, becoming more so as the alkalinity is reduced; in weakly alkaline and acid solution, water is oxidised.

7.6 Conclusion

Although there is much still to be learnt even of the simple binary compounds of the actinide elements, it is quite clear that their chemistry is considerably more complicated than that of the lanthanides. The general behaviour is much more like that of the *d*-block elements. Thus, a wide range of oxidation states is shown by the early members and only in the latter half of the series does a constant, relatively low (+3) oxidation state appear. At the beginning of the series it is relatively easy to remove (formally) all the valence electrons and, at least up to uranium(VI), the resulting oxidation state is the preferred one. Similarly, the higher oxidation states become less stable, and the lower more stable, with increasing atomic number (Fig. 7.5). Indeed, it was this behaviour which caused early doubts as to whether there really was an actinide or 5f-series. There are several analogies between the early actinide elements and the heavier d-block elements with the same number of outer electrons, especially in their maximum oxidation states, e.g. protactinium(V) resembles tantalum(V) and thorium(IV) is very similar to hafnium(IV). When neptunium and plutonium were discovered (1940) it was found that they resembled uranium much more closely than rhenium and osmium, and the isolation of americium and curium confirmed Seaborg's (1944) proposal that these elements formed the beginning of a 5f-series based on actinium.

Fig. 7.5   An alternative representation of the oxidation-state diagram. Note that for uranium onwards, all oxidation states other than +3 become progressively less stable as the atomic number increases

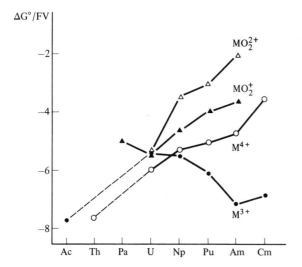

Presumably, the similarities between the 5f-elements and the d-block metals stem from similar trends in ionisation and promotion energies (cf. Ch. 3 and 5). Unfortunately, data are not available for the actinide elements, and even the electron configurations of some of the neutral atoms are still in doubt (Table 7.9). Nothing is known of the configurations of the ions nor of the ionisation energies. It is probable, however, that at least at the beginning of the series the 6d- and 5f-electrons have similar binding energies, as is suggested by the presence of both types of electron in the neutral atoms. The ionisation energies of these electrons would be expected to be less than for 5d- and 4f-electrons (this is the general trend with increasing principal quantum number), although removal of 7s-electrons (which penetrate the core) may well be harder than for 6s- or 5s-electrons. The relative constancy of oxidation state in the lanthanide series was seen (Ch. 6) to result from a fortuitous balancing of ionisation and atomisation energies, coupled with relatively high fourth ionisation energies. Such a balancing is unlikely at the beginning of the actinide series, and all the ionisation energies (beyond the second) will probably be lower than for the lanthanides. Presumably, these differences are sufficiently great to offset the larger sizes of the atoms and ions and consequent loss of lattice energy. The 5f-orbitals are also larger and extend further, relative to the 6s- and 6p-orbitals, than the 4f-orbitals relative to 5s and 5p; the 5f-orbitals are thus much more likely to be involved in the bonding, and there is some evidence for this.

Table 7.9   Electron configurations and ionic radii.

		Configuration			$r_{M^{3+}}$/pm	$r_{M^{4+}}$/pm
		5f	6d	7s		
Ac		0	1	2	111	
Th		0	2	2	—	99
Pa		2	1	2	—	96
	or	1	2	2		
U		3	1	2	103	93
Np		4	1	2	101	92
	or	5	0	2		
Pu		6	0	2	100	90
Am		7	0	2	99	89
Cm		7	1	2	98·5	88
Bk		9	0	2	98	
	or	8	1	2		
Cf		10	0	2	97·7	
Es		11	0	2		
Fm		12	0	2		
Md		13	0	2		
No		14	0	2		
Lw		14	1	2		

Just as in the other transition series, the increasing effective nuclear charge along the series, reflected in the decreasing ionic radii (Table 7.9), will lead to increases in the ionisation energies and destabilisation of the higher oxidation states, so that beyond americium the +3 state is the norm. In this part of the series some analogies with the lanthanides are seen, e.g. the two exceptions to the +3 state are Bk^{4+} and No^{2+} which have (presumably) $5f^7$ and $5f^{14}$ configurations and are the analogues of Tb^{4+} and Yb^{2+}. However, americium(II), analogous to europium(II), is not formed under normal chemical conditions; it has been observed as an unstable species trapped in a dilute CaF_2 matrix.

For oxidation states up to +4 the metals occur as simple ions, M^{2+}, M^{3+}, M^{4+}, or complexes containing these ions. As might be expected from the large radii and consequent low polarising power of these ions, large coordination numbers, particularly eight and nine, are common. In most series of comparable compounds, the coordinate number decreases with increasing oxidation state. In no other series of elements does it appear possible to obtain a simple aquated M^{4+} ion in solution (except for Ce^{4+}), again showing the relatively low polarising power of the large cation. With other elements, either polymeric, hydrolysed species are obtained, even at high acidities, or cationic oxo–complexes are formed.

With the actinides, oxo–cations appear for the higher oxidation states, for which the common form is the actinyl ion, $MO_2^{n+}(n = 1, 2)$. These ions occur in aqueous solution and in many compounds, including the oxides and oxyhalides discussed above. In all cases there is a linear O–M–O arrangement in which the M–O distance (160–200 pm) indicates multiple bonding. The bonding is evidently very strong, especially in the MO_2^{2+} ions, since the oxo ligands cannot be displaced and are not protonated even in strong acid, although the MO_2^+ ions are less stable in both respects. In principle, enough orbitals are available for each oxygen atom to form one sigma- and two pi-bonds with the metal atom [$2p_\sigma$(a $2s$-$2p$ hybrid), $2p_x$ and $2p_y$ on oxygen, and $7s$, $6d_{z^2}$, $6d_{xz}$, $6d_{yz}$, $5f_{x(x^2-y^2)}$, and $5f_{y(3y^2-x^2)}$ on the metal], accommodating twelve electrons of an O≡M≡O system. [Note that this does not necessarily mean that the bonds are actually triple bonds, but merely that the orbitals are available; the extent of interaction between them is unknown. It is probable that electron density is polarised towards the oxygen atoms, but the shortest bond lengths seem to correspond to bonds of order greater than two.] The stability of this system will depend on the relative energies of the various orbitals (and the associated promotion energies) and the degree to which they overlap. With increasing atomic number, the metal orbitals will become more compact (probably increasing the overlap with the oxygen orbitals), and lower in energy, and increasing oxidation state has a similar effect. The best situation is clearly that in UO_2^{2+}; presumably the overlaps and energies are less favourable in PaO_2^+ which is readily protonated, $Pa{=}O \rightarrow Pa{-}O{-}H$. For the other species of this type, there is an additional complication in that the metal ion has 'non-bonding' electrons which must be accommodated in $6d$- or, more probably, $5f$-orbitals of higher energy than the bonding orbitals of the OMO system (one electron for UO_2^+ and NpO_2^{2+}, two for NpO_2^+ and PuO_2^{2+}, etc.). By analogy with the d-block, these electrons are probably in weakly anti-bonding orbitals resulting from interaction of the metal atom with the other (equatorial) ligands.

Bibliography

BENT, Vol. 5; **CW**, 28; **ES**, 23; **HJ**, 31; **MM**, 11; **PW**, 22.

K. W. Bagnall, *The Actinide Elements*, Elsevier, 1972. Good, simply written survey.

J. J. Katz and G. T. Seaborg, *The Chemistry of the Actinide Elements*, Methuen, 1957. Comprehensive coverage, useful for reference.

G. T. Seaborg, *Man-Made Transuranium Elements*, Prentice-Hall, 1963, Fascinating, readable account of the production and properties of the heaviest elements.

D. Brown, *Halides of the Lanthanides and Actinides*, Wiley, 1968. Comprehensive survey of preparation, structures and properties.

L. B. Asprey and B. B. Cunningham, *Prog. Inorg. Chem.*, **2**, 267 (1960). Review of unusual oxidation states of the actinides and lanthanides.

J. J. Katz and I. Sheft, *Adv. Inorg. Chem. Radiochem.*, **2**, 195 (1961). Review of actinide halides, including description of techniques needed for handling small quantities of highly radioactive materials.

D. Brown, *Adv. Inorg. Chem. Radiochem.*, **12**, 1 (1970). Chemistry of protactinium.

L. E. J. Roberts, *Quart. Rev.*, **15**, 442 (1961). Review of actinide oxides.

J. G. Cuninghame, *Chemical Aspects of the Nucleus, Royal Institute of Chemistry Monographs for Teachers, No. 23*, The Chemical Society, 1972. A good introductory text. See also **HR**, 2–3 and **PW**, 35.

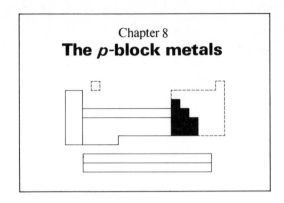

Chapter 8
The p-block metals

In the p-block, for the first time, there are elements which cannot unequivocally be classed as metals. In fact, this block contains all the non-metals, as well as the rare gases. It is therefore necessary to define more closely what is meant by a metal. A satisfactory chemical definition (as opposed to one based on physical properties such as electrical conductivity or lustre) is that a metal is an element which, in aqueous solution, displays cationic behaviour or which has an oxide which is soluble in acids. As will be seen, these are not necessarily identical criteria. On this basis, the elements shown in Fig. 8.1 will be treated as metals, although those on the boundary are probably better classed as metalloids.

		Non-metals		
B	C	N	O	F
Al	Si	P	S	Cl
Ga	Ge	As	Se	Br
In	Sn	Sb	Te	I
Tl	Pb	Bi	Po	At

Metals

Fig. 8.1 Division of the p-block into metals and non-metals

The chemistry of these elements is reasonably simple as far as the types of compound formed is concerned, as each shows at most two oxidation states. However, it is often no longer possible to describe the compounds in terms of the ionic model, and considerable covalency will be found, i.e. the compounds are molecular or polymeric with discrete, directional bonds between adjacent atoms. The appearance of covalency is hardly surprising since these elements occupy a central position in the Periodic Table, between the cationic s-block metals and the anionic chalcogens and halogens.

8.1 Occurrence, isolation, and uses

The p-block metals differ enormously in their abundances, ease of winning, price and utility. The majority are more widely useful as the elemental metals, or as alloys with each other, than as compounds. (cf. Tables 8.1 and 8 2).

Table 8.1

Element	Abundance (%)	Principal Ore	Location	Major Products
Al	8	Bauxite, $Al_2O_3.xH_2O$	Jamaica Australia Africa	Al Al_2O_3, $Al_2(SO_4)_3$
Ga	10^{-3}	Bauxite Coal, Zn-smelter flue-dust	Jamaica Australia Africa	GaAs
In	10^{-5}	Flue-dusts Zn, Pb residues		Alloys
Tl	10^{-5}	Flue-dusts Cu, Pb, Ag residues		
Ge	7×10^{-4}	Flue-dusts		Semiconductor alloys
Sn	4×10^{-3}	Cassiterite, SnO_2	Malaysia Bolivia Thailand China	Sn, alloys SnO_2, $SnCl_4$
Pb	2×10^{-4}	Galena, PbS	USA Australia USSR Canada Mexico	Pb, alloys PbO, Pb_3O_4 $(C_2H_5)_4Pb$
Sb	5×10^{-5}	Stibnite, Sb_2S_3	USA Mexico Bolivia China S. Africa	Alloys Sb_2O_3
Bi	10^{-5}	Pb, Cu, Sn residues Bismuthinite, Bi_2S_3		Alloys Bi_2O_3

Aluminium is the most abundant metal in the earth's crust, and occurs in large deposits of the hydrated oxide, formed by prolonged weathering of other minerals. The elemental metal has proved to be extremely useful, being light, strong (especially when alloyed), a good conductor of heat and electricity, and resistant to corrosion. This last property results from the formation of a tough, tightly adherent layer of the oxide, which is self-healing. When a fresh surface of aluminium is exposed (e.g. by scratching), the oxide film reforms very rapidly. Thus aluminium does not exhibit its true reactivity (which is high) unless the oxide film is removed or prevented from reforming, e.g. by amalgamation or by the presence of chloride ion. Aluminium bench tops pitted by mercury spills are a common sight in laboratories, and chloride-corrosion of aluminium is a familiar phenomenon to many motorists.

The native ore, bauxite,† contains many impurities, particularly silica and iron oxides, and purification is necessary before reduction. Fortunately, aluminium oxide is amphoteric and will dissolve in alkali. The ore is therefore treated with hot, concentrated caustic soda solution which dissolves the alumina but not the impurities. After settling and filtering, the solution is cooled and seeded with $Al_2O_3.3H_2O$ to obtain a precipitate of the finely divided trihydrate (without the seed the oxide would be gelatinous and difficult to handle). Only about half the aluminium precipitates, so the liquor is recycled.

---

† This is a generic term for the hydrated oxide. Specific minerals are gibbsite and hydrargillite ($Al_2O_3.3H_2O$), and boehmite and diaspore ($Al_2O_3.H_2O$).

The reduction of alumina with carbon is not practicable, since temperatures in excess of 2 000 °C would be needed, and electrolysis is preferred. Although alumina melts at over 2 000 °C, its solution in cryolite (Na_3AlF_6, made from Al_2O_3 and HF or H_2SiF_6) melts at about 1 000 °C and this temperature can be lowered further by the addition of calcium fluoride. Graphite-lined steel tanks are used as the cathodes with graphite anodes, at about 950 °C. Molten aluminium sinks to the bottom of the melt and is drawn off. The power requirement is large, some 10–15 kWh of electricity being required for each kilo of aluminium (1–1·5 MJ mol^{-1}). To be economic, therefore, cheap electricity is essential and most smelters are associated with hydro-electric schemes (Canada, USA, USSR, Norway, Switzerland, Africa). Some smelters are now being built on coalfields or near nuclear power stations (e.g. Lynemouth, Anglesey, and Invergordon, in the UK).

The major uses of aluminium depend on its low density, corrosion resistance and strength (see Table 8.2). The addition of small amounts of other metals (chiefly copper, iron and manganese) and silicon improve the strength considerably, and such alloys are used extensively in aircraft and ship

Table 8.2   Uses of the elemental metals and their compounds

	Metal	**Compounds**

Al	Domestic utensils
	Chemical equipment
	Electric cables
	Aircraft/ship construction
	Containers (e.g. beer cans)
		Al_2O_3 – pigments, fillers,
		  ceramics, abrasives
		$Al_2(SO_4)_3$ – water treatment
		  (coagulant)
		$NaAl(SO_4)_2 \cdot 12H_2O$ –
		  fire extinguishers,
		  baking soda
		$AlCl_3$, $Al(C_2H_5)_3$ –
		  polymerisation catalysts

Sn	Tin plate
	Alloys, bronzes
	  (see Table 8-3)
	Float-glass medium
		SnO_2 – enamels, glasses
		$SnCl_2$, $SnSO_4$ –
		tin-plating baths
		$K_3Sn(OH)_3$, SnF_2–
		  toothpaste
		Organotins – plastics
		  stabilisers, biocides

Pb	Alloys (see Table 8-3) Pipes, sheet Electric storage batteries	PbO_2 – battery plates, other Pb compounds $PbCO_3$ – white lead pigment $Pb(C_2H_5)_4$ – antiknock agent
Sb	Alloys (see Table 8-3)	Sb_2O_3 – enamels, fire-retardants

construction. As mentioned above, the corrosion resistance is due to a layer of oxide, which is normally only a few millionths of a millimetre thick (10^{-6} to 10^{-4} mm). The layer can be thickened by making the aluminium the anode in the electrolysis of sulphuric acid ('anodising'). When first formed, the extra coating is porous and will take up dyes and pigments; the layer is then sealed by heating in the bath or in water to 100 °C. A strong, decorative finish is thus achieved, usually about 0·01 mm thick. Since the oxide layer is a non-conductor of electricity, this treatment is applied to aluminium wires which are subsequently woven into cables with a conductivity, weight for weight, about twice that of copper.

In marked contrast, the other metals of Group III occur in only minute quantities and have rather specialised uses. The major commercial source of gallium is the alkaline liquor of the aluminia purification process (bauxite contains $0.003 - 0.01\%$ of gallium oxide). As the liquor is recycled, the gallium concentration increases and, after about twenty cycles, gallium oxide, Ga_2O_3, is precipitated by treating the solution with carbon dioxide (weak acid); aluminium remains in solution. Gallium metal is obtained (like sodium) by electrolysis with a mercury cathode. Its major use is in semiconductors (e.g. as GaAs, GaSb). Indium is also a useful semiconductor material but finds numerous other applications as a coating on or additive to other alloys, to improve corrosion- or wear-resistance or hardness. It is obtained primarily from zinc residues and smelter slags, by roasting, dissolution in sulphuric acid and electrolysis. Thallium is obtained similarly, but finds little commercial application.

Apart from germanium, the remaining metals of the p-block are most often used as alloys with each other. Some familiar examples are given in Table 8.3. The most desirable features are low melting point, easy working and, in the case of the type metals, expansion on freezing. Appreciable quantities of tin are used in plating onto other metals to provide a corrosion-free surface; only a small thickness is required. Molten tin is also used in the float glass process which revolutionised the manufacture of sheet glass, as it has a convenient melting point (232 °C), does not react appreciably with molten glass, and the small quantities of tin which do dissolve have no deleterious effects on the glass.

Table 8.3   Constitution and uses of p-block alloys (percent by weight)

	Sn	Pb	Sb	Bi	Other
Plumber's solder	33	67			
White solder	5	75	19		1, Cu
Aluminium solder		92			8, Cd
Soft solder	50			50	
Type metal	10	70	18		2, Cu
Pewter	85		2	6	7, Cu
Phosphor bronze	10		9·5		79.7, Cu; 0·8, P
Battery plate		94	6		

Since these metals all occur together, and small amounts of the others have marked effects on the properties of any one, careful refining is necessary, especially for tin and lead. Significant quantities of arsenic and antimony, as well as silver, gold and zinc, are recovered as by-products. Tin, lead, and antimony ores are roasted (oxidised) and then reduced in reverbatory or blast furnaces. Bismuth is obtained from the anode sludge of electrolytic copper-refining baths or from the flue-dust of tin or copper smelters, as well as from its own sulphide ore.

Germanium has achieved considerable glamour and importance with the advance of the semiconductor industry. Its principal source is the flue-dust of coal-burning gas works or zinc smelters, from which it is obtained by reduction to the volatile metal (volatilises with zinc), oxidation to GeO_2 and treatment with concentrated hydrochloric acid. This gives the molecular chloride, $GeCl_4$, which can be distilled out and hydrolysed to give pure GeO_2 which is reduced, usually with hydrogen.

8.2   The elemental metals

A tendency to the formation of covalent bonds is found even in the elemental metals, as evinced by the occurrence of low coordination numbers and directional bonds. As might be expected, this tendency becomes more pronounced from Group III to Group V (cf. Table 8.4). Thus, the Group III metals (except gallium) have recognisable metallic lattices, although slight distortions from the ideal arrangements are found. Gallium has a unique structure in which the gallium atoms form pairs (molecule-like). This metal also has an exceptionally low melting point and it is thought that the atom-pairs may persist in the liquid phase.

Table 8.4   Melting points and structures of the elemental metals

	M.P.	Structure	Internuclear distances
	°C		pm
Al	660	fcc	286(12)
Ga	30	Unique	244(1), 270(2), 273(2), 279(2)
In	156	Tetragonal ('fcc')	324(4), 336(8)
Tl	449	hcp	340(12)
Ge	937	Diamond	244(4)
Sn	232	α-diamond	280(4)
		β-tetragonal	302(4), 318(2)
Pb	327	fcc	349(12)
Sb	631	Rhombohedral	291(3), 336(3)
Bi	271	Rhombohedral	307(3), 353(3)

Numbers in parentheses are the number of neighbour atoms at that distance.

In Group IV the tendency to formation of directional bonds is quite marked in the first two members, germanium and tin. Both show the diamond structure in which each atom is bonded to four others tetrahedrally situated around it. The atoms thus appear to be sp^3-hybridised as in many of their compounds (e.g. the tetrahalides), and these metals have low electrical conductivities (both are semiconductors). For tin, this form (α-tin, grey tin) is stable only below room temperature; the conversion to this form at low temperatures causes the metal to crumble, a phenomenon known as tin plague or tin pest. As normally encountered (β-tin, white tin), tin has a tetragonal structure and the familiar metallic properties. However, each tin atom still has only four nearest neighbours, forming a flattened tetrahedron, although two other atoms rather farther away complete a very distorted octahedron. It is stated that these two forms of tin react differently with hydrochloric acid, the α-form giving tin(IV) and the β-form tin(II) in solution. This difference would be consistent with the structures and other properties of the two allotropes. By contrast, lead has a regular close-packed structure, albeit with rather large internuclear distances.

The stable forms of antimony and bismuth consist of puckered sheets in which each atom is directly bound to three neighbours by covalent bonds, but there is some metallic bonding between the sheets. Antimony also has an unstable yellow form, obtained by rapid condensation of the vapour. The vapour and, presumably, this solid consist of tetrahedral Sb_4 molecules; again each atom is bonded pyramidally to three others.

None of the metals is particularly reactive at room temperature (cf. Table 8.5), and aluminium, tin and lead are widely used for their corrosion resistance. Aluminium and gallium are known to be protected by a thin, unreactive layer of oxide. Tin and lead may be genuinely unreactive, since they remain bright in contact with water, but the redox potentials (see below) suggest that they should react, and it is possible that protective layers are formed in these cases also. All the metals react with aqueous acids, although aluminium is 'passivated' by concentrated nitric acid (i.e. the oxide layer is thickened). Germanium, tin, and antimony also react with nitric acid to give the (hydrated) oxides, the other metals dissolve to give nitrates. Lead reacts only slowly with hydrochloric or sulphuric acid owing to the formation of an insoluble layer of the chloride or sulphate. The lighter

Table 8.5 Products of reaction of the *p*-block metals with various reagents at room temperature

	Water	Acid	Alkali	Air†	F_2	Cl_2
Al	NR	Al_{aq}^{3+}	$Al(OH)_4^-$	$NR(Al_2O_3)$	AlF_3	$AlCl_3$
Ga	NR	Ga_{aq}^{3+}	$Ga(OH)_4^-$	$NR(Ga_2O_3)$	GaF_3	$GaCl_3$
In	NR	In_{aq}^{3+}	NR	$NR(In_2O_3)$	InF_3	$InCl_3$
Tl	NR	Tl_{aq}^+	NR	Tl_2O	TlF_3	$TlCl_3$
Ge	NR	$(Ge^{4+})‡$	$Ge(OH)_6^{2-}$	$NR(GeO_2)$	GeF_4	$GeCl_4$
Sn	NR	Sn_{aq}^{2+}	NR	$NR(SnO_2)$	SnF_4	$SnCl_4$
Pb	NR	Pb_{aq}^{2+}	NR	$NR(PbO)$	PbF_4	$PbCl_2$
Sb	NR	NR	NR	$NR(Sb_2O_3)$	SbF_5	$SbCl_5$
Bi	NR	NR	NR	$NR(Bi_2O_3)$	BiF_3	$BiCl_3$

NR signifies no reaction.
† Product obtained on heating shown in brackets.
‡ Complexes with anions of the acids.

metals (aluminium, gallium and germanium) dissolve in alkali with evolution of hydrogen, but the heavier metals are unaffected.

Thus, both the physical and chemical properties suggest that these elements become more metallic with increasing atomic weight in each Group.

8.3 Halides

The known halides are listed in Table 8.6.

Direct action of a *p*-block metal with a halogen leads usually to the Group oxidation state, MX_3, MX_4, or MX_5. The exceptions occur for the heaviest halogens and the heaviest metals. Thus, $BiCl_3$, $BiBr_3$, BiI_3, $SbBr_3$, SbI_3, $PbBr_2$, PbI_2, and TlI_3 are obtained (the last of these is almost certainly a thallium(I) compound, containing the I_3^- ion). Some lower halides are known for each metal and, as the above trend suggests these become more stable with increasing atomic weight of both halogen and metal. The compounds $SbCl_5$, PbF_4, $PbCl_4$, and TlX_3 (all X) all lose halogen on warming, e.g.

$$TlF_3 \rightarrow TlF + F_2$$

$$PbCl_4 \rightarrow PbCl_2 + Cl_2$$

Lower halides of germanium, tin and indium are obtained by reducing the higher halides, most conveniently with the metal. The germanium dihalides disproportionate again on heating:

$$Ge + GeX_4 \rightleftharpoons 2GeX_2$$

but the tin(II) and lead(II) halides can be melted and even boiled without decomposition. Lower halides of aluminium and gallium have been detected in the vapour state at low concentrations, and AlCl is important in the production of high-purity aluminium metal by vapour transport. The metal is treated with $AlCl_3$ at high temperature (about 1 000 °C), forming AlCl which disproportionates on cooling. The forward reaction has a positive entropy term ($\Delta S > 0$) and is favoured by raising the temperature.

$$2Al(l) + AlCl_3(g) \underset{cool}{\overset{heat}{\rightleftharpoons}} 3AlCl(g)$$

Table 8.6　　Halides of the *p*-block metals

Legend box:
Formula
Coord. no. (structure)
Melting point/°C
$\Delta H_f^0/\text{kJ mol}^{-1}$

Upper block (higher halides)

Compound	Coord. no. (structure)	mp/°C	ΔH_f^0
AlF_3	6(ReO_2)	1 290 sb	−1498
$AlCl_3$	6($CrCl_3$)	180 sb	−707
$AlBr_3$	4, dmr	98	−527
AlI_3	4, dmr	ca. 180	−310
GaF_3		800 sb	
GeF_4	4, mol	−37 sb	
$GaCl_3$	4, dmr	78	−525
$GeCl_4$	4, mol	83(BP)	−690
$GaBr_3$	4, dmr	122	−387
$GeBr_4$	4, mol	26	−328
GaI_3	4, dmr	212	−239
GeI_4	4, mol	146	
InF_3		1 170	
SnF_4	6, pol	705 sb	
SbF_5	6, pol	7	
$InCl_3$		586	−537
$SnCl_4$	4, mol	114(BP)	−545
$SbCl_5$	5, mol	5	−440
$InBr_3$	6?	436	−429
$SnBr_4$	4, mol	33	−406
InI_3	4, dmr	210	−239
SnI_3	4, mol	144	
TlF_3		550(F_2)	
PbF_4	6, pol	600	−930
BiF_5	6(UF_5)		
$TlCl_3$	6($CrCl_3$)	40 ds	−315
$PbCl_4$	4, mol		−329
$TlBr_3$	4, dmr		

Lower block (lower halides)

Compound	Coord. no. (structure)	mp/°C	ΔH_f^0
GeF_2	3, chn	300 dp	
$GeCl_2$	3, chn	450 dp	
$GeBr_2$	3, chn	122	
GeI_2	6(CdI_2)		
SnF_2	3, chn		
SbF_3	3, mol		−915
$InCl$		225	−186
$SnCl_2$	3, chn	246	−350
$SbCl_3$	3, mol		−382
$InBr$	1(TlI)		−175
$SnBr_2$	3, chn	216	−266
$SbBr_3$	3, mol		−259
InI			−116
SnI_2	3, chn	316	−144
SbI_3	6(BiI_3)		−100
TlF	6(NaCl)	327	−326
PbF_2	9($PbCl_2$)	835	−666
BiF_3			
$TlCl$	8(CsCl)	430	−204
$PbCl_2$	9	498	−359
$BiCl_3$	3, mol		−379
$TlBr$	8(CsCl)	456	−173
$PbBr_2$	9($PbCl_2$)	373	−279
$BiBr_3$	3, mol		−276
$TlIr$	4, lyr	440	−124
PbI_2	6(CdI_2)	400	−175
BiI_3	6		−150

mol = molecular, dmr = dimeric, pol = polymeric, chn = chain, lyr = layer. BP = boiling point, dp = disproportionates, ds = dissociates, sb = sublimes

Also:

$GaX_2(X = Cl, Br, I)$　$= Ga^+GaX_4^-$

$InCl_2$　$= In^+InCl_4^-$

$TlX_2(X = Cl, Br)$　$= Tl^+TlX_4^-$

TlI_3　$= Tl^+I_3^-$

$Tl_2X_3(X = Cl, Br)$　$= (Tl^+)_3TlX_6^{3-}$

$Sb_{11}F_{43}$　$= [Sb_6F_{13}]_n^{5n+}[SbF_6^-]_{5n}$

$Bi_2X_4(X = Cl, Br)$　$= (Bi^{III})(Bi^{V})X_4$

$Bi_{24}Cl_{28}$　$= (Bi_9)^{5+}(BiCl_5)^{2-}(Bi_2Cl_8)^{2-}$

A few halides are known in which the metal apparently displays an intermediate oxidation state, e.g. $GaCl_2$, but these mostly contain the metals in the conventional oxidation states, both of which occur in the one compound, e.g. $Ga^+GaCl_4^-$. Only $Bi_{24}Cl_8$ appears to be unusual (see below).

Very few of these compounds have simple ionic lattices; these are found mainly with the heavier metals in their lower oxidation states. The tri-iodides of antimony and bismuth, and lead di-iodide have hcp arrangements of iodide ions with the metal ions in octahedral positions. The other lead dihalides, having smaller anions, have more complicated structures with Pb^{2+} ions surrounded by eight or nine anions (cf. Sr^{2+}, Ba^{2+}). Of the higher halides, only those of the Group

III metals show any tendency towards ionic behaviour. All the trifluorides, the trichlorides except GaCl$_3$, and InBr$_3$ have structures involving six-coordinate metal ions. Most of these are significantly higher-melting than the other trihalides, which have molecular lattices containing halogen-bridged dimers; these should, strictly, be formulated M$_2$X$_6$. Note, however, that from a structural point of view, these could also be described as hcp halide ion lattices with M^{3+} ions in *adjacent tetrahedral* holes. When molten, all except the fluorides have the M$_2$X$_6$ molecular structure.

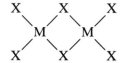

The remaining halides are all covalent materials, although this does not necessarily mean that simple, molecular structures are found. The higher fluorides, except GeF$_4$, have associated structures with fluorine atoms bridging between the metal atoms which are six-coordinate (Fig. 8.2). Germanium tetrafluoride is, however, a molecular gas (cf. SiF$_4$, CF$_4$). The other tetrahalides

(a) SnF$_4$

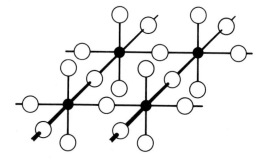

Fig. 8.2   Structures of polymeric fluorides

(b) SbF$_5$

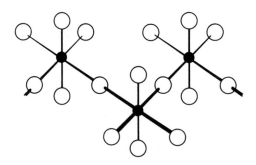

(c) BiF$_5$

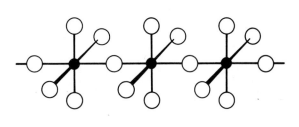

are composed of discrete tetrahedral molecules, the chlorides being fuming liquids (cf. SiCl$_4$, TiCl$_4$). Antimony pentachloride probably has a molecular, trigonal bipyramidal structure (contrast SbF$_5$) and the trihalides SbX$_3$ and BiX$_3$ (X ≠ I) form pyramidal molecules. The latter structure can be regarded as being derived from a tetrahedron with the lone pair of electrons (which presumably has some *p*-character) occupying one position. A similar situation is found for MX$_2$ (M = Ge, Sn) in which the pyramidal configuration is achieved by polymerization with bridging halogen atoms (Fig. 8.3).

Fig. 8.3   Structures of Group IV and V lower halides. In these and subsequent figures, the two dots represent the lone pair of electrons

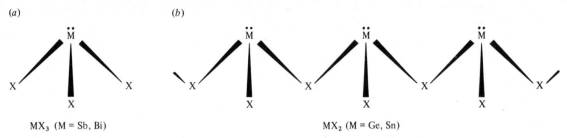

(a)   MX$_3$ (M = Sb, Bi)   (b)   MX$_2$ (M = Ge, Sn)

The tri-, tetra- and penta-halides are susceptible to hydrolysis, as would be expected for covalent compounds with polar bonds, and most react with atmospheric moisture forming first oxyhalides and then oxides, e.g.

$$GeX_4 \rightarrow GeOX_2 \rightarrow GeO_2.$$

These halides must therefore be handled only briefly, if at all, in air, and are best confined to closed systems. In contrast, many of the lower halides dissolve readily in water and can be recovered as hydrates, although dehydration cannot always be readily effected without decomposition. For example, hydrated aluminium chloride should be heated in dry hydrogen chloride to prevent formation of the oxychloride. The heaviest metals give halides which are, at best, sparingly soluble, e.g. the lead halides dissolve when heated and crystallise out again (anhydrous) when the solution is cooled, and the thallium(I) halides (except the fluoride) are very insoluble.

In many cases additional halide ions can coordinate to the metal to give anionic complexes which are usually closely related, structurally, to the parent halide. Thus, aluminium, even in aqueous solution, forms the octahedral AlF_6^{3-} ion but the other halides give only the four-coordinate AlX_4^- ions and these are formed only in non-aqueous media. Similar ions occur in the Group III dihalides, which have ionic lattices, $M^+MX_4^-$. The tetra- and penta-positive metals all give octahedral complexes MX_6^{2-} or MX_6^-, while the lower oxidation states of these metals all show the effect of the lone pair of electrons, forming MX_3^-, MX_4^- and MX_5^{2-} ions (Fig. 8.4). However, in

Fig. 8.4   Structures of complex anions

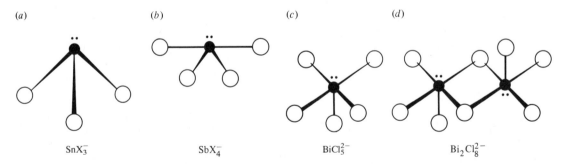

(a)   SnX$_3^-$ (b)   SbX$_4^-$ (c)   BiCl$_5^{2-}$ (d)   Bi$_2$Cl$_8^{2-}$

some cases cubic phases can be obtained in which the metal ions are surrounded by six equivalent halide ions, e.g. in $CsSnBr_3$ or $[Co(NH_3)_6][SbCl_6]$. The curious halide $Bi_{24}Cl_{28}$ contains two anionic complexes, $BiCl_5^-$ and $Bi_2Cl_8^{2-}$, with a cluster cation, Bi_9^{5+}. A number of other condensed anions is known, and many species of simple stoicheiometry actually have complex, polymeric structures.

Thermodynamic data, although incomplete, show the familiar tendency to less negative ΔH_f^0-values with increasing atomic number of metal and of halogen (Fig. 8.5). In each Group,

Fig. 8.5 Oxidation-state diagrams for the *p*-block halides. (Note: the absence of a point from the diagram does not necessarily mean that a compound is unknown, but that data are not available. e.g. SnF₂ and SnF₄ are both known)

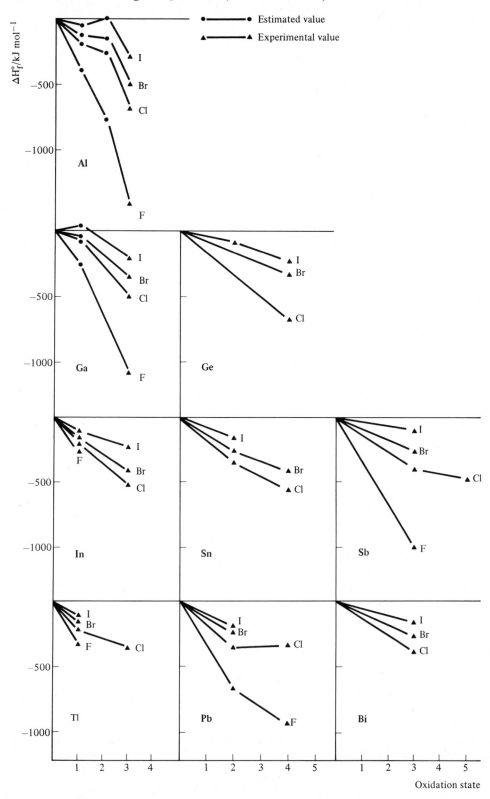

where data are available, the lower halides of the lighter metals are all unstable to disproportiona-tion but this instability also becomes less pronounced with increasing atomic weight of metal and of halogen, and the lower halides of the 5*p*- and 6*p*-metals are stable.

8.4 Oxides

The two oxidation states are displayed again in the oxides, the lower becoming more stable (to oxidation) with increasing atomic number (Table 8.7, Fig. 8.6). Thus the Group oxidation state is

Table 8.7 Oxides of the *p*-block, with metal coorination numbers (and structures), acidities, and enthalpies of formation

Formula
Coord. No. –
(Structure type)
$\Delta H_f^0/\text{kJ mol}^{-1}$

Al_2O_3						
$6(Al_2O_3)$						
ampho						
$-1\,676$						
Ga_2O_3	GeO_2			Ga_2O	GeO	
$6(Al_2O_3)$	$6(TiO_2)$			6?	4?	
ampho	ampho				ampho	
$-1\,089$	-551			-343	-212	
In_2O_3	SnO_2	Sb_2O_5		In_2O	SnO	Sb_2O_3
$6(C{-}M_2O_3)$	$6(TiO_2)$			6?	4 polym	3 molec
ampho	ampho	acidic		basic	ampho	ampho
-926	-581	-972			-286	-720
Tl_2O_3	PbO_2			Tl_2O	PbO	Bi_2O_3
$6(C{-}M_2O_3)$	$6(TiO_2)$			6?	4 polym	
basic	insol			basic	ampho	basic
-395	-277			-169	-219	-574

achieved on heating the metals in air or oxygen except for antimony, bismuth, and lead, which give Sb_2O_3, Bi_2O_3 and PbO respectively. The precise conditions chosen are important, however, as at elevated temperatures higher, mixed-valence oxides are formed, Sb_2O_4 between 300 and 900 °C and Pb_3O_4 above 400 °C. The oxide Bi_2O_5 has never been properly characterized and probably does not exist. The corresponding antimony oxide is obtained by oxidizing the metal with nitric acid, evaporating the solution and igniting the residue below 400 °C. Lead dioxide can be obtained

Fig. 8.6 Oxidation-state diagrams for *p*-block oxides

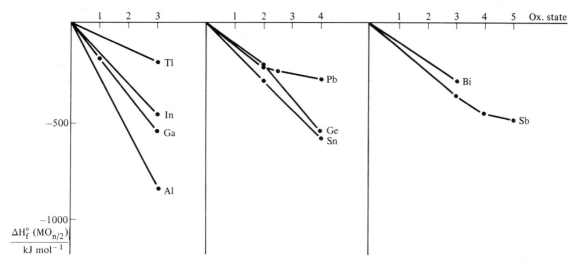

by oxidation of alkaline solutions of lead(II) salts. Both oxides are thermally unstable, as is also Tl_2O_3:

$$Sb_2O_5 \xrightarrow{300\,°C} Sb_2O_4 \xrightarrow{900\,°C} Sb_2O_3$$

$$PbO_2 \xrightarrow{500\,°C} Pb_3O_4 \xrightarrow{550\,°C} PbO$$

$$Tl_2O_3 \xrightarrow{100\,°C} Tl_2O$$

Lower oxides are also known for tin, germanium, indium and gallium, although all are susceptible to oxidation and are normally obtained under reducing conditions. Germanium monoxide disproportionates on heating to 500 °C, but SnO and In_2O are stable at high temperatures.

Most of the oxides are quite insoluble in water, and many are resistant to attack by acids and alkalis. The hydrated forms, obtained by precipitation from aqueous solutions of a salt of the metal in the appropriate oxidation state, are much more reactive. The majority of the hydrated oxides (there are probably few genuine hydroxides, although it is difficult to distinguish) are amphoteric, dissolving in acidic and in basic solutions. The exceptions are the monoxides, M_2O, and Bi_2O_3, which are basic, and Sb_2O_5, which seems to be entirely acidic.

Aluminium and gallium oxides normally crystallize with the corundum (α-Al_2O_3) structure, which consists of an hcp array of oxide ions with the M^{3+} ions in octahedral holes. With the high charges on the ions, this lattice is very stable and alumina is very hard (second only to diamond) and insoluble; it is therefore used as an abrasive. Alumina also forms the basis of many gemstones, e.g. ruby, in which about 1 per cent of the Al^{3+} ions are replaced by Cr^{3+}, and sapphire, which contains titanium and iron. It is salutary to consider that these materials are prized for their impurities! The corresponding oxides of indium and thallium have the 'C–M_2O_3' structure, which is similar to the fluorite structure except that one-quarter of the anions are missing. The metal ions are thus six-coordinate but in a rather irregular way, the anions being at the corners of an incomplete cube. The structures of the lower oxides of these metals are not known, but presumably involve six-coordination for the metal ions. The three oxides MO_2 have the rutile (TiO_2) structure, i.e. the metals are six-coordinate, although GeO_2 has a high temperature form with the cristobalite (SiO_2) structure, involving linked GeO_4-tetrahedra.

The lower oxides M–O display the effect of the lone-pair shown by the halides, with the difference that the metal atoms are bound to four oxygen atoms forming a square pyramid (Fig. 8.7). The pyramids are linked into sheets by oxygen atoms, each of which is bound tetrahedrally to four metal atoms. The mixed oxide Pb_3O_4 shows both types of environment for lead, the Pb^{IV} atoms are octahedrally coordinated and linked into chains by *cis* bridges, while the Pb^{II} atoms are three-coordinate with a pyramidal configuration, and link the $Pb^{IV}O_6$-chains together (Fig. 8.6b). Similar lone-pair effects are seen in the structures of Sb_2O_3 and Bi_2O_3. Although both compounds show more than one crystal form, all involve pyramidal MO_3-units and the forms differ only in the way these are linked together.

Fig. 8.7   Structures of (*a*) MO (M = Sn, Pb) and (*b*) Pb_3O_4 (redrawn from A. F. Wells (1975) *Structural Inorganic Chemistry*, 4th edn, OUP)

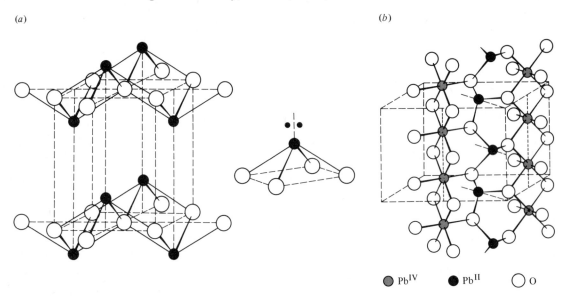

(*a*)   (*b*)

$\bullet$ Pb^{IV} $\bullet$ Pb^{II} $\bigcirc$ O

8.5   Aqueous chemistry

Since most of the oxides are amphoteric, cationic or anionic species will be formed according to the conditions. However, few simple aquated cations exist, and all are subject to hydrolysis and must be studied in strongly acidic solutions. Uni-, di-, and tri-positive cations are known, e.g. Tl^+, Sn^{2+}, Pb^{2+}, and Al^{3+} to Tl^{3+}. Except for Tl^+, which behaves as a simple cation at all times, hydrolysis often accompanied by condensation, occurs on raising the pH, e.g.

$M(H_2O)_6^{3+} \rightleftharpoons M(H_2O)_5(OH)^{2+} + H^+$

$pK_a = 4 \cdot 95$ (Al), $2 \cdot 60$ (Ga), $3 \cdot 7$ (In), $1 \cdot 16$ (Tl)

$2Al(OH)^{2+}(aq) \rightleftharpoons Al(\mu\text{-}OH)_2Al^{4+}(aq)$

The ready hydrolysis of Al^{3+}(aq) is of considerable use. On raising the pH slightly, the hydrated oxide forms readily, nucleating round fine suspended particles which are thereby precipitated; this is obviously of use in water treatment and clarification. The acidity of the aquo-ion is sufficient for solutions to react with carbonates, as in foam fire-extinguishers and baking powder; the low toxicity of aluminium is also of importance in these applications.

Similar considerations apply to the Group IV metals:

$$Pb^{2+}(aq) \rightleftharpoons Pb(OH)^+(aq) + H^+ \qquad pK_a = ca.\ 8$$

$$Sn^{2+}(aq) \rightleftharpoons Sn_3(OH)_4^{2+}(aq)$$

The last of these is probably a cyclic trimer with hydroxo bridges. Tripositive antimony and bismuth seem to occur in acidic solution only as oxo–cations, SbO^+ or BiO^+, or condensed species, e.g. those based on $Bi_6O_6^{6+}$, although there is some evidence for $Sb(OH)_2^+$. The cation $Bi_6(OH)_{12}^{6+}$ is known to have a structure in which OH-groups bridge the twelve edges of a Bi_6-octahedron.

Although some higher oxides (e.g. SnO_2, GeO_2) dissolve in acids, no cationic species are formed. These oxides dissolve only when complex-forming anions are present; e.g.

$$SnO_2 + HCl \rightarrow SnCl_6^{2-}$$

They are insoluble in, for example, nitric or perchloric acids, and the best way of obtaining the hydrated oxide is to acidify a basic solution with nitric acid (cf. the higher oxides of the d-block metals).

All the oxides except those of indium and thallium dissolve in alkali to give anionic species most of which are probably hydroxo-complexes, e.g. $Sn(OH)_3^-$, $Al(OH)_4^-$, $Sb(OH)_4^-$, $Sn(OH)_6^{2-}$, $Sb(OH)_6^-$. These species are stable only in dilute, strongly basic solution and if the pH is lowered, or the solution concentrated, condensation occurs and ultimately the hydrated oxide is precipitated. Several series of salts derived from these anions are known, although the dehydrated forms are probably best regarded as mixed oxides.

Table 8.8 Standard redox potentials (volts) for p-block metals in acid solution

M	N	$E^0(M^{(N-2)+}/M)$	$E^0(M^{N+}/M)$
Al	3	—	−1·66
Ga	3	—	−0·52
In	3	−0·25	−0·34
Tl	3	−0·34	+0·72
Ge	4	ca. 0	−0·15
Sn	4	−0·14	−0·01
Pb	4	−0·13	+0·66
Sb	5	+0·21	+0·36
Bi	5	+0·32	ca. +0·95

The thermodynamic data derived from the redox potentials (Table 8.8, Fig. 8.8) display the same trends as seen for the oxides and halides, i.e. the Group oxidation states become less stable, more oxidizing, with increasing atomic number of the metal, while the lower oxidation states become more stable. Only In^+ (and, presumably, Ga^+ and Al^+) and Ge^{2+} are unstable to disproportionation. Comparison with the potential for the half-reaction

$$O_2 + 4H^+ + 4e^- = 2H_2O \qquad E^0 = +1.23\ V$$

shows that all the lower oxidation states are susceptible to atmospheric oxidation except Tl^+, Pb^{2+}, and BiO^+, in accord with laboratory experience.

Fig. 8.8   Oxidation-state diagrams for acidic and basic aqueous solutions in the absence (upper set) and presence (lower set) of oxygen

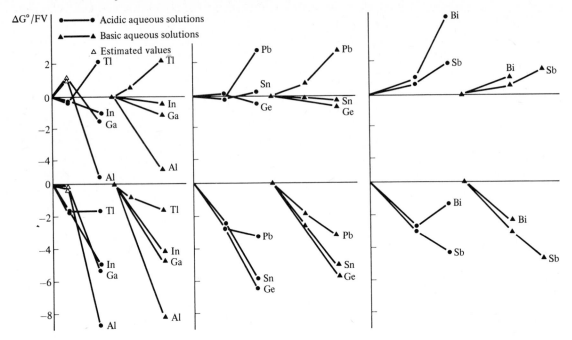

The potentials are not very sensitive to pH, but in each case the effect of increasing the pH is to destabilize the lower oxidation state relative to the higher, e.g.

$$Sn^{4+} + 2e^- = Sn^{2+} \qquad E^0 = +0.15 \text{ V}$$

$$Sn(OH)_6^{2-} + H^+ + 2e^- = HSnO_3^- + 3H_2O \qquad E_b^0 = -0.07 \text{ V}$$

$$PbO_2 + 4H^+ + 2e^- = Pb^{2+} + 2H_2O \qquad E^0 = +1.46 \text{ V}$$

$$PbO_2 + 2H^+ + 2e^- = PbO + H_2O \qquad E_b^0 = +1.01 \text{ V}$$

$$\tfrac{1}{2}Sb_2O_5 + 3H^+ + 2e^- = SbO^+ + 1{\cdot}5H_2O \qquad E^0 = +0{\cdot}58 \text{ V}$$

$$H_3SbO_6^{4-} + 5H^+ + 2e^- = SbO_2^- + 4H_2O \qquad E_b^0 = +0{\cdot}43 \text{ V}$$

This effect occurs because the oxidation reactions produce protons, so that raising the pH facilitates the reaction (changes the position of equilibrium, cf. p. 79 –80). It is common experience that oxidation occurs more easily in alkaline media; high pH is essential for the production of PbO_2, for example.

8.6   Rationale

The most striking aspect of the chemistry of the *p*-block metals is the pronounced tendency to covalency. For relatively high oxidation states, +3 and +4, some covalency would be expected; ions of such high charge would be extremely polarising. It is thus not surprising that compounds such as Al_2Br_6 or $SnCl_4$ should be molecular rather than ionic. It is more curious that the lower oxidation states should also display covalency effects. These are perhaps most apparent from the structures; compounds containing Sn^{II}, Pb^{II}, Sb^{III}, and Bi^{III} all show structures in which the metal atom is bonded to three (occasionally four) neighbours, all of which lie in a plane on one side of the metal atom, leaving a space on the other side (i.e. M–X distances are normal on one side and abnormally long on the other). The most logical explanation of this is that three (four) covalent bonds are being formed, and that the space is occupied by the remaining pair of electrons, which would repel neighbouring atoms. This pair of electrons is sometimes referred to as the 'inert pair', presumably because it is difficult to involve in the bonding or to ionise off (e.g. in Pb^{II} or Bi^{III}). This is something of a misnomer, however, since in a stereochemical sense the lone-pair is quite active. The arrangement of the other atoms about the metal atom shows that the lone pair occupies an orbital which has some p-character, i.e. the atoms are roughly sp^3-hybridized. Pure s-character for the lone pair would make the atoms appear spherical. Such behaviour can be found, e.g. in the thallium(I) halides, which have cubic structures. Mixed halides with cubic structures are also known, e.g. $CsSnCl_3$ and Cs_3SbBr_6. In these compounds the p-block elements occupy sites of cubic symmetry and thus behave as spherical ions or atoms. Similar behaviour is found for lead(II). Although in oxides lead displays the same irregular structure as tin, in the sulphide and the halides the lead atom (ion) appear spherical. This effect is sometimes referred to as *dehybridization*, since the lone pair in the spherical ion must have pure s-character rather than s-p-hybridization which would give it directional properties. This becomes more common with increasing atomic number of the ion, and is presumably related to the ease with which one of the lone pair electrons can be promoted from the s-orbital to the p-orbital (the effectiveness of mixing orbitals by hybridisation depends on their having similar energies). The promotion energies (kJ mol^{-1}) are: Ga, 582; In, 530; Tl, 639; Ga, 119; Sn; 113; Pb, *ca.* 145.

That these elements display considerable covalency is consistent with their position in the Periodic Table. The most ionic behaviour would be expected of elements which lie in the extreme Groups of the table and are thus highly electronegative (halogens, chalcogens) or highly electropositive (s-block metals). Elements of intermediate Groups would be less likely to form ionic compounds. Although the p-block metals are still electropositive (metallic) the nuclear charges are greater than for the s- and d-block metals, making the ions smaller and more polarizing and more prone to covalency. In addition, the heavier members of each Group have large numbers of electrons and are thus more *polarisable*, i.e. the metal cation would be readily polarised by a neighbouring anion, increasing the covalent character of the bond between them. This is also shown by the increasing affinity of these 'soft' metals for 'soft' non-metals – the heavier metals occur naturally as sulphides rather than as oxides.

It is also noticeable that metallic character is more pronounced in the heavier members, in that all the members of the sixth Period (Tl, Pb, Bi) and of the fifth (In, Sn, Sb) are included but only gallium and germanium of the fourth and aluminium of the third. A combination of factors is responsible for this. Metallic character was defined as being correlated with cationic (electropositive) behaviour. As the atomic number increases in any Period, the oxidation number also increases, e.g. gallium displays +1 and +3 states, germanium +2 and +4, etc. Thus, more electrons have to be involved in the bonding or ionised off, and this becomes increasingly expensive in energy. The effective nuclear charge also increases with atomic number in a Period, so that even to remove the same number of electrons becomes more difficult. The increasing effective nuclear charge is the reason for the decreasing size of the atoms and ions, and the increasing covalency. However, as each Group is descended, the atoms (ions) become larger and the ionisation energies decrease. It is thus easier to form cations and metallic behaviour is more apparent. These data are shown in Table 8.9.

The above presentation is something of a simplification. In particular, there are two further points requiring explanation, *viz.* (a) why is it that the only stable oxidation states are +N and +(N−2) (N = Group number)? and (b) why does the +N state become more difficult to attain as each Group is descended? If, as suggested above, ionisation energies decrease down a Group, the

Table 8.9   Enthalpies of formation (ΔH_f^0/kJ mol^{-1}) of gaseous atoms and ions from the solid metals

	M	M$^+$	M^{2+}	M^{3+}	M^{4+}	M^{5+}
Al	324	802	2 619	5 364	16 944	30 760
Ga	272	951	2 930	5 892	12 082	—
In	244	802	2 622	5 327	10 577	—
Tl	180	769	2 739	5 619	10 509	—
Ge	372	1 132	2 669	5 970	10 380	19 392
Sn	301	1 009	2 420	5 362	9 290	16 367
Pb	197	912	2 362	5 442	9 524	16 164
Sb	259	1 093	2 683	5 123	9 373	14 774
Bi	207	910	2 519	4 984	9 354	14 756

formation of higher oxidation states should become more facile, as is observed in the *d*-block. Clearly a more detailed examination is needed.

Since the bonding in many of these compounds has considerable covalent character, the best thermodynamic approach would be a covalent bond cycle such as that shown in Fig. 8.9.

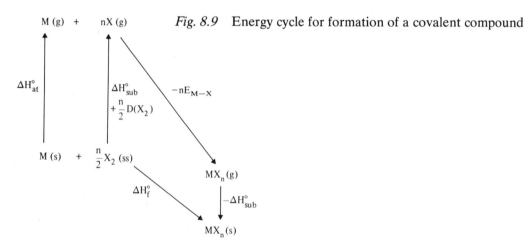

Fig. 8.9   Energy cycle for formation of a covalent compound

Unfortunately, the major term in this cycle, the bond energy E_{M-X}, is not known. It can, of course, be calculated when the other data are available, but values for hypothetical compounds cannot be estimated, and this method is of little use for the present purpose. The best which can be done is to choose the compounds which are most likely to have reasonably ionic character, e.g. oxides or fluorides, and to use an ionic Born–Haber cycle. However, even the calculation of lattice

Table 8.10   Ionic radii (pm)

M	Al	Ga	In	Tl	Ge	Sn	Pb	Sb	Bi
N	3	3	3	3	4	4	4	5	6
r_{N-2}	—	—	132	140	93	112	120	—	—
r_N	50	62	81	95	53	71	84	62	74

energies is not straightforward. In Table 8.11 some lattice energies calculated by Kapustinskii's method are compared with those derived from the Born–Haber cycle. The Kapustinskii value is

Table 8.11 Lattice energies of some oxides calculated from the Born–Haber cycle and by Kapustinkii's method (kJ mol^{-1})

	Ga_2O	Ga_2O_3	In_2O_3	SnO	SnO_2
U_{Kap}	2 486	14 950	13 907	3 326	11 551
U_{B-H}	3 208	15 724	14 436	3 658	11 786
Difference	722	774	529	332	235

always the lower and the differences are large, quite enough to upset thermochemical calculations. The discrepancies are much larger than for the *s*- or 3*d*-block metals, for instance, and reflect the irregularity of the structures and the contribution of covalency to the bond energy. As a compromise, the thermochemical values for, e.g., SnO and SnO_2 could be used to derive values for the hypothetical compounds Sn_2O and Sn_2O_3 by scaling them by the factors which the Kapustinskii treatment suggests. The Kapustinskii formula shows that lattice energies are roughly proportional to the product $\nu Z_+ Z_-$, the values of which for the tin oxides are: Sn_2O, 6; SnO, 8; Sn_2O_3, 30; SnO_2, 24. Thus, estimated values would be

$$U(Sn_2O) = 6U(SnO)/8$$

and

$$U(Sn_2O_3) = 30U(SnO_2)/8 = 24U(SnO_2)/30.$$

In practice the last two values will be different, but they may be averaged to obtain $U(Sn_2O_3) \approx$ 14 212 kJ mol^{-1}; the first relationship gives $U(Sn_2O) \approx 2\,744$ kJ mol^{-1}. An alternative approach would be to use the lattice energy of a similar compound of a neighbouring element, i.e. to assume that $U(Sn_2O) \approx U(In_2O)$; this method gives rather larger values. The enthalpies of formation calculated in these two ways are shown in Table 8.12 and plotted in Fig. 8.10. Both intermediate

Table 8.12 Enthalpies of formation and disproportionation of tin oxides (kJ mol^{-1})

	n	$-U_{Kap}$	$-U(InO_{n/2})$	$-U_{B-H}$	$\Delta H_f^0(Sn^{n+})$	$\frac{n}{2}\Delta H_f^0(O^{2-})$	$\Delta H_f^0(SnO_{n/2})$	ΔH_{disp}
$SnO_{0.5}$	1	−1 372	—	—	1 009	475	+112	−255·5
		—	−1 604	—			−120	−23·5
SnO	2	—	—	−3 658 (−1 829)	2 420	951	−287	
$SnO_{1.5}$	3	−7 106 (−2 365)	—	—	5 362	1 426	−318	−122·5
			−7 218 (−2 406)				−430	−10·5
SnO_2	4			−11 786 (−2 946)	9 290	1 902	−594	

Figures in parentheses are $\frac{1}{n}U(SnO_{n/2})$

compounds are unstable to disproportionation. Similar calculations have been performed for the aluminium halides, to give the values shown in Fig. 8.1. In this case, all except the trihalides are unstable to disproportionation. It may reasonably be assumed, therefore, that, as in the other

Fig. 8.10   Oxidation-state diagram for tin oxides. The vertical bars represent the range of calculated enthalpies for Sn_2O and Sn_2O_3

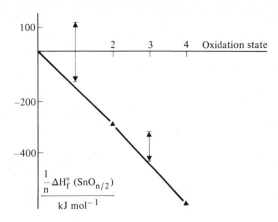

blocks, those oxidation states which are consistently not obtained are unstable to disproportionation.

As discussed in detail in Appendix D, the quantity which determines the relative stability of a series of compounds MX_n is $(1/n)\Delta H_f^0(MX_n)$, the enthalpy of formation per unit of oxidation. If this quantity becomes progressively less negative with increasing n, all the compounds in the series will be stable to disproportionation, if not then some compounds will be unstable as discussed above. Two major terms contribute to $\Delta H_f^0(MX_n)$, *viz.* $\Delta H_f^0(M^{n+})$ and $U(MX_n)$, of which the first increases fairly smoothly with increasing n (see Table 8.11) but the second does not. The irregularity in the change of $\Delta H_f^0(M^{n+})$ is due to the ionisation energies, which is most clearly brought out by plotting the ionisation energy divided by the final charge on the ion, $(1/n) I_n$, as in Figure 8.11. It is then apparent that the ionisation energies are roughly proportional to the charge while electrons of the same type are being removed. That is, to remove a second *p*- or *s*-electron requires about twice as

Fig. 8.11   Proportional ionisation energies $(\frac{1}{n}I_n)$ *vs* electron configuration

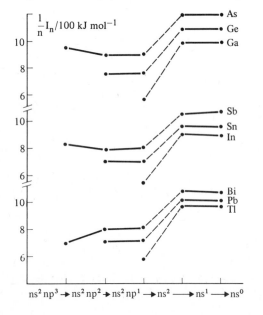

much energy as to remove the first. It is more difficult to remove s-electrons than p-electrons because s-electrons penetrate the atomic core more effectively and come more under the influence of the nuclear charge. This means that, if it is worthwhile, energetically, to remove the first electron of a particular type (p or s), it will be worth removing them all. Suppose three p-electrons are present; to remove two requires three times $(1+2)$ the energy required to remove the first, and to ionise off all three requires six times this amount $(1+2+3)$. The lattice energy is also increasing; on Kapustinskii's model it increases roughly in the ratio $1:3:6$. The actual rate of increase is greater than this because the radius of M^{n+} is decreasing. Therefore, $(1/n)\Delta H_f^0(MX_n)$ is becoming increasingly more negative as n increases, and the intermediate compounds MX and MX_2 will be unstable with respect to M and MX_3.

Similar considerations apply to the removal of the s-electrons, so that the only oxidation states which will appear are $+(N-2)$, corresponding to removal of all the p-electrons, and $+N$, corresponding to removal of all the valence electrons. This contrasts sharply with the situation in the d-block where ionisation energies for removal of d-electrons increase more rapidly, resulting in stepwise ionisation and the formation of a range of oxidation states differing by unity (see Ch. 3).

This leaves the problem of the relative stabilities of the two oxidation states. For the lighter members of a Group, the higher oxidation state appears more stable, while for the heavier members the reverse is true. This trend could result either from an increasing stability of the lower state with increasing atomic number, or from a decreasing stability of the higher state. The thermodynamic data show that the lower oxidation state remains roughly constant in energy while the upper state becomes rapidly less stable with increasing atomic weight of the metal. This is shown, for instance in the redox potential data in Fig. 8.6 and, very strikingly, by the enthalpies of formation of the halides (Table 8.6). Particularly for the $5p$- and $6p$-metals, the enthalpies of formation of the lower halides are almost identical, while those of the higher halides become rapidly less negative down the Group. This behaviour is again due to the combination of two factors, ionisation energies and hydration or lattice energies. Ionisation energies would be expected to decrease with increasing atomic number, as shielding effects normally outweigh the increase in nuclear charge. As Table 8.9 and Fig. 8.12 show, this decrease occurs between the fourth and fifth periods and also between the fifth and sixth Periods for ionisation of p-electrons. The $(N-2)$-state would be expected, on this basis alone, to become more stable. However, the decrease in ionisation energy is offset by a decrease in hydration and lattice energies as the ions become larger, and these two effects roughly balance.

To form the $+N$-state, the two remaining electrons must be removed from the valence-shell s-orbital. As remarked previously, s-electrons are those most directly influenced by the nuclear charge (least shielded). The nuclear charge is increased between the fifth and sixth periods by an extra 14 units, over and above the 'normal' increase of 18 units, by the appearance of the $4f$-block. The sudden decrease in stability of the $+N$-state in the sixth Period is thus due to the 'lanthanide' effect coupled with a further decrease in hydration and lattice energies. (The increased effective nuclear charge for s-electrons is also responsible for the increase in promotion energy referred to above.)

The reduction by dissociation which occurs when many of the higher-oxidation state compounds (e.g. PbO_2) are heated, is the entropy effect discussed previously (p. 27). Since more of the gaseous component (e.g. O_2) is consumed in forming the higher oxidation state compound, the free energy

$$Pb + O_2(g) = PbO_2(s)$$

$$Pb + \tfrac{1}{2}O_2(g) = PbO(s)$$

of formation becomes less negative with increasing temperature more rapidly, i.e. the higher oxidation state becomes less stable relative to the lower.

Fig. 8.12   Successive ionisation energies. Note the general decrease in I_n down each Group for *p*-ionisation and the different trend for *s*-ionisation

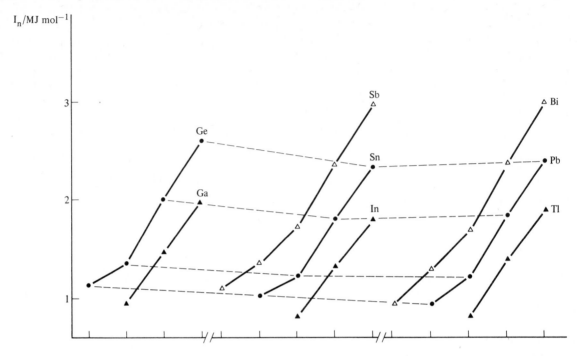

The increasing metallic character found with increasing atomic weight down a Group is also related to the polarizing power of the cation. Thus, Al_2O_3 is amphoteric, Ga_2O_3 less so, and In_2O_3 and Tl_2O_3 are basic. The acidity of the aquo ions decreases in the same sequence. Both these trends result from the decreasing polarisation of coordinated water by the cation. The greater the polarising power of the cation, the more readily is a proton lost by the water and the more likely is the formation of anionic hydroxo-complexes, as discussed in previous chapters. Similar effects are seen in the structures of the halides and halide complexes. All the fluorides of the trivalent metals have six-coordinate metal atoms, but with the more polarizable halogens four-coordination is found for the lighter metals and six-coordination for the heavier metals. (The formation of fluoro-complexes in aqueous solution is mainly an entropy effect, since the small anion imposes a 'structure' on the solvent by hydrogen-bonding, which is broken when the anion coordinates.) The greater polarization of the halogen by the smaller cation results in greater transfer of charge, so that electroneutrality for the metal is attained with a smaller coordination number.

Bibliography

BENT, 12, 16–8, 21; **CW,** 9, 11, 13; **HJ,** 15–6, 21, 23; **MM,** 15; **PW,** 30–2.

J. D. Donaldson, *Prog. Inorg. Chem.*, **8**, 287 (1967). The chemistry of tin(II).

J. D. Dunitz and L. E. Orgel, *Adv. Inorg. Chem. Radiochem.*, **2**, 1 (1960). Critical, readable review of the stereochemistry of ionic compounds.

F. Glockling, '*The Chemistry of Germanium*', Academic Press, 1969. A useful survey.

N. N. Greenwood, *Adv. Inorg. Chem. Radiochem.*, **5**, 91 (1963). The chemistry of gallium.

J. E. Huheey and C. L. Huheey, *J. Chem. Educ.*, **49**, 227 (1970). Discussion of the effects of the lanthanide contraction in the $6p$-elements.

L. Kolditz, *Adv. Inorg. Chem. Radiochem.*, **7**, 1 (1965). Halides of the Group V metals.

Chapter 9

Elemental metals and intermetallic compounds

Attention has been focussed in the preceding chapters on the binary compounds formed between the metallic elements and the non-metals. However, the metals form compounds with all the other elements of the Periodic Table, excluding only the rare gases, and this treatment would be incomplete without some discussion of the structures and properties of the elemental metals themselves and the compounds which they form with each other.

9.1 The structures of the elements

The structures of the solid forms of the elements vary in a systematic way throughout the Periodic Table, reflecting the electronic structures of the atoms. The rare gases have atomic configurations with complete valence shells, and the solid form involves an fcc array of atoms held together only by weak, non-directional van der Waals' forces. As would be expected, the solids are formed only at very low temperatures. The halogens give solids composed of diatomic molecules in which pairs of atoms are tightly bound to each other, but are only weakly bound to other pairs. This behaviour, of course, arises from the single unpaired electron of the free atoms which allows the formation of a single covalent bond. The chalcogens of the next Group can form two such bonds, either a double bond to one other atom, as in oxygen, or single bonds to two other atoms; since these atoms themselves form two bonds, chain or ring structures result. Similar trends are found for the elements of Groups V and IV, where three-dimensional structures are found with each atom forming single bonds to three or four neighbours, although nitrogen (but not carbon) forms stable diatomic molecules. In all these cases the structures follow logically from the electronic configurations of the free atoms and obey the '8–N' rule (N = Group number): the number of covalent electron-pair bonds formed is in each case 8–N, giving a closed-shell configuration to each atom.

When the free atom has less than four valence electrons it is no longer possible to achieve a closed-shell configuration in this way. Consequently these elements, the metals, adopt different structures which are bonded in a rather different way. It is convenient to describe the structures first and to deal with the bonding separately.

9.2 Structures of metals

The particular crystal structure adopted by a metal depends on the precise conditions of temperature and pressure obtaining. Usually at least two (often more) structures are found and the energy differences between them are very small (a few kJ mol^{-1}). Attention will here be concentrated on the form stable under 'normal' conditions, i.e. at pressures of not more than one atmosphere (101·3 kN m^{-2}) and at temperatures up to room temperature (300 K); usually these are the most thermodynamically stable forms. It should be emphasised, however, that a change of conditions will often lead to a change of structure.

Most metals adopt one of the three basic lattices, hcp, fcc or bcc. A characteristic feature of these, as of all metallic structures, is that each atom has a large coordination number. In both the close-packed lattices, every atom has an identical environment (except those at the surface), and has twelve nearest neighbours – six in its own layer and three from each of the adjacent layers. The bcc structure is slightly less compact, as each atom has only eight nearest neighbours but six more atoms are only a little more distant.

The distribution of these structures throughout the Periodic Table is shown in Fig. 9.1. Although there are local variations, as might be expected in a collection of sixty-odd different elements, there is a fair degree of regularity in the distribution. The d- and f-block metals adopt the highly symmetrical hcp, fcc, or bcc lattices, and usually all the metals of one Group show the same structure, suggesting that the electronic structure of the atoms plays a rôle in determining the packing of the atoms (see below). In some cases, additional interactions are possible, favouring the adoption of a different structure, which is why the ferromagnetic metals, iron and cobalt, appear to be anomalous (note, however, that nickel is also ferromagnetic).

The two close-packed structures, hcp and fcc, differ only in the relative positions of layers of atoms which are not in contact, the stacking sequences being ABABAB or ABCABC, respectively. Consequently the energy differences between these structures are small and the stacking sequences are often not perfect through the entire lattice. More complicated regular sequences also occur but, in pure metals, are relatively rare; an example is samarium in which a sequence of nine layers is repeated, ABABCBCAC.

Fig. 9.1 Crystal structures of the metals

* hcp at low temperatures

† tetragonal at room temperature

Li* bcc	Be hcp															Al fcc	
Na* bcc	Mg hcp															Al fcc	
K bcc	Ca hcp	Sc hcp	Ti hcp	V bcc	Cr bcc	Mn cubic	Fe bcc	Co hcp	Ni fcc	Cu fcc	Zn hcp	Ga ortho	Ge diam
Rb bcc	Sr hcp	Y hcp	Zr hcp	Nb bcc	Mo bcc	Tc hcp	Ru hcp	Rh fcc	Pd fcc	Ag fcc	Cd hcp	In tetrag	Sn† diam
Cs bcc	Ba bcc	La hcp	Hf hcp	Ta bcc	W bcc	Re hcp	Os hcp	Ir fcc	Pt fcc	Au fcc	Hg hexag	Tl hcp	Pb fcc

Ce hcp	Pr hcp	Nd hexag	Pm ?	Sm hexag	Eu bcc	Gd hcp	Tb hcp	Dy hcp	Ho hcp	Er hcp	Tm hcp	Yb fcc	Lu hcp

As might be anticipated, the borderline metals of Groups III and IV of the p-block have non-standard structures. Gallium has a complex, orthorhombic structure in which each atom has one unique close neighbour and six others farther away, rather as though it were displaying the univalency sometimes seen in the chemistry of this element. Indium has a structure which is almost bcc, except that the 'cube' is elongated in one direction by 8 per cent. Thallium has a conventional hcp structure, so that the elements of this Group become more 'metallic' as the atomic number increases. The same trend is found in Group IV. Germanium has the 'covalent' diamond structure which is also shown by tin below 18 °C. Above this temperature, tin has a metallic, tetragonal structure which has been described as a distorted diamond structure or as a body-centred tetragonal lattice. Lead has the regular fcc structure. The increasing tendency to metallic behaviour in the Group has a strong parallel in the chemistry (see Ch. 8).

Even the Group II metals, zinc, cadmium, and mercury, have structures slightly distorted from the ideal, hard-sphere arrangement, which has been interpreted as showing weak directional (i.e. covalent) bonding.

9.3   Intermetallic systems

The metals form binary compounds with nearly all the other elements, the nature of the compounds depending on how similar or different the two elements are. If they differ widely, as in metal halides or oxides, salt-like structures of fairly definite composition result. When the elements are not greatly different in electronegativity but their atoms have very different radii, interstitial phases may result, as in the carbides and nitrides. If, however, the two elements are closely similar, e.g. two metals, they will probably form substitutional solid solutions, i.e. atoms of one metal will randomly replace those of the other in the crystal lattice. When the metals are very similar in atomic size, electronegativity, electronic structure, etc., they may be completely miscible in all proportions in the solid state, so that if the metals are melted together and then cooled, the resulting solid is homogeneous and has the same crystal structure for all compositions. Some pairs of metals which exhibit complete miscibility are potassium-rubidium, potassium-caesium, copper-nickel, and titanium-zirconium. This behaviour can be expressed more formally in a **phase-diagram**, which shows graphically the stability ranges of the various phases as a function of composition and temperature (for a particular pressure, usually one atmosphere). The diagram for the potassium-rubidium system is shown in Fig. 9.2. The area at the top of the diagram, at high temperature, represents the liquid phase. When the liquid is cooled, solid begins to separate at a temperature which depends on the composition, but the solid phase has the same crystal structure at all compositions. There is also a region in which solid and liquid coexist, the extent of which depends on the composition; only at one precise composition (66·8 atom per cent rubidium) does the system show a sharp melting point.

Fig. 9.2   K-Rb phase diagram (after M. Hansen (1936) *Constitution of Binary Alloys*, Springer-Verlag, Berlin)

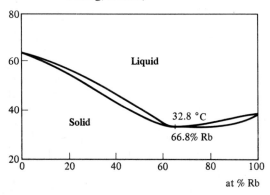

at % Rb

When the two pure metals have different lattices, complete miscibility is impossible. Each structure can be maintained only over a certain composition range, and the two structures will usually be separated in the phase diagram by a region in which the two solid phases coexist. Consider two metals, A and B. When B is dissolved in A, a substitutional solid solution (the α-phase) is formed which has the same crystal structure as pure A. Eventually, however, this structure will become unstable, and at high concentrations of B the stable structure is that of B with A atoms substituted at some of the sites (the β-phase). At intermediate compositions the system will consist of an intimate physical mixture of both phases, as shown in the hypothetical phase diagram of Fig. 9.3a. This behaviour, rather than a sudden change from pure α-phase to pure β-phase, results from the thermodynamics of the system, i.e. the way in which the free energy of the phases depend on composition. Figure 9.3b shows the situation for one particular temperature. The free energy of pure A with the α structure is G(A, α); this is the stable form at this temperature, since pure A with structure β has a higher free energy, G(A, β). Similarly, the stable form of pure B has the β structure. For a purely mechanical mixture of pure A and pure B the free energy would lie on the straight line joining G(A, α) and G(b, β). The formation of a substitutional solid solution between A and B results in a lowering of energy, mainly because of the increase in entropy

Fig. 9.3   (*a*) Hypothetical phase diagram for the A–B system. T₁ is the temperature at which the free-energy curves in (*b*) apply

Fig. 9.4   Hypothetical free-energy curves and phase diagram for metals of appreciably different electronegativity

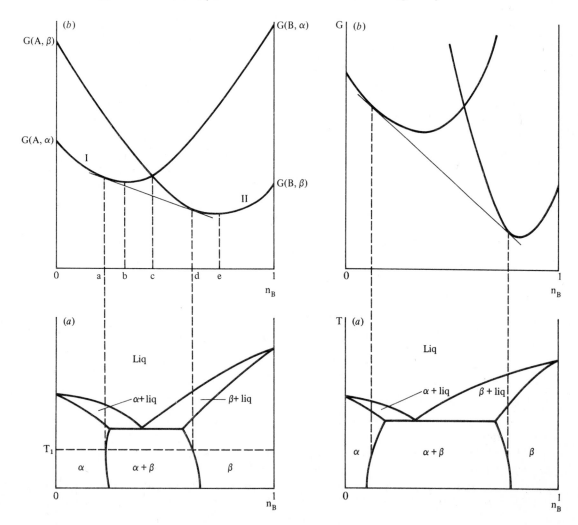

(configurational entropy, cf. the isothermal mixing of two gases). Thus, the energy of the α-phase falls with increasing B-content, n_B (curve I) and reaches a minimum at $n_B = b$, beyond which the loss of enthalpy resulting from the distortion of the lattice outweighs the entropy effect. Similarly, the β-phase (curve II) has a minimum energy at $n_B = e$. The two curves cross when $n_B = c$, and it might seem that the lowest energy for the system would correspond to phase α in the composition range $0 \leqslant n_B \leqslant c$ and phase β in the range $c \leqslant n_B \leqslant 1$, i.e. that there would be a sharp phase change at $n_B = c$. However, at this composition the free energy will be lower still if the system breaks up into a physical mixture of the two phases, α with composition a and β with composition d. These critical compositions are those for which the common tangent intersects the two curves. For any composition in the range $a \leqslant n_B \leqslant d$, the tangent represents the lowest possible energy, and the system will consist of a mixture of the two phases in such proportions as to give the appropriate overall composition. In this region, the two phases are in equilibrium, and the tangent represents the fact that the chemical potential of each component is the same in both phases. This result is perfectly general, and it is invariably found that regions corresponding to pure phases are separated by regions in which mixtures of the phases occur (this is an expression of the phase rule).

The positions of the phase boundaries thus depend on the shapes of the free-energy curves for the phases and on their relative positions. In general these will change with temperature, so that the phase boundaries in the phase diagrams are not usually vertical lines. If one phase is much more stable than the other, i.e. lies lower in the G/n diagram (see Fig. 9.4), the range of stability of the phases becomes less. That is, metals which form the most stable compounds (with each other) have the least mutual solubility. [The free energy of the compound (or solid solution) is the difference between the common tangent and the line joining $G(A, \alpha)$ and $G(B, \beta)$.]

Actual phase diagrams can be very complicated, showing many intermediate phases between the terminal phases. Typical examples are shown in Fig. 9.5. For some systems, it has been found possible to generalize; the four basic rules formulated by Hume-Rothery in the 1930s are still widely quoted. These are:

1. The mutual solubility of a pair of metals will be relatively restricted if their atomic radii differ by more than 15 per cent. If the radii are closer than this, the extent of solid solution is governed by the other factors.
2. The greater the electronegativity difference between the two metals, the greater the likelihood of formation of stable compounds with relatively narrow composition ranges. As shown above, this effect also reduces the mutual solubility of the metals.
3. As a general rule, the solubility of the metal with the higher Group number in the metal with the lower Group number is greater than the converse. For example, almost 40 atom per cent of zinc can be dissolved in copper before a second phase begins to form, but only about 2 per cent of copper can be dissolved in zinc.
4. In many systems the composition ranges of particular phases seem to be governed by the average Group number or *electron concentration* of the alloy. The weighted average of the Group numbers (which are taken to represent the number of valence electrons available for binding the solid) seems to have roughly reproducible values at the phase boundaries. Several systems based on copper, silver and gold give the same sequence of phases with increasing content of a second metal: α (fcc), β (bcc), γ (complex cubic, approximately bcc), and ε (hcp). (Some systems also have a δ-phase, but this usually occurs only at high temperatures and has a very limited composition range.) The electron concentrations at the phase boundaries are shown in Table 9.1 for some copper and silver alloys (values for gold alloys are often rather lower).

Similar trends are found for the d-block metals, in systems in which a metal from Groups IV–VI is combined with a metal from Groups VII–VIIIc. These systems show some or all of the

Fig. 9.5   Phase-diagrams for (*a*) Cu–Ag, (*b*) Cu–Zn, (*c*) Cu–Ga and (*d*) Cu–Ge. Note the decreasing solubility with increasing Group number of the solute (after C. J. Smithells (Ed.), *Metals Reference Book*, Butterworths, 1976)

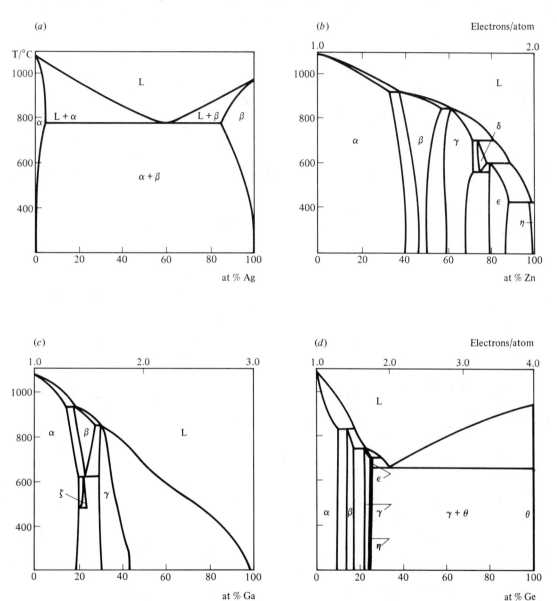

following phases, which always occur in the same order, with boundaries at roughly the same average Group number: α (bcc), Cr$_3$Si-type (nearly bcc), σ (nearly hcp), μ (hexagonal), χ (nearly bcc), hcp, fcc.

The occurrence of such regular sequences with fairly well-defined boundaries suggests that the total number of electrons available is an important factor in determining which structure is formed, and these materials have become known as *electron compounds*.

Table 9.1   Electron concentration limits of various copper- and silver-based phases (expressed in electrons per atom).

System	α-phase fcc	β-phase bcc	γ-phase cubic	ε-phase hcp	η-phase
Cu–Zn	1·00–1·32	1·32–1·48	1·57–1·68	1·77–1·87	1·97–2·00
Cu–Al	1·00–1·40	1·42–1·60	1·64–1·76	1·78–1·80	
Cu–Ga	1·00–1·44	1·40–1·56	1·60–1·74		
Cu–In	1·00–1·24	1·38–1·46	1·58–1·64		
Cu–Si	1·00–1·34	1·42–1·51	1·53–1·60	1·63–1·64	
Cu–Sn	1·00–1·30	1·39–1·48	1·60–1·63	1·72–1·78	
Ag–Zn	1·00–1·38	1·42–1·53	1·58–1·62	1·66–1·90	1·94–2·00
Ag–Cd	1·00–1·42	1·49–1·51	1·57–1·61	1·64–1·81	1·92–2·00
Ag–Al	1·00–1·40	1·44–1·56		1·56–1·80	2·82–3·00
Ag–Ga	1·00–1·38				
Ag–Ge	1·00–1·33				
Ag–Sn	1·00–1·36	1·36–1·66	1·69–1·72		

These figures represent the extreme composition for each phase; the temperatures involved are therefore different in each case. (See Fig. 9 for phase diagrams for some copper-based systems.)

9.4   Theory of metallic structure and bonding

Many attempts have been made to rationalise the structures of metals and intermetallic phases and to provide theories of bonding. Until quite recently (the last decade or so), little real progress was made, owing to the extreme difficulty of performing realistic calculations. To be satisfactory, a theory should be able to explain, quantitatively, the particular crystal structures which are adopted, the composition limits of the various phases in intermetallic systems, the strength of binding of the metal atoms to each other, the electrical and magnetic properties, etc. etc. It ought, eventually, to be possible to describe *all* solid materials in terms of a single theory, regardless of whether they are ionic, metallic or covalent (or even molecular). Progress is being made in the treatment of pure metals; extension to intermetallic phases is complicated.

Two extreme approaches have been adopted as starting points in the calculations: the valence electrons may be considered to be delocalised over the whole lattice and free to move through the crystal [nearly-free electron (NFE) approach], or they may be considered to be closely associated with the individual atoms [the tight-binding (TB) approximation].

The TB method would obviously be well-suited to treating ionic solids, in which electron delocalisation is minimal, and it is also useful for systems in which the bonds are essentially localised to one atom and its immediate neighbours. It is in many ways similar to the molecular orbital approach for molecules, and its chief value here is that it allows the introduction of the concept of **energy bands**. When two atoms are brought together their orbitals overlap and interact, forming bonding and antibonding molecular orbitals covering both atoms. As more atoms are added more molecular orbitals are formed, the total number of molecular orbitals being equal to the total number of atomic orbitals, so that bands of orbitals (energy levels) are formed. The bands grow wider as more atoms are included but the rate of change is relatively small, i.e. the energy of the lowest orbital falls slowly and that of the highest orbital rises slowly, so that the energy gap between them becomes filled with energy levels increasingly closer in energy. When there is a very large number of atoms, as in a crystal, the levels are very closely spaced, e.g. there may be some 10^{20} levels covering an energy range of 2–4 eV. Obviously this number of levels cannot be displayed on a

Fig. 9.6   (*a*) Typical density of states curve. E_F is the Fermi level. (*b*) Representation on an expanded scale showing the excitation of electrons above the Fermi level for $T > 0$ K

(*a*)   (*b*)

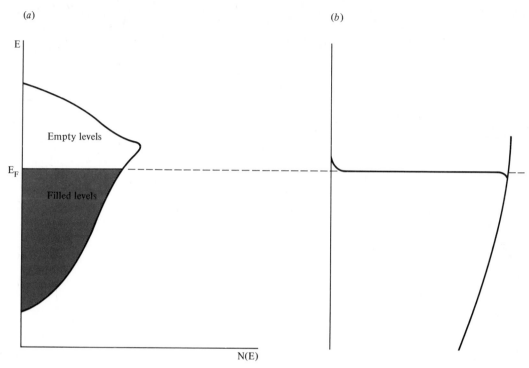

conventional energy-level diagram, and the usual representation is to plot the **density of states**. That is, the number of levels having a given energy is plotted against the energy; Fig. 9.6a shows a typical density of states curve. (In most texts these are drawn with the energy axis horizontal. It seems more logical to maintain here the chemical convention of plotting energy vertically.)

Electrons are fed into the energy levels in accordance with the Pauli principle – two per level. The level at which all the electrons has been accommodated is called the **Fermi level**, and this represents the highest energy available to the electrons at absolute zero. At higher temperatures, provided the Fermi level lies below the top of the band, some electrons will be excited above the Fermi level by the thermal energy (kT), so that the boundary of the density of states curve becomes slightly sigmoidal in shape, representing the depopulation of some levels just below the Fermi level and the partial filling of the adjacent, excited levels (Fig. 9.6b). It is principally this relatively small number of electrons which is responsible for the electrical conductivity (see below).

The NFE method takes its cue from this high electrical conductivity which is typical of metals. The electrons are clearly free to move through the lattice under the influence of an electric field. The earliest approach treated the electrons as being completely free, as an *electron gas* occupying the volume of the crystal, but it soon became clear that this was incorrect. The electrons must interact with the cationic atomic cores, they will be scattered by the cationic lattice in a way similar to that found in X-ray or electron diffraction, so that some wavelengths (i.e. energies) are forbidden. Although the potential which the atomic cores generate is large and difficult to calculate accurately, it has recently been realised that its effect in scattering the electrons is relatively weak and can be accurately simulated by a simple model. This *pseudo-potential* can be applied as a perturbation on the (relatively) straightforward calculation of the behaviour of the free electron gas (which is effectively the 'particle in a box' calculation). The precise form of the pseudo-potential is easily obtained from measurements of, for instance, the optical properties of the metal, and the density of states curve can then be calculated.

For many metals (those of the *s*-, *p*- and *f*-blocks – see next section), the pseudo-potential approach works well, since there is virtually complete delocalisation of the valence electrons, i.e. the valence orbitals of one atom overlap significantly not only with those of the nearest-neighbour atoms but also with those of next-nearest and even further neighbours. The *f*-electrons do not contribute significantly to the metallic bonding, being effectively completely localised on individual atoms and overlap with even nearest neighbours is very small. For the metals of the *d*-block, the situation is more complicated since the *s*- and *p*-levels can be adequately treated by the NFE method but the *d*-orbitals effectively form localised bonds between adjacent atoms only, requiring the TB treatment also. The results of some of these calculations are given in Section 9.6.

9.5   Enthalpy of atomisation and related properties

One of the most important physical properties of a metal, from the chemist's viewpoint, is its enthalpy of atomisation, the energy required to divide the solid metal into separate, gaseous atoms. This term appears in nearly every thermochemical cycle involving the metals and their compounds.

The enthalpy of atomisation is a direct measure of the binding energy of the solid metal, although it depends also on the electronic configuration of the gas-phase atoms. It might therefore be expected that the values of other properties which involve the disruption or distortion of the lattice would be related to ΔH_{at}^0, and correlations may be found with melting and boiling points, Young's modulus of elasticity, hardness, thermal conductivity, thermal expansion coefficient, and compressibility. Figure 9.7 shows the correlations between ΔH_{at}^0 and the melting and boiling points of the metals. The latter correlation presumably means that some interatomic bonding is retained

Fig. 9.7   Melting and boiling points of metals *vs* ΔH_{at}^0

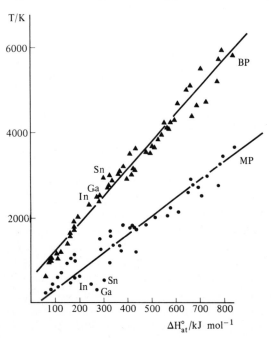

in the melt, which is similar to that in the solid. Melting need not, of course, involve the complete breakdown of the solid lattice, and the liquid will usually contain a range of atomic aggregates of various sizes. Even for those atoms which, in their Groups, appear to have anomalous ΔH^0_{at}-values, the correlations are maintained. The elements gallium, indium, and tin seem to have anomalously low melting points by comparison with their congeners, and which do not fit the correlation; these elements also have irregular crystal structures. Thus, in solid gallium there are pairs of atoms which are presumably bonded more tightly to each other than to other pairs. In melting, the pairs may be maintained while in atomisation they must be dissociated. For each of the three metals the boiling point is as expected, suggesting that the structure of the liquid is normal.

For the s- and p-block metals, the enthalpies of atomisation rise with increasing Group number (Fig. 9.8). For these metals the NFE approach works very well, and detailed calculations have been made for all the elements of these blocks. In this treatment the electron gas is assumed to

Fig. 9.8   Enthalpies of atomisation of s- and p-block metals

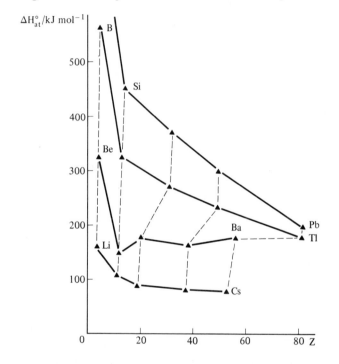

be composed of all the valence electrons, which are (nearly) free to move through the entire lattice; interaction with the pseudo-potential of the cations and exchange and correlation effects have to be taken into account. It is observed that the energies of phase transitions in metals (the energy required to convert one crystal structure into another) are very small, which means that the energy of the lattice is insensitive to details of the structures. This simplifies the calculations, since account need not be taken of the different structures adopted by the different metals. The quantity which is calculated is the energy of the metal lattice relative to the separated electrons and cations, i.e. the enthalpy of atomisation plus the sum of the ionisation energies for removal of all the valence electrons (in this way, correction for the differing electron configurations of the gaseous atoms is not needed). This quantity is found to be roughly proportional to the square of the cation charge (the Group number, the number of valence electrons), reflecting the rapid increase in binding energy from Group to Group. The results of some calculations are given in Table 9.2. Considering

Table 9.2   Calculated and experimental binding energies, $U = \Delta H^0_{at} + \Sigma I$.

Metal	U/MJ mol^{-1}	
	Observed	**Calculated**
Li	0·672	0·673
Na	0·614	0·600
K	0·509	0·484
Be	2·97	2·61
Mg	2·34	2·24
Ca	1·92	1·90
Ba	1·62	1·61
Zn	2·76	2·60
Cd	2·61	2.46
Hg	2·89	2·76
Al	5·43	5·20
Ga	5·79	5·43
In	5·38	5·04
Tl	5·63	5·43
Si	10·3	9·55
Ge	10·3	9·61
Sn	9·29	8·87
Pb	9·50	9·08

Values converted from those given by D. Weaire, quoted by V. Heine, *The Physics of Metals*, C.U.P., 1969.

the (relative!) simplicity of the theory, the agreement with experiment is good. Usually the calculated values are a little low, which is due mainly to the neglect of the structure-dependent terms, particularly the band energy.

In the *p*-block, ΔH^0_{at} decreases sharply with increasing atomic number. This represents partly the decrease in overlap of *ns*- and *np*-orbitals, which results in a raising in energy of the lowest occupied levels. There is also an increase in the energy gap between the *s*- and *p*-orbitals, caused by the interaction of the *s*-electrons with the nuclear charge. In the 6*p*-metals, the 6*s*-electrons are effectively localised and do not contribute to the metallic bonding [cf. the chemistry of these metals, (Ch. 8)].

The case of the *d*-block metals is much more difficult because, in addition to the nearly-free behaviour of the *s*-electrons, there are also the *d*-electrons which have to be treated by the TB method. The enthalpies of atomisation are much larger than for the *s*- and *p*-block metals, indicating that the *d*-electrons make a substantial contribution to the binding. It seems that each metal has about the same number of *s*-electrons (about 0·6 electrons per atom) forming a conduction band, and the remaining electrons are accommodated in the *d*-band. The shape of the *d*-band depends somewhat on the structure of the lattice (see below), but the approximate shape is as shown in Fig. 9.9. For a metal with few *d*-electrons, the lower part of the band is filled. These are bonding levels. With increasing atomic number along the period, more of these bonding levels are filled and the binding energy increases. After about five electrons per atom have been fed in, the bonding levels are full and further electrons must go into the upper, antibonding levels (there is, of course, no energy gap between the bonding and anti-bonding levels, but a continuous gradation through zero binding energy). This population of the upper levels destabilises the system and the binding energy decreases. Even when the *d*-band is completely filled, some cohesion is obtained from the *s*-electrons and from hybridisation of *s*- and *d*-levels.

This is roughly the trend observed (Fig. 9.10); ΔH^0_{at} increases in each period, reaching a maximum in Group V or VI. Within each Group, ΔH^0_{at} usually increases with increasing atomic

E

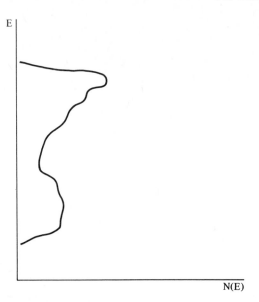

Fig. 9.9   Density of states curve for a *d*-band (after J. Friedel (1969) *The Physics of Metals*, CUP)

N(E)

Fig. 9.10   Enthalpies of atomisation of *d*-block metals

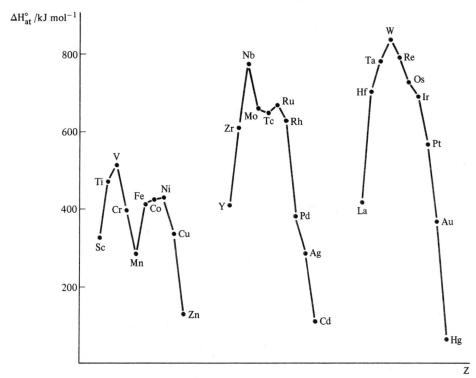

number. This effect, and the apparently anomalous structures of some of the 3*d*-metals, are related to overlap and exchange energy effects. Exchange energy is maximised by keeping electrons unpaired, with parallel spins, while for strong bonding electrons must be paired in the bonding orbitals. For the 3*d*-metals, exchange effects are dominant, as shown by the magnetic properties of chromium, manganese, iron, cobalt, and nickel (the last three are the ferromagnetic metals, chromium is antiferromagnetic, and manganese is paramagnetic with spins localised on individual atoms; manganese also has a relatively low ΔH_{at}^{0}-value and a unique crystal structure, showing that the d-electrons here make a much smaller contribution to the cohesive energy of the crystal). As a Group is descended, the d-orbitals become larger and their overlap increases, thus raising the contribution of the d-electrons to the cohesive energy. (Note that p- and d-orbitals differ in the way their overlap integrals depend on the main quantum number.) In the $5d$-metals the exchange effect is completely lost but the binding energy is high, rising to a maximum in the middle of the series where most electrons are available for bonding.

9.6   Crystal structure

As mentioned above, the major part of the energy which binds a metal lattice together is governed by factors which do not depend on the actual arrangement of the atoms (provided the interatomic distances do not change appreciably from structure to structure). The most important structure-dependent term is the band structure energy. The pattern of energy levels depends on the symmetry of the metal lattice, since this determines the way in which the orbitals can interact, so that different structures will have different density of states curves. The most stable structure is that which allows the appropriate number of electrons to be given the lowest energy. As an example, Fig. 9.11 shows the calculated band shapes for the d-block metals for the three major structures.

Fig. 9.11   Density of states for d-bands for three different crystal structures (after D. G. Pettifor, *J. Phys. C.* **3**, 367 (1970))

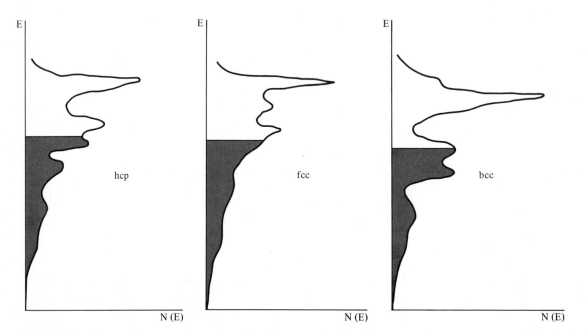

The shaded areas represent the filling of the states by five electrons per atom (i.e. vanadium or chromium), and it is clear that the lowest energy is obtained for the bcc structure as is actually found for these metals. If this type of comparison is made for all numbers of electrons per atom which are of interest, curves like those of Fig. 9.12 are obtained. The structure with most negative energy is

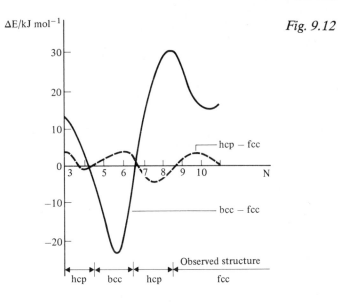

Fig. 9.12   Relative stabilities of the three crystal lattices *vs* number of *d*-electrons (the effect of *s*- and *p*-electrons is also included). Agreement with observation is good except when the number of electrons is small. Note that (*a*) the energy of the fcc lattice is taken as zero for each metal, (*b*) the stable structure is that with the lowest energy e.g. for N = 9 both hcp and bcc have higher energies than fcc (after D. G. Pettifor, *J. Phys. C.* **3**, 367 (1970))

that which will be adopted, and agreement between the calculated and observed structures is very good.

Similar calculations for the *s*- and *p*-block metals and alloys show that at about one electron per atom the hcp structure is favoured, as found for lithium and sodium at low temperatures; the fcc structure might be stable at about 1·4 electrons per atom, but bcc is the stable lattice above this level. At 1·6 electrons per atom, hcp is favoured again and fcc is preferred at about 2·2 electrons per atom. Agreement with observation is not very good at low electron-per-atom numbers (1·0–1·4), but the calculated electron numbers for change from one structure to another agree quite well with those found for the electron compounds (see Table 9.1). It has also been shown that the calculated energies of the actual, somewhat irregular structures of metals such as zinc, cadmium, indium and gallium are lower than those of any of the normal structures.

9.7   Electrical conductivity and semiconductivity

The most characteristic property of metals is that they are good conductors of electricity, the conductivity being inversely proportional to the absolute temperature. The current which passes is carried by the electrons, which migrate through the crystal lattice under the influence of the electric field; the atoms (cations) do not move from their normal positions. Such electronic conduction is much more efficient than the ionic conduction which occurs in, for example, some oxide systems, where the current is carried by ions migrating through the lattice (metallic conduction is also possible, however, in mixed-valence oxides). It has already been seen that, in a metallic crystal, the electrons occupy orbitals which extend over the entire crystal. However, the same could be said of a crystal such as diamond,† which certainly does not show marked electrical conductivity, so that delocalisation cannot by itself explain conduction.

---

† A description of structures such as that of diamond in terms of localised covalent bonds between pairs of atoms is an approximation. The building up of molecular orbitals over all the atoms, as discussed earlier, is obviously just as applicable to the non-metals as it is to the metals; bands of energy levels are obtained from the *s*- and *p*-orbitals (or the *sp³*-hybrids derived from them).

When a current passes there is a net flow of electrons in the direction of the applied field. The only electrons which can contribute to this flow are unpaired electrons in partly-filled levels around the Fermi level. The great majority of electrons, paired in the lower levels, contribute nothing to the net flow, equal numbers being displaced in each direction. By interaction with the electric field, further electrons at the Fermi level are excited, energy being drawn from the field. Since the energies involved are very small, the empty levels must lie very close to the Fermi level for appreciable conduction to occur. That is, such excitations can occur only within one energy band, the **conduction band**. In a conductor, therefore, the conduction band must be partly empty, as shown schematically in Fig. 9.13a for a metal with one electron per atom, when the Fermi level lies in the centre of the band. When the field is applied, electrons close to the Fermi level are excited into empty levels just above, and it is these electrons which are responsible for the conductivity, only a small proportion of total electron population.

If the conduction band (assumed here to be an s-band) were completely full, with two electrons per atom, and the lowest levels of the next band (p-band) were higher in energy (Fig. 9.13b), no excitation would be possible except at extremely high voltages or temperatures. This energy difference between the bands is usually referred to as the **band gap**. Materials with large band gaps are therefore insulators. On this basis it might seem that a metal such as magnesium, with two electrons per atom, should be an insulator. However, in most metals the energy bands overlap considerably (Fig. 9.13c), so that in this case the Fermi level would lie in the overlap region, and

Fig. 9.13   Filling of the conduction bands by (a) one, or (b) and (c) two electrons per atom

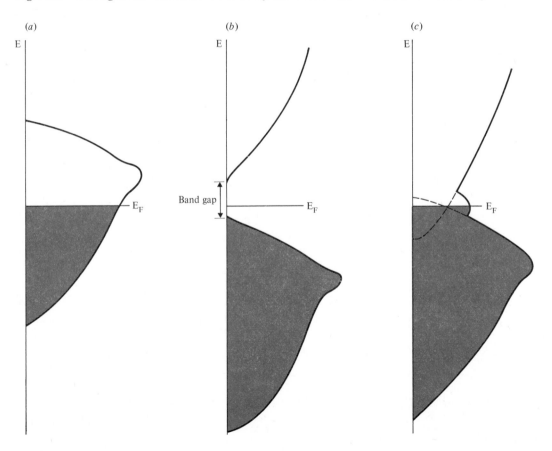

empty levels would be available. (This overlapping of energy levels is equivalent to some hybridisation of s- and p-orbitals.) Magnesium therefore conducts electricity almost as well as sodium. For a metal with three electrons per atom, e.g. aluminium, the Fermi level would lie in the lower half of the p-band. The conductivity which any particular metal exhibits is thus not directly related to the number of valence electrons, but depends on the density of states at the Fermi level.

The above description applies strictly only at absolute zero. At temperatures above this some electrons will have energies above the Fermi level. However, raising the temperature has only a small effect on the number of electrons available for excitation by the electric field, but the increased vibration of the atoms interferes with the motion of the electrons, resulting in the familiar linear decrease of conductivity with increasing temperature.

In some materials the reverse behaviour is found, the conductivity increases as the temperature is raised. These are the **semiconductors**, such as silicon, germanium, and grey tin, so called because they have conductivities between those of metals and insulators. These substances have band structures like that of Fig. 9.13b except that the band gap is quite small, e.g. 1·09, 0·60 and 0·08 eV for silicon, germanium and tin (106, 58, and 7·7 kJ mol^{-1} respectively). It then becomes possible for electrons to be excited across the band gap by thermal energy (kT = 2·47 kJ mol^{-1} at 300 K); the higher the temperature the greater the number of electrons promoted, and the conductivity increases accordingly. The band gap in a typical insulator such as sodium chloride, is about 10 eV (965 kJ mol^{-1}), so that thermal excitation is completely impossible in this case. Materials such as silicon are called intrinsic semiconductors because the semiconduction is a property of the band structure of the pure material. Extrinsic semiconductors are those in which the band structure has been modified by the deliberate introduction of impurities. If silicon is doped with, say, phosphorus or arsenic, an extra electron is introduced for every silicon atom replaced. These electrons do not go directly into the conduction band, but lie in additional levels within the band gap, and can therefore be readily excited into the conduction band, enhancing the conductivity. An alternative approach is to use a dopant which has less valence electrons than silicon, e.g. boron or indium. There will now be empty levels lying just above the Fermi level which can accept electrons by excitation from the filled band. Such an acceptor level leads, formally, to conduction by the *positive* holes left by the promotion of electrons, giving a p-type semiconductor. In the first case, with the Group V dopant, the current is carried by *negative* electrons excited into the upper band from the donor level, i.e. n-type semiconduction (see Fig. 9.14). Such materials have enormous utility, and whole industries have grown up around their manufacture and use. As the above discussion implies, extremely close control of purity and of the deliberate addition of impurities is required.

Fig. 9.14   Band gaps in (a) an intrinsic semiconductor, (b) an n-type semiconductor (the levels in the band gaps are filled donor levels), (c) a p-type semiconductor (the levels in the band gap are empty acceptor levels), (d) an insulator

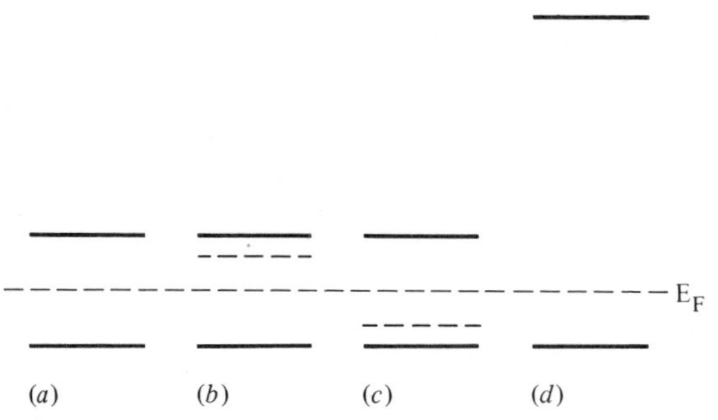

(a) (b) (c) (d)

Another class of compounds with special electrical properties is that of the **superconductors**. With these, the electrical resistivity becomes effectively zero below a certain (very low) critical temperature. This allows very high currents to be sustained easily and is used, for instance, to produce very high magnetic fields. The theory of superconduction is not well developed, but this property seems to be related to band structure. Systems with about five or seven electrons per atom are expected to have relatively high critical temperatures. Some of the better materials are listed in Table 9.3.

Table 9.3   Critical temperatures and electron concentrations for some superconductors.

Material	T_c/K	Electrons/atom
$AlNb_3$	17·5	4·5
GaV_3	16·8	4·5
Nb_3Sn	18·0	4·75
SiV_3	17·0	4·75

9.8   Mechanical strength

The major use of the metallic elements is as structural materials, they are employed for their strength. It is tempting to relate strength, hardness, etc. to the binding energy. Indeed, the alkali and alkaline earth metals, with small enthalpies of atomisation and low melting points, are characterised by their softness and malleability, while the d-block metals are very tough. However, this correlation is only partly valid. It is noticeable that most metals are not used in the pure state. This is because a pure metal is usually rather soft and deforms easily. The deliberate addition of an impurity considerably increases the mechanical strength, e.g. copper is alloyed with zinc or tin to obtain brass or bronze, iron has carbon and other metals added to give steel, and so on. It is the additives which govern the mechanical properties.

The effect of the impurities arises from the way in which they are incorporated into the metal lattice. It is extremely difficult to grow structurally good crystals for two reasons. Firstly, it is theoretically impossible to produce a perfect crystal lattice in which every atom is in its correct place. There will always be some atoms missing or some in interstitial positions (see Ch. 10). Although such irregularities weaken the lattice and decrease the binding energy, the randomisation of these defects throughout the lattice gives a positive entropy term which offsets this loss. Even at very low temperatures and in crystals which are grown very slowly, there is a finite number of such defects in the lattice. In practice, however, crystals are usually grown relatively rapidly and the atoms are not always able to adopt the equilibrium configuration. It frequently happens, for example, that a plane of atoms is incomplete, extending only part way through a crystallite, so that the atoms at its edge are each surrounded by one atom less than those in the regular part of the lattice forming a discontinuity or dislocation. There will be a line of such atoms extending along the edge of this plane, forming an **edge dislocation**. Screw dislocations are also possible in which the discontinuities form a spiral through the crystal.

It is very difficult to grow crystals which do not contain dislocations, and it is the dislocations which (largely) determine the mechanical properties. Consider the edge dislocation shown in Fig. 9.15. In the immediate vicinity of the dislocation the lattice is distorted to accommodate the extra layer of atoms. The edge consists of a row of atoms with one neighbour less than usual, and two other atoms have moved towards each other into the gap. It would not require very much further distortion for one of these atoms to move completely into the gap to continue the extra row of

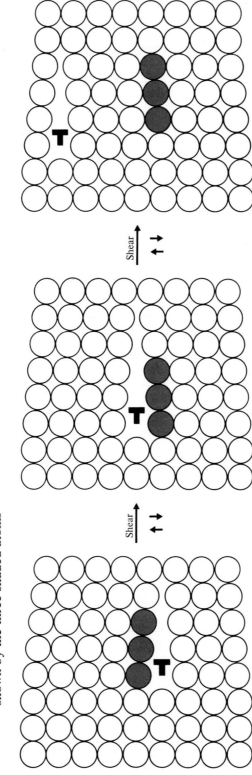

Fig. 9.15 Plastic deformation of a metal by movement of an edge dislocation under shear. The original position of the dislocation is shown by the three shaded atoms

atoms. The dislocation is thus moved into the next plane. Such movement of the atoms could be induced by applying a shearing stress to the crystal, so that if dislocations are present, the crystal will deform easily as the dislocations move. The real mechanical strength of the metal will therefore be much less than the intrinsic strength calculated from the binding energy. Pure metals are therefore relatively soft.

The strength of the crystal could be increased by eliminating the dislocations, and recently there has been much interest in the growing of 'whiskers' of various materials (e.g. carbon, silicon carbide, aluminium); each whisker is effectively a single crystal containing very few dislocations. Used in a suitable matrix, materials of excellent mechanical properties can be obtained but at present are too expensive for widespread use.

More practically, the strength can also be improved by the addition of a second component, the atoms of which are of different radius from those of the host lattice, since these foreign atoms tend to become localised at the dislocation. At an edge dislocation the lattice is slightly compressed at one side of the edge and slightly expanded at the other. Larger atoms can therefore be accommodated easily in the expanded region, as happens for example when zinc is added to copper to make bronze. There is a mutually advantageous interaction between the dislocation and the zinc atoms, so that it becomes more difficult to move the dislocation, and the metal becomes harder. Similar effects are obtained by the introduction of smaller atoms which fit into interstitial positions; these also help to fix the dislocations, e.g. the use of carbon in steels.

Bibliography

PW, 19.

D. M. Adams, *Inorganic Solids*, Wiley, 1974. Chapter 8 gives a useful introductory survey of metallic bonding.

L. V. Azaroff, *Introduction to Solids*, McGraw-Hill, 1969. Readable account of structures, dislocations, phase-diagrams, and properties of metals.

C. S. Barrett and T. B. Massalski, *Structures of Metals*, 3rd edn., McGraw-Hill, 1966. Structures of solids (ionic, metallic and interstitial), theories of bonding, dislocations.

W. Hume-Rothery, R. E. Smallman, and C. W. Haworth, *The Structures of Metals and Alloys*, 5th edn., The Institute of Metals, 1969. A classic. Good, readable presentation.

R. S. Nyholm, *Adv. Sci.*, 421 (1967). Interesting review of bonding properties of metals from the chemist's viewpoint.

P. S. Rudman, J. Stringer, and K. I. Jaffee (eds.), *Phase Stability in Metals and Alloys*, McGraw-Hill, 1967. Conference papers, some very detailed, some at introductory level, of structures, constitution, and theory of alloys and intermetallic systems.

J. H. Westbrook (ed.), *Intermetallic Compounds*, Wiley, 1967. A comprehensive text with some sections at introductory level.

In previous chapters many examples have been mentioned of compounds which do not have simple compositions, e.g. the oxides of the *d*- and *f*-block metals. Such compounds are said to be **non-stoicheiometric**, that is, they appear to deviate from the law of simple proportions. This phenomenon is not restricted to oxides; it appears, for instance, in sulphides and other chalcogenides and could, in principle, be found in any system forming an ionic lattice. Molecular compounds, of necessity, must show the same, definite composition under all conditions and, even if the crystal lattice is not perfect, imperfections can only arise by disorientation or the omission or inclusion of entire molecules, so that the composition is not affected.

10.1 Defective crystal lattices

The implication of deviation from simple stoicheiometry in an ionic solid is that the crystal lattice is not perfect. Indeed, it can be shown that even a stoicheiometric lattice will usually be imperfect, either by the omission of ions from their regular sites (Schottky defects) or by some ions occupying abnormal sites (interstitial sites, Frenkel defects);† such defects must also occur in metallic and other systems. While the formation of these defects involves losses of lattice energy, their randomisation throughout the lattice gives a positive contribution to the entropy of the system. At any temperature above absolute zero, therefore, there will be a certain equilibrium concentration of defects, and the crystal must be imperfect. (Even at absolute zero, some configurational entropy will remain.) As the temperature is increased, more defects will form until, at the melting point, the lattice can no longer maintain its rigidity. At normal temperatures these defects are usually present in only very small concentrations, e.g. in sodium chloride at 25 °C only one ion site in about 3×10^{16} is vacant. Defects such as these are bound to occur in all crystals, they are *intrinsic defects*, and have no direct effect on the stoicheiometry.

If the stoicheiometry of a binary compound departs from the simple, idealised value, at least one of the constituent elements must be present in more than one oxidation state. For instance, when zinc oxide, ZnO, is heated it loses oxygen and becomes yellow. At 800 °C, 0·000035 moles of

---

† These two types of defect can be distinguished by e.g. density or electrical conductivity measurements. Frenkel defects do not affect the density, whereas Schottky defects result in a density lower than that calculated from the unit-cell dimensions (which can be obtained by X-ray diffraction). Provided electronic conduction does not occur, an electric current must be carried by the migration of ions through the lattice. Determination of the sign of the charge carriers then allows a distinction to be drawn, since Frenkel defects affect only one sublattice (which is therefore that responsible for the conduction) while Schottky defects must occur in equal numbers in both sublattices, so that the current will be carried both by cations and anions.

O_2 are lost per mole of ZnO. To preserve the electrical neutrality of the crystal, either some of the Zn^{2+} ions or some of the remaining O^{2-} ions must be reduced. It is found that the basic crystal lattice is preserved and that, as oxygen is lost, zinc ions are reduced to zinc atoms which occupy interstitial sites which are normally vacant. From the point of view of the ideal crystal lattice, this form contains an excess of the metal, and the formula is written $Zn_{1 \cdot 00007}O$ to show this. Cadmium oxide also loses oxygen on heating, becoming yellow or even black, and $0 \cdot 00025$ moles of O_2 are lost at 650 °C, but in this case the metal lattice is preserved and some oxide ions are omitted from their proper sites, $CdO_{0 \cdot 9995}$. For every vacancy, one Cd^{2+} ion must be reduced to a cadmium atom. In both cases the colours shown are associated with the occurrence of two oxidation states: light absorption supplies energy for electron transfer from M^0 to M^{2+} to occur. The different behaviour of the two systems, which can be detected by, e.g., careful density measurement, is related to their different structures. Zinc oxide has the wurtzite structure, with tetrahedral coordination of Zn^{2+}, while CdO has the NaCl-structure. In the latter case, cadmium atoms cannot be accommodated in the tetrahedral interstitial sites, resulting in an oxide-deficient lattice. As might be expected, both are n-type semiconductors.

As in these two cases, it is usually the metallic element which undergoes an oxidation-state change. This is for energetic reasons; clearly the electron affinity of Zn^{2+} or Cd^{2+} is greater than that of O^{2-}. Even this process is not very favourable, however, as is shown by the small deviations from ideal composition and the high temperatures involved.

In the formation of a metal-deficient or non-metal-rich phase, one of the components must be oxidised. Again, it is usually easier to oxidise the metal than the non-metal, although exceptions do occur. For example, a very small excess of iodine may be incorporated into potassium iodide, giving cation vacancies and a corresponding number of iodine atoms; it is much more feasible, energetically, to form I^0 from I^- than K^{2+} from K^+.

In all these cases, the deviations from ideal stoicheiometry are very small. This is primarily because the additional material incorporated in the lattice is uncharged, thus there is no gain in lattice energy (even if, as in some cases, extensive charge delocalisation occurs). Formation of vacancies also reduces the lattice energy. The gain in configurational entropy is quite small, so that the equilibrium composition lies very close to the ideal value, except, perhaps, at very high temperatures. Wide variations in composition are much more likely when two or more oxidation states are readily available, as with many of the d- and f-block metals, and it is the oxides and sulphides of these elements which often show quite gross deviations from ideal composition and give highly defective structures. When such deviations from simple stoicheiometry occur they will, of course, do so in the direction of another stable oxidation state of the metal. For instance, the composition of Fe_2O_3 varies towards that of FeO (or Fe_3O_4), corresponding to the reduction of Fe^{3+} to Fe^{2+}, whereas that of Cu_2O changes towards CuO, with oxidation of Cu^+ to Cu^{2+}. In some cases (e.g. TiO, VO) changes in both directions are observed.

Although it is almost always the oxidation state of the metal which is adjusted, the composition change need not involve modification of the metal sublattice. An oxidative-variation may be achieved by omitting metal ions to give a metal-deficient structure, e.g. $Fe_{1-x}O$, or by incorporating extra non-metal ions in interstitial sites (non-metal excess), as in UO_{2+x}. The omission of a cation or the introduction of an interstitial anion involves a decrease in lattice energy, but this is offset by a gain due to the oxidation of some of the cations, Fe^{2+} to Fe^{3+} or U^{4+} to U^{6+}. Similarly, deviation towards a lower oxidation state may occur in a metal-excess (e.g. $Ti_{1+x}S_2$) or a non-metal-deficient (e.g. CeO_{2-x}) manner. The incorporation of extra metal ions, albeit with a lower charge than the rest, in interstitial positions will usually result in an increase in lattice energy, while the inclusion of neutral atoms generally destabilises the structure; the latter process therefore usually gives rise to only small deviations from ideal composition. Some examples of these types of behaviour are given in Table 10.1.

Table 10.1   Some non-stoicheiometric systems

Deviation towards a higher oxidation state:

Metal-deficient	Non-metal-excess
$Mn_{1-x}O$	UO_{2+x}
$Fe_{1-x}O$	Pu_2O_{3+x}
$Fe_{1-x}S$	Cm_2O_{3+x}
$Cu_{2-x}O$	PaO_{2+x}

Deviation towards a lower oxidation state:

Metal-excess	Non-metal-deficient
$Zn_{1-x}O$	CdO_{1-x}
$Fe_{2+x}O_3$	CeO_{2-x}
$Ti_{1+x}S_2$	PrO_{2-x}

It is not always possible to give a precise description in terms of excess or deficiency of a particular component, particularly when the composition range is large and spans two 'normal' simple stoicheiometries. For example, cerium, praseodymium, and the actinides form a series of oxides with compositions varying from M_2O_3 to MO_2. All the structures are based on the fluorite structure: in MO_2 the structure is perfect (apart from intrinsic defects), in M_2O_3 one-quarter of the anions is missing in an orderly fashion, so that a distinct, regular lattice is formed, although this could be described as an oxygen-deficient form of MO_2. Equally, the intermediate phases may be described either as oxygen-deficient, MO_{2-x}, or as oxide-excess, M_2O_{3+x}. It is also possible for both sub-lattices to be defective simultaneously, e.g. in: 'TiO' and 'VO', both of which show wide ranges of composition about the ideal stoicheiometry, arising from different numbers of vacancies in the metal and oxide sub-lattices.

10.2   Ordering of defects

At high temperatures the entropy contribution to the free energy is significant but in many cases the loss of enthalpy in forming the defective lattice is, as suggested above, not necessarily very great. If the energy difference between the two oxidation states of the metal is not large, and the radii of the cations are suitable, it is conceivable that there could be an increase in lattice energy, particularly if the defects are ordered into a 'super-lattice'. As the temperature is lowered, there may then be a transition from the random structure to an ordered phase (**order-disorder transition**). For example, CeO_2 exhibits a randomly oxygen-deficient fluorite structure above 685 °C with a lower composition limit of $CeO_{1.72}$, and continuous variations appear possible between the limits, truly CeO_{2-x}. At lower temperatures this phase is unstable and breaks up into a mixture of appropriate proportions of stoicheiometric CeO_2 and an ordered phase of composition $Ce_{32}O_{58}$, in which oxide ion vacancies are arranged regularly through the lattice so that the new unit cell corresponds to eight unit cells of the fluorite lattice, there being six oxide vacancies in this unit..

It seems likely that the majority of, if not all, non-stoicheiometric phases adopt ordered structures at moderate temperatures, although the ordering involved may occur over large distances, i.e. the unit cell may be very large. Many systems are now known in which the aggregation of defects into recognisable units occurs. One system which has been studied for many years is FeO_{1-x}, formed by heating iron in oxygen above 570 °C; this is an intriguing system in that the observable composition ranges do not include the ideal stoicheiometry. On cooling, this phase decomposes, giving Fe_3O_4 and, initially, an oxide closer in composition to FeO, and finally more Fe_3O_4 and iron metal are formed. The basic lattice of FeO is of the NaCl-type, and the variations in composition occur by the omission of Fe^{2+} ions and the oxidation of two of the remaining cations to

Fe^{3+}. At very high temperatures or compositions close to FeO the vacancies are probably distributed randomly throughout the lattice, but at most temperatures some ordering is detectable. Some of the Fe^{3+} ions are on tetrahedral sites (the radius is favourable and there are no ligand-field stabilisation effects for Fe^{3+}) and a defect unit is created consisting of one of the tetrahedral Fe^{3+} ions associated with two octahedral cation vacancies (one being the 'missing' Fe^{2+}, the other being obtained by resiting an octahedral Fe^{3+} on a tetrahedral site). Such clusters of defects have been shown to occur, for instance, in Fe$_{0.947}$O. For higher degrees of oxidation, e.g. Fe$_{0.918}$O, further aggregation may occur, with four tetrahedral Fe^{3+} ions forming a tetrahedral unit associated with thirteen octahedral vacancies (see Fig. 10.1). The negative charges which these units would have is offset by the surrounding octahedral Fe^{3+} ions. The local structure is thus very similar to the inverse spinel structure of Fe$_3$O$_4$ (see Fig. 3.11), and provides a reasonable mechanism for the disproportionation reaction. When Fe$_{1-x}$O is cooled, aggregation of defects occurs, giving Fe$_3$O$_4$ nuclei and leaving the remainder of the lattice less imperfect and closer to ideal FeO.

Fig. 10.1   The cluster of four tetrahedral Fe^{3+} ions and thirteen cation vacancies in Fe$_{1-x}$O, shown with parts of its surrounding NaCl lattice (after Adams, *Inorganic Solids*, Wiley, 1974)

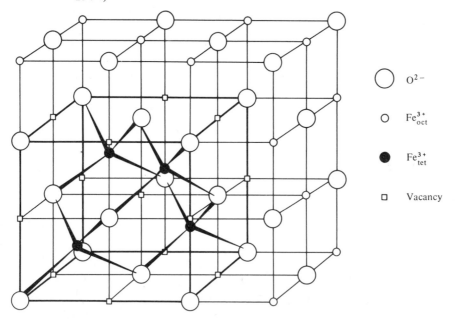

O^{2-}

Fe$^{3+}_{oct}$

Fe$^{3+}_{tet}$

Vacancy

The wide range of stoicheiometry of Fe$_{1-x}$O ($0.84 \leqslant x \leqslant 0.95$) is related to the ease of formation of Fe^{3+} from Fe^{2+}. For other metals, the corresponding ionisation energy is often greater and the composition range narrower, as with Co$_{1-x}$O ($0.988 \leqslant x \leqslant 1.000$) and N$_{1-x}$O ($0.999 \leqslant x \leqslant 1.000$). The monoxides of titanium and vanadium show extremely wide variations in composition, and both the cation and anion lattices are defective. At temperatures below 900 °C, the vacancies in TiO form well-ordered lattices. There is almost certainly some overlap between the d-orbitals of adjacent metal ions, allowing delocalisation of charge and reductive deviations from the ideal composition. The metallic conductivity shown by these phases is consistent with this idea.

It is probable that many compounds which exhibit a wide range of composition actually form a series of discrete phases, each having its own, characteristic, regular lattice, and that genuine non-stoicheiometry (involving a single structure with varying degrees of defectiveness) occurs only over quite narrow composition ranges (except at high temperatures). For example, in the Cr-S system the sulphide ions form an hcp array and the metal atoms occupy octahedral sites. When all these sites are filled the stoicheiometry is CrS (this is the NiAs-structure). The composition Cr_2S_3, the upper limit, is obtained by omitting, in an orderly fashion, two-thirds of the metal ions in alternate layers. Intermediate phases, each with a narrow composition range, are obtained by ordering different proportions of vacancies within alternate layers, giving the series CrS, $Cr_{0.85-0.87}S$, $Cr_{0.85}S$, $Cr_{0.70-0.76}S$, $Cr_{0.69}S$, and $Cs_{0.67}S$. The second of these, 'Cr_7S_8', does exhibit some disorder, in that the cation vacancies are randomised but are still restricted to alternate cation layers. The corresponding iron compound, Fe_7S_8, shows the same structure between 360 and 400 °C; below 360 °C the vacancies are ordered while above 300 °C they are randomised over all the octahedral sites in all the layers.

The occurrence of such ordered phases, each with its own distinct lattice, implies that defects in the 'normal' lattice are able to interact and that the energy of the crystal lattice can be affected by such interactions over large distances. This is illustrated by the **shear structures** (sometimes called Magnéli phases after the Swedish worker who investigated them). These represent yet another different method of ordering anion vacancies: the vacancies are brought together, localised into particular parallel planes, and eliminated, giving rise to a local discontinuity in the crystal lattice with the normal lattice extending on both sides. This is exemplified by the ReO_3-structure, for which such behaviour is common. In an fcc array of oxide ions, one quarter of the octahedral sites is occupied by Re^{6+} ions. A section through this structure is shown in Fig. 10.2a. If oxide ion vacancies are localised into a {100} plane they can be eliminated by moving one half of the structure relative to the other half (Fig. 10.2b). The crystal now appears to have undergone a slipping or shearing along the plane of eliminated vacancies, and this process is known as *crystallographic shear*. Along the crystallographic shear (c.s.) plane, one oxide ion has been eliminated for each

Fig. 10.2   (*a*) A {001} plane in the ReO_3 lattice. Above and below this layer are planes consisting only of oxide ions, completing the octahedral coordination about each metal ion. Each oxide ion thus lies between two metal ions, giving the stoicheiometry MO_3. The dashed lines indicate one unit of the fcc lattice; note the two vacant octahedral sites. The oxide ions in the {100} plane (shaded) are eliminated to give the sheared structure shown in (*b*)

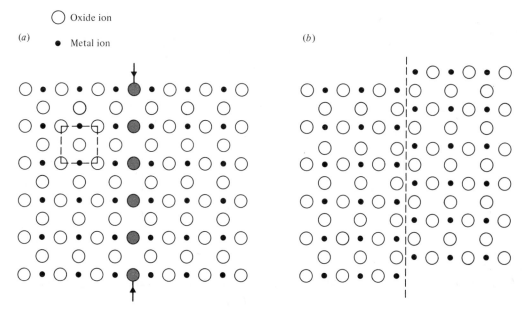

metal ion, so that the local structure corresponds to the stoicheiometry MO_2; this composition would be achieved by letting the c.s. planes approach as closely as possible (Fig. 10.3a) – this is effectively a $CdCl_2$-type structure in which all octahedral sites of alternate layers are occupied). As the c.s. planes are moved apart the stoicheiometry changes: MO_2, M_2O_5, M_3O_8, M_4O_{11}, etc. (Fig. 10.3a–d). Provided the c.s. planes are regularly spaced through the lattice, as appears to happen in practice, an homologous series is obtained with the general formula M_nO_{3n-1}, as found for the oxides of molybdenum and tungsten. Such structures appear to be quite common; other examples are based on the rutile structure, giving the homologous series M_nO_{2n-1} (e.g. for M = Ti, V), and it is also possible for two independent sets of c.s. planes to intersect, giving block structures in which the lattice is composed of infinite columns of various, but well-defined, cross-sections, as in the niobium and tantalum oxides.

Fig. 10.3   Regular spacing of {100} crystallographic shear planes in the ReO_3-lattice, giving the compositions (*a*) MO_2, (*b*) M_2O_5, (*c*) M_3O_8 and (*d*) M_4O_{11}

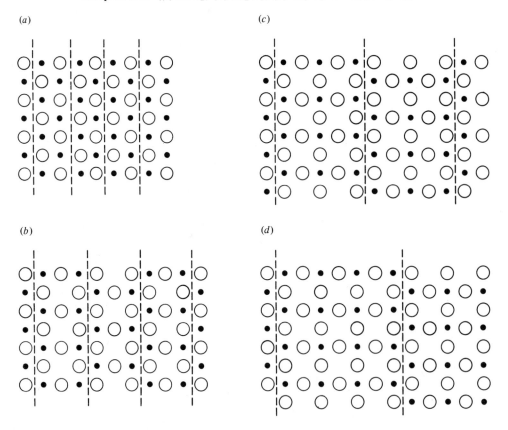

(*a*)   (*c*)

(*b*)   (*d*)

In all these cases, many members of each series are known, and for large values of n very small changes in stoicheiometry occur, yet each has a well-defined crystal structure with the c.s. planes regularly spaced through the lattice. For instance, all the compounds Ti_nO_{2n-1} with $16 \leqslant n \leqslant 36$ have the same basic structure (the c.s. plane is $\{1\bar{3}2\}$), but these 21 compounds cover a composition range of only $TiO_{1.9375}$ to $TiO_{1.9722}$. It has recently been realised that, although in any one phase all the c.s. planes are parallel, they may adopt different orientations in different phases; each orientation corresponds to the elimination of a different proportion of vacancies (Fig. 10.4 shows one alternative orientation). It thus becomes possible to describe *any* composition in terms of

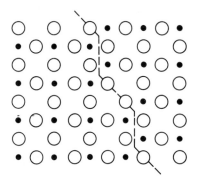

Fig. 10.4 A {210} crystallographic shear plane

regular, appropriately spaced c.s. planes of suitable orientation. Such systems, which can be based on the TiO_2-, ReO_3- or α-PbO_2 structures, have been called *infinitely adaptive*. It is, of course, still necessary to have two oxidation states close in energy.

It should be noted that some crystal structures are less tolerant of defects than others. Clearly, the NaCl-, TiO_2-, and ReO_3-lattices are readily adaptable, although in different ways, and many systems based on these structures have been mentioned above. On the other hand, the corundum (α-Al_2O_3) and A-M_2O_3 lattices are apparently less well-suited to the creation of vacancies or the inclusion of interstitial ions, since phases crystallising with these lattices exhibit relatively narrow composition ranges even when higher or lower oxidation states are readily available, e.g. 'Ti_2O_3' covers the range $TiO_{1.501}$ to $TiO_{1.512}$ in marked contrast to the wide ranges shown by 'TiO' and 'TiO_2'.

The above survey has covered the major ways in which defects may be incorporated and organised in ionic lattices. Unfortunately, with the present state of knowledge, little systematisation appears possible, the long-range interactions involved are subtle and not understood, and it is not in general possible to predict whether a particular material is likely to be non-stoicheiometric nor what type of defect structure will be adopted. Obviously, to form shear structures the basic lattice must be relatively open and there must be a lower oxidation state readily available; such behaviour could not be expected for NaCl-type lattices, which must adopt some other method of including or eliminating vacancies. It is also not clear why some compounds, notably oxides and sulphides, should be very prone to non-stoicheiometry while others, e.g. halides, are not. Much remains for further investigation in this field, which has important practical applications. It should also be emphasized that the concepts and types of defect structures illustrated here are not confined to ionic materials but apply also to interstitial compounds, such as hydrides, carbides, nitrides, and to intermetallic compounds and alloys, further extending the range of technologically important materials.

10.3 Thermodynamic considerations

Since chemical behaviour is governed by free energy relationships, the essential difference between a highly stoicheiometric compound and a non-stoicheiometric phase is the way in which the free energy of the system varies with composition: the former is thus a special case of the latter. For compounds of closed-shell ions (oxides, halides, etc. of *s*- and *p*-block metals) the enthalpy of creation of an oxidative or reductive defect is very high and positive. The free energy of such a system is a minimum at the stoicheiometric composition and rises sharply on either side, and this behaviour is found at all temperatures. In a three-dimensional representation, free energy-composition-temperature, such a system would appear as a very narrow wedge or knife-edge, lying

Fig. 10.5   Free-energy surfaces for phases with (*a*) well-defined stoicheiometry (the line pro-
jected on to the χ–T plane resents the conventional phase diagram), and (*b*) a large
potential composition range (the phase diagram now depends on the presence of other
phases – see text)

(*a*)   (*b*)

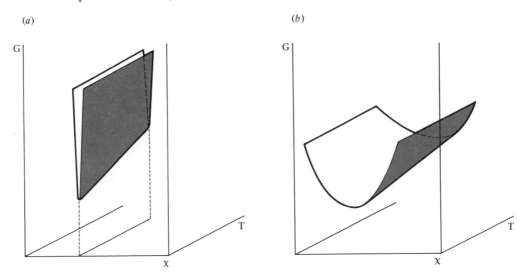

in the composition-temperature plane (Fig. 10–5a). On the conventional phase diagram (composition *vs* temperature) such a system would appear as a vertical line, and is often known as a *line
phase*.

The corresponding free-energy surface for a non-stoicheiometric system would be much less
strongly curved, a shallow, gently varying surface, representing the ease with which oxidation or
reduction can be achieved (Fig. 10.5b). In the majority of cases the formation of reductive and
oxidative defects requires different amounts of energy, so that the curvature is not necessarily
symmetrical about the minimum. There is also no requirement that the minimum should correspond to any particular, simple stoicheiometry.

Whether the non-stoicheiometric phase will be able to exhibit a large range of composition
depends not only on the shallowness of the free-energy surface, but also on its position and the
relative positions of the surfaces for the neighbouring phases. Fig. 10.6a shows a hypothetical
example of a system consisting of the pure metal, M, a broad phase of nominal composition MO,
and a line phase of composition M_2O_3. The region of stability of the non-stoicheiometric phase,
MO_a to MO_b, is given by the common tangent method (see Ch. 9), the tangent on the pure metal
side being drawn from the free energy of the metal, G_M^0 (i.e. the metal is here treated as an infinitely
thin line phase). The relative positions and shapes of the free-energy curves will depend on the
temperature, so that the composition range will also be a function of temperature (Fig. 10.6b). In
general, the free energy of the phase containing the metal in the highest oxidation state will vary
most rapidly with temperature, so that there will frequently be a temperature below which the
tangent between the extreme phases lies below the free energy curve for the intermediate
compound (Fig. 10.6c), i.e. the intermediate compound is now unstable to disproportionation.
These features are illustrated by the partial phase diagram for the Ti–O system (Fig. 10.7). The
cubic NaCl-type phase, TiO (high), is stable only at high temperatures and also exhibits a widening
composition range as the temperature is increased. Below about 500 °C, this phase disproportionates into monoclinic, highly ordered TiO (low) together with either $TiO_{0.5}$ (the δ-phase) or Ti_2O_3,
depending on the composition.

Fig. 10.6 Free-energy diagrams for a broad-range phase, MO, and a narrow phase, M_2O_3. The composition range of MO is given by the contact points of the two tangents. (*b*) represents a higher temperature than (*a*), giving a wider range, while in (*c*), representing a lower temperature, MO is unstable to disproportionation

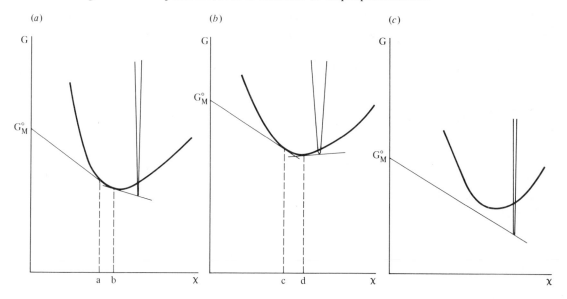

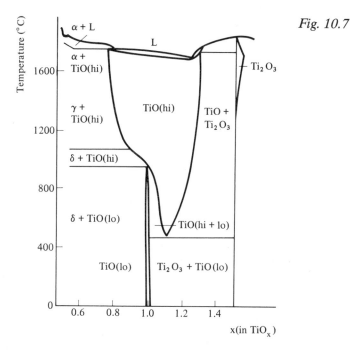

Fig. 10.7 Part of the phase diagram for the Ti–O system (redrawn from M. D. Banus and T. Reed (1970) *The Chemistry of Extended Defects in Non-Metallic Solids* (Ed. L. Eyring and M. O'Keefe) North-Holland Publish Co.)

Similar variations in the rate of change of free energy with temperature (i.e. in entropy) account for order-disorder transitions, such as those in the CeO_2 or PrO_2 systems. Here a phase with continuously variable composition and randomised defects, and therefore with relatively high entropy, is stable at high temperatures but on cooling an homologous series of narrow, ordered

Fig. 10.8   Free-energy diagrams for a broad, non-stoicheiometric phase and an associated homologous series. At the higher temperature, (*a*), the broad phase is formed, at the lower, (*b*), the series of compounds is obtained but the composition may still appear to vary smoothly since the succession of tangents approximates to a smooth curve.

(*a*)

(*b*)

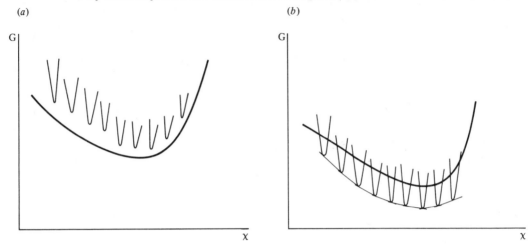

Fig. 10.9   Phase-diagram of part of the Pr–O system. The arrowed line phases represent part of the homologous series Pr_nO_{2n-2} (redrawn from M. S. Jenkins, R. P. Tureotte and L. Eyring (1970) *The Chemistry of Extended Defects in Non-Metallic Solids*, (Ed. L. Eyring and M. O'Keefe) North-Holland Publishing Co.)

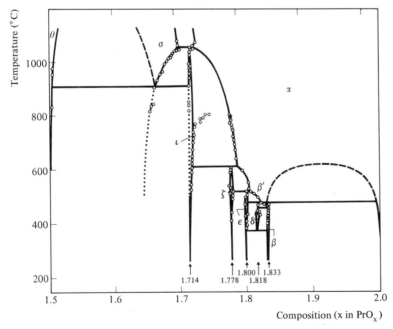

phases is formed. This effect is shown in Fig. 10.8 and exemplified in Fig. 10.9 by the Pr_2O_3–PrO_2 system. The high-temperature phase (α) is stable in the range $PrO_{1.72}$–$PrO_{2.00}$, but on cooling gives a series of oxides of general formula Pr_nO_{2n-2}; those with n = 7(ι), 9(ζ), 10(ϵ), 11(δ), and 12(β) are shown. It will be appreciated that, particularly for the higher members of homologous series, experimental differentiation between a series of ordered compounds and a wide, non-stoicheiometric phase is very difficult.

Bibliography

ES, 4

D. M. Adams, *Inorganic Solids*, Wiley, 1974. Chapter 9 is a good, short, readable account of defects and non-stoicheiometry.

N. N. Greenwood, *Ionic Crystals, Lattice Defects, and Non-stoichiometry*, Butterworth, 1968. Readable, detailed account of ionic lattices, intrinsic defects and non-stoicheiometry.

W. J. Moore, *Seven Solid States*, Benjamin, 1967. Good, brief, readable account. Chapter 1 treats intrinsic defects in NaCl, Chapter 5 deals with non-stoicheiometry in NiO.

J. S. Anderson, *J. Chem Soc. Dalton Trans*, 1107 (1973). Good description of crystallographic shear and infinitely adaptive systems. Fairly technical.

L. Eyring and M. O'Keefe (Eds), *The Chemistry of Extended Defects in Non-Metallic Compounds*, North-Holland, 1970. Mainly specialised papers on particular systems, but the first two contributions are useful (Reed, $3d$-oxides; Anderson, thermodynamics).

L. Mandelcorn (Ed.), *Non-Stoichiometric Compounds*, Academic Press, 1964. Chapter 3 (Wadsley) gives a good account of different structure types and Chapter 5 (Subbarao) a fairly technical treatment of physical properties.

A. Rabeneau (Ed.), *Problems of Non-Stoichiometry*, North-Holland, 1970. Detailed and technical. Good general reviews by Anderson and Jeannin.

C. N. R. Rao (Ed.), *Modern Aspects of Solid State Chemistry*, Plenum Press, 1970. Highly technical articles.

Ionisation energies (kJ mol^{-1})

s-block

Li	520	7 297	
Na	496	4 561	
K	419	3 069	
Rb	403	2 650	
Cs	376	2 420	
Be	899	1 758	14 850
Mg	738	1 450	7 731
Ca	590	1 146	4 942
Sr	549	1 064	
Ba	502	965	

p-block

Al	578	1 817	2 745	11 580	
Ga	579	1 979	2 962	6 190	
In	558	1 820	2 705	5 250	
Tl	589	1 970	2 880	2 890	
Ge	760	1 537	3 301	4 410	8 975
Sn	708	1 411	2 942	3 928	7 778
Pb	715	1 450	3 080	4 082	6 694
Sb	834	1 590	2 440	4 250	5 401
Bi	703	1 609	2 465	4 370	5 402

3*d*-block

Sc	631	1 235	2 389	7 130		
Ti	656	1 309	2 650	4 173	96 273	
V	650	1 414	2 828	4 600	6 293	12 434
Cr	652	1 592	2 986	4 900	7 050	8 744	15 520
Mn	717	1 509	3 251	5 021	7 322	9 456	11 460
Fe	762	1 561	2 956	5 502	7 531	9 832	12 340
Co	758	1 644	3 231	5 104	8 054	10 230	12 720
Ni	736	1 752	3 489	5 397	7 531	10 630	13 140
Cu	745	1 958	3 545	5 682	7 908	10 230	13 510
Zn	906	1 734	3 831				

4d-block

Y	616	1 180	1 979				
Zr	674	1 268	2 217	3 313	7 991	9 540	11 380
Nb	664	1 381	2 416	3 700	4 770	9 958	12 050
Mo	685	1 558	2 618	4 480	5 397	6 945	12 050
Tc	703	1 472	2 850	4 146	5 690	7 322	9 058
Ru	711	1 617	2 746	4 477	6 067	7 824	9 665
Rh	720	1 744	2 996	4 393	6 464	8 201	10 120
Pd	804	1 874	3 177	4 707	6 360	8 661	10 580
Ag	731	2 072	3 360	5 012	6 736	8 577	11 170
Cd	876	1 630	3 615				

5d-block

La	541	1 103	1 849				
Hf	760	1 440	2 250	3 210	7 991		
Ta	760	1 560	2 155	3 192	4 513		
W	770	1 710	2 322	3 410	4 623	5 878	
Re	759	1 600	2 510	3 632	4 916	6 171	7 615
Os	840	1 640	2 410	3 849	5 188	6 569	7 991
Ir	879	1 648	2 602	3 766	5 481	6 945	8 494
Pt	870	1 791	2 745	3 958	5 314	7 238	8 870
Au	889	1 980	2 895	4 192	5 606	7 029	9 242
Hg	1 007	1 809	3 300				

4f-block

La	538	1 067	1 850
Ce	540	1 047	1 938
Pr	521	1 018	2 081
Nd	530	1 035	2 129
Pm	536	1 051	
Sm	542	1 068	2 286
Eu	547	1 085	2 404
Gd	595	1 168	1 988
Tb	570	1 111	2 093
Dy	567	1 126	2 213
Ho	574	1 139	2 201
Er	581	1 151	2 165
Tm	589	1 163	2 273
Yb	603	1 174	2 416
Lu	513	1 341	2 046

Appendix B
E^0 values

Couple	Acid Solution Reaction	E^0/V	Basic Solution Reaction	E_b^0/V
s-block				
Li^+/Li	$Li^+ + e^- = Li$	$-3\cdot04$		
Na^+/Na	$Na^+ + e^- = Na$	$-2\cdot71$		
K^+/K	$K^+ + e^- = K$	$-2\cdot92$		
Rb^+/Rb	$Rb^+ + e^- = Rb$	$-2\cdot92$		
Cs^+/Cs	$Cs^+ + e^- = Cs$	$-2\cdot92$		
Be^{2+}/Be	$Be^{2+} + 2e^- = Be$	$-1\cdot85$	$BeO + H_2O + 2e^- = Be + 2OH^-$	$-1\cdot78$
Mg^{2+}/Mg	$Mg^{2+} + 2e^- = Mg$	-2.37	$Mg(OH)_2 + 2e^- = Mg + 2OH^-$	$-1\cdot86$
Ca^{2+}/Ca	$Ca^{2+} + 2e^- = Ca$	-2.87	$Ca(OH)_2 + 2e^- = Ca + 2OH^-$	$-2\cdot19$
Sr^{2+}/Sr	$Sr^{2+} + 2e^- = Sr$	$-2\cdot89$	$Sr(OH)_2 + 2e^- = Ba + 2OH^-$	$-2\cdot05$
Ba^{2+}/Ba	$Ba^{2+} + 2e^- = Ba$	$-2\cdot90$	$Ba(OH)_2 + 2e^- = Ba + 2OH^-$	$-2\cdot16$
Ra^{2+}/Ra	$Ra^{2+} + 2e^- = Ra$	$-2\cdot92$		
p-block				
Al^{3+}/Al	$Al^{3+} + 3e^- = Al$	$-1\cdot66$	$Al(OH)_3 + 3e^- = Al + 3OH^-$	$-1\cdot47$
Ga^{3+}/Ga	$Ga^{3+} + 3e^- = Ga$	$-0\cdot53$	$Ga(OH)_4^- + 3e^- = Ga + 4OH^-$	$-0\cdot39$
In^{3+}/In	$In^{3+} + 3e^- = In$	$-0\cdot34$	$In(OH)_3 + 3e^- = In + 3OH^-$	$-0\cdot17$
In^+/In	$In^+ + e^- = In$	$-0\cdot25$		
Tl^{3+}/Tl	$Tl^{3+} + e^- = Tl$	$+0\cdot72$	$Tl(OH)_3 + 3e^- = Tl + 3OH^-$	$+0\cdot69$
Tl^+/Tl	$Tl^+ + e^- = Tl$	$-0\cdot34$	$TlOH + e^- = Tl + OH^-$	$+0\cdot49$
Ge^{4+}/Ge	$GeO_2 + 4H^+ + 4e^-$ $= Ge + 2H_2O$	$-0\cdot15$	$HGeO_3^- + 2H_2O + 4e^-$ $= Ge + 5OH^-$	$-0\cdot20$
Ge^{2+}/Ge	$Ge^{2+} + 2e^- = Ge$	$0\cdot0$		
Sn^{4+}/Sn^{2+}	$Sn^{4+} + 2e^- = Sn^{2+}$	$+0\cdot15$	$Sn(OH)_6^- + 2e^-$ $= HSnO_2^- + H_2O + 3OH^-$	$-0\cdot10$
Sn^{2+}/Sn	$Sn^{2+} + 2e^- = Sn$	$-0\cdot14$	$HSnO_2^- + H_2O + 2e^-$ $= Sn + 3OH^-$	$-0\cdot08$
Pb^{4+}/Pb^{2+}	$PbO_2 + 4H^+ + 2e^-$ $= Pb^{2+} + 2H_2O$	$+1\cdot46$	$PbO_2 + H_2O + 2e^-$ $= PbO + 2OH^-$	$+1\cdot08$
Pb^{2+}/Pb	$Pb^{2+} + 2e^- = Pb$	$-0\cdot13$	$PbO + H_2O + 2e^- = Pb + 2OH^-$	$+0\cdot25$
Sb^{5+}/Sb^{3+}	$Sb_2O_5 + 6H^+ + 4e^-$ $= 2SbO^+ + 3H_2O$	$+0\cdot58$		
Sb^{3+}/Sb	$Sb_2O_3 + 6H^+ + 3e^-$ $= Sb + 3H_2O$	$+0\cdot15$	$SbO_2^- + 2H_2O + 3e^-$ $= Sb + 4OH^-$	$+0\cdot17$
Bi^{5+}/Bi^{3+}	$Bi_2O_4 + 4H^+ + 2e^-$ $= 2BiO^+ + 2H_2O$	$+1\cdot59$		
Bi^{3+}/Bi	$BiO^+ + 2H^+ + 3e^-$ $= Bi + H_2O$	$+0\cdot32$	$Bi_2O_3 + 3H_2O + 6e^-$ $= 2Bi + 6OH^-$	$+0\cdot37$

Couple	Acid Solution		Basic Solution	
	Reaction	E^0/V	Reaction	E_b^0/V
3d-block				
Sc^{3+}/Sc	$Sc^{3+}+3e^-=Sc$	$-2\cdot08$	$Sc(OH)_3+3e^-=Sc+3OH^-$	$-1\cdot78$
Ti^{2+}/Ti	$Ti^{2+}+2e^-=Ti$	$-1\cdot63$		
Ti^{3+}/Ti	$Ti^{3+}+3e^-=Ti$	$-1\cdot21$		
Ti^{4+}/Ti	$Ti(OH)_2^{2+}+2H^++4e^-$			
	$=Ti+2H_2O$	$-0\cdot88$		
V^{2+}/V	$V^{2+}+2e^-=V$	$-1\cdot19$		
V^{3+}/V^{2+}	$V^{3+}+e^-=V^{2+}$	$-0\cdot26$		
V^{4+}/V^{3+}	$VO^{2+}+2H^++e^-$			
	$=V^{3+}+H_2O$	$+0\cdot36$		
V^{5+}/V	$VO_2^++4H^++5e^-$		$VO_4^{3-}+4H_2O+5e^-$	
	$=V+4H_2O$	$-0\cdot25$	$=V+8OH^-$	$-0\cdot33$
Cr^{2+}/Cr	$Cr^{2+}+2e^-=Cr$	$-0\cdot91$		
Cr^{3+}/Cr	$Cr^{3+}+3e^-=Cr$	$-0\cdot74$	$Cr(OH)_3+3e^-=Cr+3OH^-$	$-0\cdot65$
Cr^{4+}/Cr			$CrO_2+2H_2O+4e^-$	
			$=Cr+4OH^-$	$-0\cdot44$
Cr^{6+}/Cr^{3+}	$Cr_2O_7^{2-}+14H^++6e^-$		$CrO_4^{2-}+4H_2O+6e^-$	
	$=2Cr^{3+}+7H_2O$	$+1\cdot33$	$=Cr+8OH^-$	$+0\cdot10$
Mn^{2+}/Mn	$Mn^{2+}+2e^-=Mn$	$-1\cdot18$	$Mn(OH)_2+2e^-=Mn+2OH^-$	$-0\cdot72$
Mn^{3+}/Mn^{2+}	$Mn^{3+}+e^-=Mn^{2+}$	$+1\cdot51$	$Mn(OH)_3+e^-=Mn(OH)_2+OH^-$	$+0\cdot98$
Mn^{4+}/Mn^{2+}	$MnO_2+4H^++2e^-$		$MnO_2+2H_2O+2e^-$	
	$=Mn^{2+}+2H_2O$	$+1\cdot23$	$=Mn(OH)_2+2OH^-$	$+0\cdot78$
Mn^{6+}/Mn^{4+}			$MnO_4^{2-}+3H_2O+2e^-$	
			$=MnO_2+4OH^-$	$+1\cdot43$
Mn^{7+}/Mn^{2+}	$MnO_4^-+8H^++5e^-$			
	$=Mn^{2+}+4H_2O$	$+1\cdot51$		
Mn^{7+}/Mn^{4+}			$MnO_4^-+2H_2O+3e^-$	
			$=MnO_2+4OH^-$	$+1\cdot42$
Mn^{7+}/Mn^{6+}	$MnO_4^-+e^-=MnO_4^{2-}$	$+0\cdot56$		
Fe^{2+}/Fe	$Fe^{2+}+2e^-=Fe$	$-0\cdot44$	$Fe(OH)_2+2e^-=Fe+2OH^-$	$-0\cdot05$
Fe^{3+}/Fe^{2+}	$Fe^{3+}+e^-=Fe^{2+}$	$+0\cdot77$	$Fe(OH)_3+e^-=Fe(OH)_2+OH^-$	$+0\cdot27$
Fe^{6+}/Fe^{3+}	$FeO_4^{2-}+8H^++3e^-$		$FeO_4^{2-}+4H_2O+3e^-$	
	$=Fe^{3+}+4H_2O$	$+2\cdot20$	$=Fe(OH)_3+5OH^-$	$+1\cdot55$
Co^{2+}/Co	$Co^{2+}+2e^-=Co$	$-0\cdot28$	$Co(OH)_2+2e^-=Co+2OH^-$	$-0\cdot10$
Co^{3+}/Co^{2+}	$Co^{3+}+e^-=Co^{2+}$	$+1\cdot81$	$Co(OH)_3+e^-=Co(OH)_2+OH^-$	$+1\cdot00$
Ni^{2+}/Ni	$Ni^{2+}+2e^-=Ni$	$-0\cdot25$	$Ni(OH)_2+2e^-=Ni+2OH^-$	$+0\cdot11$
Ni^{4+}/Ni	$NiO_2+4H^++4e^-$			
	$=Ni+2H_2O$	$+1\cdot68$		
Ni^{4+}/Ni^{2+}			$NiO_2+2H_2O+2e^-$	
			$=Ni(OH)_2+2OH^-$	$+1\cdot32$
Cu^+/Cu			$Cu_2O+H_2O+2e^-=2Cu+2OH^-$	$+0\cdot47$
Cu^{2+}/Cu	$Cu^{2+}+2e^-=Cu$	$+0\cdot34$		
Cu^{2+}/Cu^+	$Cu^{2+}+e^-=Cu^+$	$+0\cdot15$	$2Cu(OH)_2+2e^-$	
			$=Cu_2O+2OH^-+H_2O$	$+0\cdot75$
Zn^{2+}/Zn	$Zn^{2+}+e^-=Zn$	$-0\cdot76$	$Zn(OH)_2+2e^-=Zn+2OH^-$	$-0\cdot41$
4d-block				
Y^{3+}/Y	$Y^{3+}+3e^-=Y$	$-2\cdot37$	$Y(OH)_3+3e^-=Y+3OH^-$	$-1\cdot98$
Nb^{3+}/Nb	$Nb^{3+}+3e^-=Nb$	$-1\cdot10$		
	$Nb_2O_3+6H^++3e^-$			
	$=Nb+3H_2O$	$-0\cdot64$		
Mo^{3+}/Mo	$Mo^{3+}+3e^-=Mo$	$-0\cdot20$		
Mo^{6+}/Mo			$MoO_4^{2-}+4H_2O+6e^-$	
			$=Mo+8OH^-$	$-0\cdot22$

continued

Couple	Acid Solution		Basic Solution	
	Reaction	E^0/V	Reaction	E_b^0/V
Tc^{2+}/Tc	$Tc^{2+}+2e^-=Tc$	$+0.4$		
Tc^{4+}/Tc^{2+}	$TcO_2+4H^++2e^-$ $=Tc^{2+}+2H_2O$	$+0.6$		
Tc^{7+}/Tc^{4+}	$TcO_4^-+4H^++3e^-$ $=TcO_2+2H_2O$	$+0.7$		
Ru^{7+}/Ru^{6+}			$RuO_4^-+e^-=RuO_4^{2-}$	$+1.43$
Rh^{3+}/Rh	$Rh^{3+}+3e^-=Rh$	$+0.80$		
	$Rh_2O_3+6H^++6e^-$ $=2Rh+3H_2O$	$+0.87$	$Rh_2O_3+3H_2O+6e^-$ $=2Rh+6OH^-$	$+0.87$
	$RhCl_6^{3-}+3e^-$ $=Rh+6Cl^-$	$+0.43$		
Ru^{2+}/Ru	$RuCl_5^{3-}+2e^-$ $=Ru+5Cl^-$	$+0.61$		
Pd^{2+}/Pd	$Pd^{2+}+2e^-=Pd$	$+0.99$	$Pd(OH)_2+2e^-=Pd+2OH^-$	$+0.90$
	$PdCl_4^{2-}+2e^-$ $=Pd+4Cl^-$	$+0.62$		
	$PdBr_4^{2-}+2e^-$ $=Pd+4Br^-$	$+0.60$		
Pd^{4+}/Pd^{2+}	$PdCl_6^{2-}+2e^-$ $=PdCl_4^{2-}+2Cl^-$	$+1.29$		
Ag^+/Ag	$Ag^++e^-=Ag$	$+0.80$	$Ag_2O+H_2O+2e^-=2Ag+2OH^-$	$+1.17$
Ag^{2+}/Ag^+	$Ag^{2+}+e^-=Ag^+$	$+1.98$	$2AgO+H_2O+2e^-=Ag_2O+2OH^-$	$+1.44$
Ag^{3+}/Ag^+			$Ag_2O_3+H_2O+2e^-$ $=2AgO+2OH^-$	$+1.57$
Cd^{2+}/Cd	$Cd^{2+}+2e^-=Cd$	-0.40	$Cd(OH)_2+2e^-=Cd+2OH^-$	$+0.02$

5d-block

Couple	Acid Solution		Basic Solution	
La^{3+}/La	$La^{3+}+3e^-=La$	-2.52	$La(OH)_3+3e^-=La+3OH^-$	-2.07
La^{3+}/La^{2+}	$La^{3+}+e^-=La^{2+}$	(-3.8)		
Zr^{4+}/Zr	$Zr^{4+}+4e^-=Zr$	-1.53	$H_2ZrO_3+H_2O+4e^-$ $=Zr+4OH^-$	-1.53
Ta^{3+}/Ta	$Ta_2O_3+6H^++6e^-$ $=2Ta+3H_2O$	-0.81		
W^{6+}/W	$WO_3+6H^++6e^-$ $=W+3H_2O$	-0.09	$WO_4^{2-}+4H_2O+6e^-$ $=W+8OH^-$	-0.22
Re^{4+}/Re	$ReO_2+4H^++4e^-$ $=Re+2H_2O$	$+0.25$	$ReO_2+2H_2O+4e^-$ $=Re+4OH^-$	$+0.25$
Re^{6+}/Re	$ReO_4^{2-}+8H^++6e^-$ $=Re+4H_2O$	$+0.36$		
Re^{6+}/Re^{4+}	$ReO_4^{2-}+4H^++2e^-$ $=ReO_2+2H_2O$	$+0.51$		
Re^{7+}/Re			$ReO_4^-+4H_2O+7e^-$ $=Re+8OH^-$	$+0.25$
Re^{7+}/Re^{4+}			$ReO_4^-+2H_2O+3e^-$ $=ReO_2+4OH^-$	$+0.24$
Os^{8+}/Os	$OsO_4+8H^++8e^-$ $=Os+4H_2O$	$+0.85$	$HOsO_5^-+4H_2O+8e^-$ $=Os+9OH^-$	$+0.85$
Ir^{3+}/Ir	$IrCl_6^{3-}+3e^-=Ir+6Cl^-$	$+0.77$	$Ir_2O_3+3H_2O+6e^-$ $=2Ir+6OH^-$	$+0.73$
Ir^{4+}/Ir^{3+}	$IrCl_6^{2-}+e^-=IrCl_6^{3-}$	$+1.02$		

	Acid Solution		**Basic Solution**	
Couple	Reaction	E^0/V	Reaction	E_b^0/V
Pt^{2+}/Pt	$Pt(OH)_2 + 2H^+ + 2e^-$ $= Pt + 2H_2O$	+0·98	$Pt(OH)_2 + 2e^- = Pt + 2OH^-$	+0·98
	$PtCl_4^{2-} + 2e^- = Pt + 4Cl^-$	+0·73		
	$PtBr_4^{2-} + 2e^- = Pt + 4Br^-$	+0·58		
Pt^{4+}/Pt^{2+}	$PtO_2 + 2H^+ + 2e^- = Pt(OH)_2$	$ca.$ +1·1	$Pt(OH)_6^{2-} + 2e^-$ $= Pt(OH)_2 + 4OH^-$	$ca.$ +1·0
	$PtCl_6^{2-} + 2e^-$ $= PtCl_4^{2-} + 2Cl^-$	+0·68		
Au^+/Au	$Au^+ + e^- = Au$	+1·69		
	$AuBr_2^- + e^- = Au + 2Br^-$	+0·96		
Au^{3+}/Au	$Au^{3+} + 3e^- = Au$	+1·50		
	$Au(OH)_3 + 3H^+ + 3e^-$ $= Au + 3H_2O$	+1·45		
	$AuCl_4^- + 3e^- = Au + 4Cl^-$	+1·00		
	$AuBr_4^- + 3e^- = Au + 4Br^-$	+0·87 (60 °C)		
Hg^+/Hg	$Hg_2^{2+} + 2e^- = 2Hg$	+0·79		
	$Hg_2Cl_2 + 2e^- = 2Hg + 2Cl^-$	+0·27		
	$Hg_2Br_2 + 2e^- = 2Hg + 2Br^-$	−0·14		
	$Hg_2I_2 + 2e^- = 2Hg + 2I^-$	−0·04		
Hg^{2+}/Hg^+	$2Hg^{2+} + 2e^- = Hg_2^{2+}$	+0·92		
Hg^{2+}/Hg	$HgBr_4^{2-} + 2e^- = Hg + 4Br^-$	+0·22	$HgO + H_2O + 2e^- = Hg + 2OH^-$	+0·93
	$HgI_4^{2-} + 2e^- = Hg + 4I^-$	−0·04		
4f-block				
Ce^{3+}/Ce	$Ce^{3+} + 3e^- = Ce$	−2·48	$Ce(OH)_3 + 3e^- = Ce + 3OH^-$	−2·07
Ce^{3+}/Ce^{2+}	$Ce^{3+} + e^- = Ce^{2+}$	(−3·5)		
Ce^{4+}/Ce^{3+}	$Ce^{4+} + e^- = Ce^{3+} (2M\ HClO_4)$	+1·74		
Pr^{3+}/Pr	$Pr^{3+} + 3e^- = Pr$	−2·46	$Pr(OH)_3 + 3e^-$ $= Pr + 3OH^-$	−2·02
Pr^{3+}/Pr^{2+}	$Pr^{3+} + e^- = Pr^{2+}$	(−3·0)		
Pr^{4+}/Pr^{3+}	$Pr^{4+} + e^- = Pr^{3+}$	+2·86		
Nd^{3+}/Nd	$Nd^{3+} + 3e^- = Nd$	−2·43	$Nd(OH)_3 + 3e^-$ $= Nd + 3OH^-$	−2·01
Nd^{3+}/Nd^{2+}	$Nd^{3+} + e^- = Nd^{2+}$	(−2·8)		
Pm^{3+}/Pm	$Pm^{3+} + 3e^- = Pm$	−2·42	$Pm(OH)_3 + 3e^- = Pm + 3OH^-$	−2·01
Pm^{3+}/Pm^{2+}	$Pm^{3+} + e^- = Pm^{2+}$	(−2·5)		
Sm^{3+}/Sm	$Sm^{3+} + 3e^- = Sm$	−2·41	$Sm(OH)_3 + 3e^- = Sm + 3OH^-$	−2·00
Sm^{3+}/Sm^{2+}	$Sm^{3+} + e^- = Sm^{2+}$	−1·15		
Eu^{3+}/Eu	$Eu^{3+} + 3e^- = Eu$	−2·41	$Eu(OH)_3 + 3e^- = Eu + 3OH^-$	−2·00
Eu^{3+}/Eu^{2+}	$Eu^{3+} + e^- = Eu^{2+}$	−0·43		
Gd^{3+}/Gd	$Gd^{3+} + 3e^- = Gd$	−2·40	$Gd(OH)_3 + 3e^- = Gd + 3OH^-$	−1·99
Gd^{3+}/Gd^{2+}	$Gd^{3+} + e^- = Gd^{2+}$	(−3·6)		
Tb^{3+}/Tb	$Tb^{3+} + 3e^- = Tb$	−2·39	$Tb(OH)_3 + 3e^- = Tb + 3OH^-$	−1·96
Tb^{3+}/Tb^{2+}	$Tb^{3+} + e^- = Tb^{2+}$	(−3·5)		
Dy^{3+}/Dy	$Dy^{3+} + 3e^- = Dy$	−2·35	$Dy(OH)_3 + 3e^- = Dy + 3OH^-$	−1·95
Dy^{3+}/Dy^{2+}	$Dy^{3+} + e^- = Dy^{2+}$	(−2·6)		
Ho^{3+}/Ho	$Ho^{3+} + 3e^- = Ho$	−2·32	$Ho(OH)_3 + 3e^- = Ho + 3OH^-$	−1·94
Ho^{3+}/Ho^{2+}	$Ho^{3+} + e^- = Ho^{2+}$	(−2·9)		
Er^{3+}/Er	$Er^{3+} + 3e^- = Er$	−2·30	$Er(OH)_3 + 3e^- = Er + 3OH^-$	−1·92
Er^{3+}/Er^{2+}	$Er^{3+} + e^- = Er^{2+}$	(−3·0)		
Tm^{3+}/Tm	$Tm^{3+} + 3e^- = Tm$	−2·28	$Tm(OH)_3 + 3e^- = Tm + 3OH^-$	−1·91
Tm^{3+}/Tm^{2+}	$Tm^{3+} + e^- = Tm^{2+}$	(−2·1)		
Yb^{3+}/Yb	$Yb^{3+} + 3e^- = Yb$	−2·27	$Yb(OH)_3 + 3e^- = Yb + 3OH^-$	−1·90

continued

Couple	Acid Solution Reaction	E^0/V	Basic Solution Reaction	E_b^0/V
Yb^{3+}/Yb^{2+}	$Yb^{3+}+e^-=Yb^{2+}$	$-1\cdot21$		
Lu^{3+}/Lu	$Lu^{3+}+3e^-=Lu$	$-2\cdot26$	$Lu(OH)_3+3e^-=Lu+3OH^-$	$-1\cdot89$

5f-block

Couple	Acid Solution Reaction	E^0/V	Basic Solution Reaction	E_b^0/V
Ac^{3+}/Ac	$Ac^{3+}+3e^-=Ac$	$-2\cdot58$		
Th^{4+}/Th	$Th^{4+}+4e^-=Th$	$-2\cdot4$		
Th^{4+}/Th^{3+}	$Th^{4+}+e^-=Th^{3+}$	$-2\cdot48$		
Pa^{5+}/Pa	$PaO_2^++4H^++5e^-$ $=Pa+2H_2O$	$-1\cdot0$		
Pa^{5+}/Pa	$PaO_2^++4H^++e^-$ $=Pa^{4+}+2H_2O$	$ca.\ -0\cdot1$		
U^{3+}/U	$U^{3+}+3e^-=U$	$-1\cdot80$	$U(OH)_3+3e^-=U+3OH^-$	$-1\cdot34$
U^{4+}/U^{3+}	$U^{4+}+e^-=U^{3+}$	$-0\cdot60$	$U(OH)_4+e^-=U(OH)_3+OH^-$	$-1\cdot31$
U^{5+}/U^{3+}	$UO_2^++4H^++2e^-$ $=U^{3+}+2H_2O$	$-0\cdot02$		
U^{5+}/U^{4+}	$UO_2^++4H^++e^-$ $=U^{4+}+2H_2O$	$+0\cdot56$		
U^{6+}/U^{3+}	$UO_2^{2+}+4H^++3e^-$ $=U^{3+}+2H_2O$	$+0\cdot01$		
U^{6+}/U^{4+}	$UO_2^{2+}+4H^++2e^-$ $=U^{4+}+2H_2O$	$+0\cdot32$	$UO_2(OH)_2+2H_2O+2e^-$ $=U(OH)_4+2OH^-$	$+0\cdot21$
	$UO_2^{2+}+2e^-=UO_2$	$+0\cdot45$		
U^{6+}/U^{5+}	$UO_2^{2+}+e^-=UO_2^+$	$+0\cdot08$		
Np^{3+}/Np	$Np^{3+}+3e^-=Np$	$-1\cdot83$	$Np(OH)_3+3e^-=Np+3OH^-$	$-1\cdot42$
Np^{4+}/Np^{3+}	$Np^{4+}+e^-=Np^{3+}$	$+0\cdot19$	$Np(OH)_4+e^-=Np(OH)_3+OH^-$	$-0\cdot93$
Np^{5+}/Np^{3+}	$NpO_2^++4H^++2e^-$ $=Np^{3+}+2H_2O$	$+0\cdot44$		
Np^{5+}/Np^{4+}	$NpO_2^++4H^++e^-$ $=Np^{4+}+2H_2O$	$+0\cdot68$	$NpO_2OH+2H_2O+e^-$ $=Np(OH)_4+OH^-$	$+1\cdot22$
Np^{6+}/Np^{3+}	$NpO_2^{2+}+4H^++3e^-$ $=Np^{3+}+2H_2O$	$+0\cdot68$		
Np^{6+}/Np^{4+}	$NpO_2^++4H^++2e^-$ $\bullet=Np^{4+}+2H_2O$	$+0\cdot92$	$NpO_2(OH)_2+2H_2O+2e^-$ $=Np(OH)_4+2OH^-$	$+1\cdot26$
Np^{6+}/Np^{5+}	$NpO_2^{2+}+e^-=NpO_2^+$	$+1\cdot15$	$NpO_2(OH)_2+e^-=NpO_2OH$ $+OH^-$	$+1\cdot31$
Np^{7+}/Np^{6+}	$NpO_2^{3+}+e^-=NpO_2^{2+}$	$>2\cdot1$	$NpO_5^{3-}+H_2O+e^-$ $=NpO_4^{2-}+2OH^-$	$+1\cdot37$
Pu^{3+}/Pu	$Pu^{3+}+3e^-=Pu$	$-2\cdot03$	$Pu(OH)_3+3e^-=Pu+3OH^-$	$-1\cdot59$
Pu^{4+}/Pu^{3+}	$Pu^{4+}+e^-=Pu^{3+}$	$+1\cdot02$	$Pu(OH)_4+e^-=Pu(OH)_3+OH^-$	$-0\cdot12$
Pu^{5+}/Pu^{3+}	$PuO_2^++4H^++2e^-$ $=Pu^{3+}+2H_2O$	$+1\cdot07$	$PuO_2OH+2H_2O+2e^-$ $=Pu(OH)_3+2OH^-$	$+0\cdot73$
Pu^{5+}/Pu^{4+}	$PuO_2^++4H^++e^-$ $=Pu^{4+}+2H_2O$	$+1\cdot12$	$PuO_2OH+2H_2O+e^-$ $=Pu(OH)_4+OH^-$	$+1\cdot59$
Pu^{6+}/Pu^{3+}	$PuO_2^{2+}+4H^++3e^-$ $=Pu^{3+}+2H_2O$	$+1\cdot02$	$PuO_2(OH)_3^-+2H_2O+3e^-$ $=Pu(OH)_3+4OH^-$	$+0\cdot85$
Pu^{6+}/Pu^{4+}	$PuO_2^{2+}+4H^++2e^-$ $=Pu^{4+}+2H_2O$	$+1\cdot02$	$PuO_2(OH)_3^-+2H_2O+2e^-$ $=Pu(OH)_4+3OH^-$	$+1\cdot34$
Pu^{6+}/Pu^{5+}	$PuO_2^{2+}+e^-=PuO_2^+$	$+0\cdot93$	$PuO_2(OH)_3^-+e^-=PuO_2OH+2OH^-$	$+1\cdot09$
Pu^{7+}/Pu^{6+}			$PuO_5^{3-}+H_2O+e^-$ $=PuO_4^{2-}+2OH^-$	$+1\cdot69$
Am^{3+}/Am	$Am^{3+}+3e^-=Am$	$-2\cdot38$	$Am(OH)_3+3e^-=Am+3OH^-$	$-1\cdot88$
Am^{3+}/Am^{2+}	$Am^{3+}+e^-=Am^{2+}$	$-2\cdot9$		

Couple	Acid Solution		Basic Solution	
	Reaction	E^0/V	Reaction	E_b^0/V
Am^{4+}/Am^{3+}	$Am^{4+} + e^- = Am^{3+}$	$+2\cdot38$	$Am(OH)_4 + e^- = Am(OH)_3 + OH^-$	$+1\cdot33$
Am^{5+}/Am^{3+}	$AmO_2^+ + 4H^+ + 2e^-$ $= Am^{3+} + 2H_2O$	$+1\cdot74$	$AmO_2OH + 2H_2O + 2e^-$ $= Am(OH)_3 + 2OH^-$	$+1\cdot43$
Am^{5+}/Am^{4+}	$AmO_2^+ + 4H^+ + e^-$ $= Am^{4+} + 2H_2O$	$+1\cdot10$	$AmO_2OH + 2H_2O + e^-$ $= Am(OH)_4 + OH^-$	$+1\cdot53$
Am^{6+}/Am^{3+}	$AmO_2^{2+} + 4H^+ + 3e^-$ $= Am^{3+} + 2H_2O$	$+1\cdot70$	$AmO_2(OH)_2 + 3H_2O + 3e^-$ $= Am(OH)_3 + 3OH^-$	$+1\cdot53$
Am^{6+}/Am^{4+}	$AmO_2^{2+} + 4H^+ + 2e^-$ $= Am^{4+} + 2H_2O$	$+1\cdot36$	$AmO_2(OH)_2 + 2H_2O + 2e^-$ $= Am(OH)_4 + 2OH^-$	$+1\cdot73$
Am^{6+}/Am^{5+}	$AmO_2^{2+} + e^- = AmO_2^+$	$+1\cdot62$	$AmO_2(OH)_2 + e^- = AmO_2OH + OH^-$	$+1\cdot93$
Cm^{3+}/Cm	$Cm^{3+} + 3e^- = Cm$	$-2\cdot29$		
Cm^{3+}/Cm^{2+}	$Cm^{3+} + e^- = Cm^{2+}$	$-5\cdot0$		
Cm^{4+}/Cm^{3+}	$Cm^{4+} + e^- = Cm^{3+}$	$+3\cdot28$		
Bk^{3+}/Bk^{2+}	$Bk^{3+} + e^- = Bk^{2+}$	$-3\cdot4$		
Bk^{4+}/Bk^{3+}	$Bk^{4+} + e^- = Bk^{3+}$	$+1\cdot68$		
Cf^{3+}/Cf	$Cf^{3+} + 3e^- = Cf$	$-2\cdot28$		
Cf^{3+}/Cf^{2+}	$Cf^{3+} + e^- = Cf^{2+}$	$-1\cdot9$		
Cf^{4+}/Cf^{3+}	$Cf^{4+} + e^- = Cf^{3+}$	$>1\cdot64$		
Es^{3+}/Es^{2+}	$Es^{3+} + e^- = Es^{2+}$	$-1\cdot57$		
Fm^{3+}/Fm^{2+}	$Fm^{3+} + e^- = Fm^{2+}$	$-1\cdot3$		
Md^{3+}/Md^{2+}	$Md^{3+} + e^- = Md^{2+}$	$-0\cdot12$		
No^{3+}/No^{2+}	$No^{3+} + e^- = No^{2+}$	$+1\cdot48$		

Appendix C
Enthalpies of formation

(ΔH_f^0, 298K, of solids unless otherwise specified
values in parentheses are estimates)

Column 1 — $\Delta H_f^0/\text{kJ mol}^{-1}$

s-block

Species	$\Delta H_f^0/\text{kJ mol}^{-1}$
Li(g)	+161
Li$^+$(g)	+681
LiF	−613
LiCl	−408
LiBr	−350
LiI	−270
Li$_2$O	−599
Li$_2$O$_2$	−633
LiOH	−485
Na(g)	+108
Na$^+$(g)	+604
NaF	−574
NaCl	−411
NaBr	−361
NaI	−288
Na$_2$O	−418
Na$_2$O$_2$	−513
NaO$_2$	−261
NaOH	−428
K(g)	+90
K$^+$(g)	+509
KF	−567
KCl	−437
KBr	−394
KI	−328
K$_2$O	−363
K$_2$O$_2$	−496
KO$_2$	−283
KOH	−425
Rb(g)	+82
Rb$^+$(g)	+485
RbF	−549
RbCl	−431
RbBr	−389
RbI	−328
Rb$_2$O	−330

Column 2 — $\Delta H_f^0/\text{kJ mol}^{-1}$

Species	$\Delta H_f^0/\text{kJ mol}^{-1}$
Cs(g)	+78
Cs$^+$(g)	+454
CsF	−555
CsCl	−443
CsBr	−395
CsI	−337
Cs$_2$O	−318
Be(g)	+326
Be$^+$(g)	+1 225
Be^{2+}(g)	+2 983
BeF$_2$	−1 014
BeCl$_2$	−496
BeBr$_2$	−370
BeI$_2$	−212
BeO	−599
Be(OH)$_2$	−906
Mg(g)	+149
Mg$^+$(g)	+887
Mg^{2+}(g)	+2 337
MgF$_2$	−1 123
MgCl$_2$	−641
MgBr$_2$	−519
MgI$_2$	−360
MgO	−601
Mg(OH)$_2$	−925
Ca(g)	+177
Ca$^+$(g)	+767
Ca^{2+}(g)	+1 913
CaF$_2$	−1 221
CaCl$_2$	−801
CaBr$_2$	−683
CaI$_2$	−536
CaO	−634
Ca(OH)$_2$	−986
Sr(g)	+164
Sr$^+$(g)	+713

Column 3 — $\Delta H_f^0/\text{kJ mol}^{-1}$

Species	$\Delta H_f^0/\text{kJ mol}^{-1}$
Sr^{2+}(g)	+1 777
SrF$_2$	−1 218
SrCl$_2$	−829
SrBr$_2$	−716
SrI$_2$	−561
SrO	−603
Sr(OH)$_2$	−654
Ba(g)	+178
Ba$^+$(g)	+680
Ba^{2+}(g)	+1 645
BaF$_2$	−1 204
BaCl$_2$	−859
BaBr$_2$	−755
BaI$_2$	−605
BaO	−554

p-block

Species	$\Delta H_f^0/\text{kJ mol}^{-1}$
Al(g)	+326
Al$^+$(g)	+802
Al^{2+}(g)	+2 619
Al^{3+}(g)	+5 364
AlF$_3$	−1 490
AlF$_2$	(−774)
AlF	(−393)
AlCl$_3$	−705
AlCl$_2$	(−272)
AlCl	(−188)
AlBr$_3$	−527
AlBr$_2$	(−146)
AlBr	(−125)
AlI$_3$	−364
AlI$_2$	(+8)
AlI	(−46)
Al$_2$O$_3$	−1 676
Al(OH)$_3$	−1 284
Ga(g)	+272

Column 4 — $\Delta H_f^0/\text{kJ mol}^{-1}$

Species	$\Delta H_f^0/\text{kJ mol}^{-1}$
Ga$^+$(g)	+951
Ga^{2+}(g)	+2 930
Ga^{3+}(g)	+5 892
GaF$_3$	−1 163
GaF	−252
GaCl$_3$	−525
GaCl	−86
GaBr$_3$	−387
GaBr	−50
GaI$_3$	−239
GaI	+29
Ga$_2$O$_3$	−1 089
Ga$_2$O	−356
In(g)	+244
In$^+$(g)	+802
In^{2+}(g)	+2 622
In^{3+}(g)	+5 327
InF	−203
InCl$_3$	−538
InCl	−186
InBr$_3$	−429
InBr	−175
InI$_3$	−238
InI	−116
In$_2$O$_3$	−926
Tl(g)	+180
Tl$^+$(g)	+769
Tl^{2+}(g)	+2 739
Tl^{3+}(g)	+5 619
TlF	−325
TlCl$_3$	−315
TlCl	−204
TlBr	−173
TlI	−124
Tl$_2$O$_3$	−326
Tl$_2$O	−179
Ge(g)	+372

	$\Delta H_f^0/\text{kJ mol}^{-1}$		$\Delta H_f^0/\text{kJ mol}^{-1}$		$\Delta H_f^0/\text{kJ mol}^{-1}$		$\Delta H_f^0/\text{kJ mol}^{-1}$
$Ge^+(g)$	+1 132	$Bi(g)$	+207	V_2O_5	−1 560	Fe_2O_3	−825
$Ge^{2+}(g)$	+2 669	$Bi^+(g)$	+910	VO_2	−718	Fe_3O_4	−1 118
$Ge^{3+}(g)$	+5 970	$Bi^{2+}(g)$	+2 519	V_2O_3	−1 238	$Fe_{0.947}O$	−266
$Ge^{4+}(g)$	+10 380	$Bi^{3+}(g)$	+4 984	VO	−420		
$GeCl_4(l)$	−532	$Bi^{4+}(g)$	+9 354			$Co(g)$	+425
$GeBr_4(l)$	−348	$Bi^{5+}(g)$	+14 756	$Cr(g)$	+397	$Co^+(g)$	+1 183
GeI_4	−142	$BiCl_3$	−379	$Cr^+(g)$	+1 049	$Co^{2+}(g)$	+2 827
GeI_2	−88	$BiBr_3$	−276	$Cr^{2+}(g)$	+2 641	$Co^{3+}(g)$	+6 058
GeO_2	−551	BiI_3	−150	$Cr^{3+}(g)$	+5 627	CoF_3	−811
GeO	−212	Bi_2O_3	−574	$Cr^{4+}(g)$	+10 527	CoF_2	−692
				$Cr^{5+}(g)$	+17 577	$CoCl_2$	−313
		3d-block		$Cr^{6+}(g)$	+26 321	$CoBr_2$	−221
$Sn(g)$	+301			CrF_3	−1 112	CoI_2	−89
$Sn^+(g)$	+1 009	$Sc(g)$	+326	CrF_2	−757	Co_3O_4	−900
$Sn^{2+}(g)$	+2 420	$Sc^+(g)$	+957	$CrCl_4$	−427	CoO	−239
$Sn^{3+}(g)$	+5 362	$Sc^{2+}(g)$	+1 235	$CrCl_3$	−560		
$Sn^{4+}(g)$	+9 290	$Sc^{3+}(g)$	+2 389	$CrCl_2$	−397	$Ni(g)$	+430
$SnCl_4(l)$	−472	$ScCl_3$	−924	$CrBr_3$	−302	$Ni^+(g)$	+1 186
$SnCl_2$	−325	$ScBr_3$	−751	CrI_3	−204	$Ni^{2+}(g)$	+2 918
$SnBr_4$	−377	Sc_2O_3	−1 906	CrI_2	−159	$Ni^{3+}(g)$	+6 407
$SnBr_2$	−244			CrO_3	−590	NiF_2	−651
SnI_2	−144	$Ti(g)$	+473	CrO_2	−598	$NiCl_2$	−316
SnO_2	−581	$Ti^+(g)$	+1 129	Cr_2O_3	−1 140	$NiBr_2$	−226
SnO	−286	$Ti^{2+}(g)$	+2 438			NiI_2	−86
		$Ti^{3+}(g)$	+5 088			Ni_2O_3	−490
		$Ti^{4+}(g)$	+9 261	$Mn(g)$	+281	NiO	−240
$Pb(g)$	+197	TiF_4	−1 649	$Mn^+(g)$	+998		
$Pb^+(g)$	+912	TiF_3	−1 436	$Mn^{2+}(g)$	+2 507	$Cu(g)$	+339
$Pb^{2+}(g)$	+2 362	$TiCl_4(l)$	−805	$Mn^{3+}(g)$	+5 785	$Cu^+(g)$	+1 084
$Pb^{3+}(g)$	+5 442	$TiCl_3$	−722	$Mn^{4+}(g)$	+10 779	$Cu^{2+}(g)$	+3 042
$Pb^{4+}(g)$	+9 524	$TiCl_2$	−515	$Mn^{5+}(g)$	+18 101	$Cu^{3+}(g)$	+6 587
PbF_4	−942	$TiBr_4$	−618	$Mn^{6+}(g)$	+27 556	CuF_2	−543
PbF_2	−677	$TiBr_3$	−550	MnF_3	−996	$CuCl_2$	−206
$PbCl_4(l)$	−314	$TiBr_2$	−397	MnF_2	−795	$CuCl$	−135
$PbCl_2$	−360	TiI_4	−425	$MnCl_2$	−481	$CuBr_2$	−142
$PbBr_2$	−278	TiI_3	−335	$MnBr_2$	−385	$CuBr$	−105
PbI_2	−175	TiI_2	−255	MnI_2	−243	CuI	−68
PbO_2	−277	TiO_2	−945	$Mn_2O_7(l)$	−742	CuO	−157
Pb_3O_4	−733	Ti_2O_3	−1 536	MnO_2	−520	Cu_2O	−169
PbO	−218			Mn_2O_3	−958		
		$V(g)$	+515	Mn_3O_4	−1 388	$Zn(g)$	+125
		$V^+(g)$	+1 165	MnO	−385	$Zn^+(g)$	+1 031
$Sb(g)$	+259	$V^{2+}(g)$	+2 579			$Zn^{2+}(g)$	+2 765
$Sb^+(g)$	+1 093	$V^{3+}(g)$	+5 407	$Fe(g)$	+416	$Zn^{3+}(g)$	+6 596
$Sb^{2+}(g)$	+2 683	$V^{4+}(g)$	+10 007	$Fe^+(g)$	+1 185	ZnF_2	−764
$Sb^{3+}(g)$	+5 123	$V^{5+}(g)$	+16 299	$Fe^{2+}(g)$	+2 739	$ZnCl_2$	−415
$Sb^{4+}(g)$	+9 373	$VF_5(l)$	−1 473	$Fe^{3+}(g)$	+5 695	$ZnBr_2$	−328
$Sb^{5+}(g)$	+14 774	VF_4	−1 343	$Fe^{4+}(g)$	+11 197	ZnI_2	−209
SbF_3	−915	$VCl_4(l)$	−598	$Fe^{5+}(g)$	+18 728	ZnO	−348
$SbCl_5(l)$	−440	VCl_3	−586	$Fe^{6+}(g)$	+28 560		
$SbCl_3$	−382	VCl_2	−460	FeF_3	−1 045		
$SbBr_3$	−260	VBr_4	−393	FeF_2	−706	**4d-block**	
SbI_3	−98	VBr_3	−494	$FeCl_3$	−399	$Y(g)$	+410
Sb_2O_5	−972	VBr_2	−348	$FeCl_2$	−342	$Y^+(g)$	+1 026
Sb_2O_4	−908	VI_3	−280	$FeBr_3$	−265	$Y^{2+}(g)$	+2 206
Sb_2O_3	−720	VI_2	−264	$FeBr_2$	−250	$Y^{3+}(g)$	+4 185
				FeI_2	−110		

continued

	$\Delta H_f^0/\text{kJ mol}^{-1}$
YCl_3	-982
YI_3	-599
Y_2O_3	$-1\,905$
$Zr(g)$	$+611$
$Zr^+(g)$	$+1\,285$
$Zr^{2+}(g)$	$+2\,553$
$Zr^{3+}(g)$	$+4\,770$
$Zr^{4+}(g)$	$+8\,083$
ZrF_4	$-1\,912$
ZrF_3	$-1\,510$
ZrF_2	-962
$ZrCl_4$	-981
$ZrCl_3$	-870
$ZrCl_2$	-552
$ZrBr_4$	-760
$ZrBr_3$	-632
$ZrBr_2$	-418
ZrI_4	-485
ZrI_3	-397
ZrI_2	-285
ZrO_2	$-1\,097$
$Nb(g)$	$+774$
$Nb^+(g)$	$+1\,438$
$Nb^{2+}(g)$	$+2\,819$
$Nb^{3+}(g)$	$+5\,235$
$Nb^{4+}(g)$	$+8\,935$
$Nb^{5+}(g)$	$+13\,705$
NbF_5	$-1\,814$
$NbCl_5$	-797
$NbCl_4$	-695
$NbCl_{3.13}$	-601
$NbCl_{2.67}$	-538
$NbCl_{2.33}$	-475
$NbBr_5$	-565
NbI_5	-427
Nb_2O_5	$-1\,902$
NbO_2	-794
NbO	-407
$Mo(g)$	$+659$
$Mo^+(g)$	$+1\,344$
$Mo^{2+}(g)$	$+2\,902$
$Mo^{3+}(g)$	$+5\,520$
$Mo^{4+}(g)$	$+9\,424$
$Mo^{5+}(g)$	$+14\,821$
$Mo^{6+}(g)$	$+21\,766$
$MoF_6(l)$	$-1\,621$
$MoCl_5$	-530
$MoCl_4$	-477
$MoCl_3$	-393
$MoCl_2$	-289
$MoBr_4$	-321
$MoBr_2$	-261
MoI_2	-105

	$\Delta H_f^0/\text{kJ mol}^{-1}$
MoO_3	-745
MoO_2	-588
$Tc(g)$	$+649$
$Tc^+(g)$	$+1\,352$
$Tc^{2+}(g)$	$+2\,824$
$Tc^{3+}(g)$	$+5\,674$
$Tc^{4+}(g)$	$+9\,820$
$Tc^{5+}(g)$	$+15\,510$
$Tc^{6+}(g)$	$+22\,832$
$Tc^{7+}(g)$	$+31\,890$
Tc_2O_7	$-1\,113$
$Ru(g)$	$+669$
$Ru^+(g)$	$+1\,380$
$Ru^{2+}(g)$	$+2\,997$
$Ru^{3+}(g)$	$+5\,743$
$Ru^{4+}(g)$	$+10\,220$
$Ru^{5+}(g)$	$+16\,287$
$Ru^{6+}(g)$	$+24\,111$
$Ru^{7+}(g)$	$+33\,776$
RuF_5	-893
$RuCl_3$	-253
$RuBr_3$	-184
RuI_3	-160
RuO_4	-239
RuO_2	-305
$Rh(g)$	$+577$
$Rh^+(g)$	$+1\,297$
$Rh^{2+}(g)$	$+3\,041$
$Rh^{3+}(g)$	$+6\,037$
$Rh^{4+}(g)$	$+10\,430$
$Rh^{5+}(g)$	$+16\,892$
$RhCl_3$	-299
Rh_2O_3	-343
$Pd(g)$	$+381$
$Pd^+(g)$	$+1\,185$
$Pd^{2+}(g)$	$+3\,059$
$Pd^{3+}(g)$	$+6\,236$
$Pd^{4+}(g)$	$+10\,943$
$PdCl_2$	-172
$PdBr_2$	-104
PdI_2	-64
PdO	-85
$Ag(g)$	$+286$
$Ag^+(g)$	$+1\,017$
$Ag^{2+}(g)$	$+3\,089$
$Ag^{3+}(g)$	$+6\,499$
AgF_2	-353
AgF	-203
$AgCl$	-126
$AgBr$	-115
AgI	-64

	$\Delta H_f^0/\text{kJ mol}^{-1}$
Ag_2O_3	$+34$
AgO	-12
Ag_2O	-31
$Cd(g)$	$+111$
$Cd^+(g)$	$+987$
$Cd^{2+}(g)$	$+2\,617$
CdF_2	-700
$CdCl_2$	-391
$CdBr_2$	-316
CdI_2	-203
CdO	-258

5d-block

	$\Delta H_f^0/\text{kJ mol}^{-1}$
$La(g)$	$+431$
$La^+(g)$	$+969$
$La^{2+}(g)$	$+2\,036$
$La^{3+}(g)$	$+3\,886$
$LaCl_3$	$-1\,072$
$LaCl_2$	(-406)
LaI_3	-791
La_2O_3	$-1\,794$
$La(OH)_3$	$-1\,309$†
$Hf(g)$	$+703$
$Hf^+(g)$	$+1\,463$
$Hf^{2+}(g)$	$+2\,903$
$Hf^{3+}(g)$	$+5\,153$
$Hf^{4+}(g)$	$+8\,363$
HfF_4	$-1\,930$
$HfCl_4$	-992
$HfCl_3$	-778
$HfCl_2$	-544
$HfBr_4$	-836
$HfBr_3$	-647
$HfBr_2$	-452
HfO_2	$-1\,145$
$Ta(g)$	$+781$
$Ta^+(g)$	$+1\,541$
$Ta^{2+}(g)$	$+3\,101$
$Ta^{3+}(g)$	$+5\,256$
$Ta^{4+}(g)$	$+8\,448$
$Ta^{5+}(g)$	$+12\,961$
TaF_5	$-1\,904$
$TaCl_5$	-858
$TaCl_4$	-707
$TaCl_{2.5}$	-474
$TaBr_5$	-686
TaI_5	-490
Ta_2O_5	$-2\,046$
$W(g)$	$+837$

† ΔG_f^0

	$\Delta H_f^0/\text{kJ mol}^{-1}$
$W^+(g)$	$+1\,607$
$W^{2+}(g)$	$+3\,317$
$W^{3+}(g)$	$+5\,639$
$W^{4+}(g)$	$+9\,049$
$W^{5+}(g)$	$+13\,672$
$W^{6+}(g)$	$+19\,550$
$WF_6(g)$	$-1\,748$
WCl_6	-682
WCl_5	-513
WCl_4	-469
WCl_2	-256
WBr_6	-349
WBr_5	-314
WO_3	-843
WO_2	-590
$Re(g)$	$+791$
$Re^+(g)$	$+1\,550$
$Re^{2+}(g)$	$+3\,150$
$Re^{3+}(g)$	$+5\,660$
$Re^{4+}(g)$	$+9\,292$
$Re^{5+}(g)$	$+14\,208$
$Re^{6+}(g)$	$+20\,379$
$Re^{7+}(g)$	$+27\,994$
$ReCl_5$	-372
$ReCl_3$	-264
$ReBr_3$	-167
Re_2O_7	$-1\,240$
ReO_3	-605
ReO_2	-987
$Os(g)$	$+728$
$Os^+(g)$	$+1\,568$
$Os^{2+}(g)$	$+3\,208$
$Os^{3+}(g)$	$+5\,618$
$Os^{4+}(g)$	$+9\,467$
$Os^{5+}(g)$	$+14\,655$
$Os^{6+}(g)$	$+21\,224$
$Os^{7+}(g)$	$+29\,215$
$OsCl_4$	-255
$OsCl_3$	-190
OsO_4	-394
OsO_3	-284
$Ir(g)$	$+690$
$Ir^+(g)$	$+1\,569$
$Ir^{2+}(g)$	$+3\,217$
$Ir^{3+}(g)$	$+5\,819$
$Ir^{4+}(g)$	$+9\,585$
$Ir^{5+}(g)$	$+15\,066$
$Ir^{6+}(g)$	$+22\,011$
IrF_6	-580
$IrCl_3$	-244
IrO_2	-274
$Pt(g)$	$+339$
$Pt^+(g)$	$+1\,209$

	ΔH_f^0/kJ mol^{-1}		ΔH_f^0/kJ mol^{-1}		ΔH_f^0/kJ mol^{-1}		ΔH_f^0/kJ mol^{-1}
$Pt^{2+}(g)$	+3 000	$Pr^{3+}(g)$	+3 993	$Tb^{3+}(g)$	+4 167	**5f-block**	
$Pt^{3+}(g)$	+5 745	$PrCl_3$	−1 054	$TbCl_3$	−997	ThF_4	−2 113
$Pt^{4+}(g)$	+9 703	$PrCl_2$	(−649)	$TbCl_2$	(−573)	$ThCl_3$	−1 192
$Pt^{5+}(g)$	+15 017	$PrBr_3$	−931	Tb_2O_3	−1 864	$ThBr_4$	−967
$Pt^{6+}(g)$	+22 255	PrI_3	−636			ThI_4	−669
$PtCl_4$	−236	PrO_2	−979	$Dy(g)$	+297	ThO_2	−1 222
$PtCl_3$	−174	Pr_2O_3	−1 823	$Dy^+(g)$	+864	$Th(OH)_4$	−1 764
$PtCl_2$	−111	$Pr(OH)_3$	−1 300†	$Dy^{2+}(g)$	+1 990		
$PtBr_4$	−159			$Dy^{3+}(g)$	+4 203	PaF_6	(−2 260)
$PtBr_3$	−129	$Nd(g)$	+328	$DyCl_3$	−996	PaF_5	(−1 925)
$PtBr_2$	−97	$Nd^+(g)$	+858	$DyCl_2$	(−674)	$PaCl_4$	(−1 120)
PtI_4	−73	$Nd^{2+}(g)$	+1 893	DyI_3	−605	$PaBr_4$	(−887)
Pt_3O_4	−163	$Nd^{3+}(g)$	+4 022	Dy_2O_3	−1 869	PaI_4	(−602)
		$NdCl_3$	−1 042	$Dy(OH)_3$	−1 279		
		$NdCl_2$	−707			UF_6	−2 188
$Au(g)$	+368	NdI_3	−884	$Ho(g)$	+297	UF_5	−2 059
$Au^+(g)$	+1 257	Nd_2O_3	−1 809	$Ho^+(g)$	+871	UF_4	−1 883
$Au^{2+}(g)$	+3 237			$Ho^{2+}(g)$	+2 010	UF_3	−1 469
$Au^{3+}(g)$	+6 132	$Pm(g)$	+296	$Ho^{3+}(g)$	+4 211	UCl_6	−1 134
AuF_3	−364	$Pm^+(g)$	+832	$HoCl_3$	−1 005	UCl_5	−1 096
$AuCl_3$	−118	$Pm^{2+}(g)$	+1 883	$HoCl_2$	(−665)	UCl_4	−1 063
$AuCl$	−35	$PmCl_3$	−1 033	HoI_3	−686	UCl_3	−895
$AuBr_3$	−53	$PmCl_2$	(−720)	Ho_2O_3	−1 881	UBr_4	−799
$AuBr$	−14					UBr_3	−720
AuI	0	$Sm(g)$	+203	$Er(g)$	+343	UI_4	−510
Au_2O_3	−81	$Sm^+(g)$	+745	$Er^+(g)$	+924	UI_3	−477
		$Sm^{2+}(g)$	+1 813	$Er^{2+}(g)$	+2 074	UO_3	−1 264
		$Sm^{3+}(g)$	+4 099	$Er^{3+}(g)$	+4 240	U_3O_8	−3 757
		$SmCl_3$	−1 022	$ErCl_3$	−995	UO_2	−1 130
$Hg(g)$	+62	$SmCl_2$	(−816)	$ErCl_2$	(−615)		
$Hg^+(g)$	+1 069	SmI_3	−642	ErI_3	−586	NpF_6	(−1 932)
$Hg^{2+}(g)$	+2 878	Sm_2O_3	−1 815	Er_2O_3	−1 898	NpF_5	(−1 900)
HgF_2	−423	$Sm(OH)_3$	−1 292†	$Er(OH)_3$	−1 425	NpF_4	(−1 791)
Hg_2F_2	−485					NpF_3	(−1 506)
$HgCl_2$	−230	$Eu(g)$	+180	$Tm(g)$	+247	$NpCl_4$	−987
Hg_2Cl_2	−265	$Eu^+(g)$	+727	$Tm^+(g)$	+836	$NpCl_3$	(−904)
$HgBr_2$	−169	$Eu^{2+}(g)$	+1 812	$Tm^{2+}(g)$	+1 999	$NpBr_4$	−799
Hg_2Br_2	−204	$Eu^{3+}(g)$	+4 216	$Tm^{3+}(g)$	+4 272	$NpBr_3$	(−728)
HgI_2	−105	$EuCl_3$	−920	$TmCl_3$	−987	NpI_3	(−502)
Hg_2I_2	−102	$EuCl_2$	−808	$TmCl_2$	−709		
HgO	−91	Eu_2O_3	−1 641	TmI_3	−577		
				Tm_2O_3	−1 889		
		$Gd(g)$	+397	$Yb(g)$	+153	PuF_6	−1 803
4f-block		$Gd^+(g)$	+992	$Yb^+(g)$	+756	PuF_4	−1 778
$Ce(g)$	+469	$Gd^{2+}(g)$	+2 160	$Yb^{2+}(g)$	+1 930	PuF_3	−1 552
$Ce^+(g)$	+1 009	$Gd^{3+}(g)$	+4 148	$Yb^{3+}(g)$	+4 346	$PuCl_3$	−962
$Ce^{2+}(g)$	+2 056	$GdCl_3$	−1 004	$YbCl_3$	−960	$PuBr_3$	−787
$Ce^{3+}(g)$	+3 994	$GdCl_2$	−410	$YbCl_2$	−799	PuI_3	−544
$CeCl_3$	−1 055	GdI_3	−618	Yb_2O_3	−1 815	PuO_2	−1 050
$CeCl_2$	(−494)	Gd_2O_3	−1 815				
CeI_3	−774	$Gd(OH)_3$	−1 289	$Lu(g)$	+428	AmF_4	−1 674
CeO_2	−975			$Lu^+(g)$	+941	AmF_3	−1 648
Ce_2O_3	−1 803	$Tb(g)$	+393	$Lu^{2+}(g)$	+2 282	$AmCl_3$	−1 046
		$Tb^+(g)$	+963	$Lu^{3+}(g)$	+4 328	AmI_3	−611
$Pr(g)$	+373	$Tb^{2+}(g)$	+2 074	$LuCl_3$	−953		
$Pr^+(g)$	+894			LuI_3	−557	$CmCl_3$	−946
$Pr^{2+}(g)$	+1 912	† ΔG_f^0		Lu_2O_3	−1 878		

One of the major features which distinguish the metals of the d-block from those of the s- and p-blocks is the relative stability of successive oxidation states. In the d-block each metal exhibits a range of oxidation states which usually vary in single steps up to the maximum which is, in the early Groups at least, numerically equal to the Group number, e.g. vanadium shows the oxidation states +2, +3, +4, and +5. In contrast, the metals of the s- and p-blocks usually show only one oxidation state, corresponding to the Group number; lower states, found only in the p-block, are always two units less than this, e.g. gallium(I) and gallium(III). The known oxidation states (for binary compounds) of the $4s$-, $3d$- and $4p$-metals are shown in Table D-1. The differences between the various metals may be rationalised in terms of the thermodynamic factors at work.

Table D.1   Oxidation states found in binary compounds

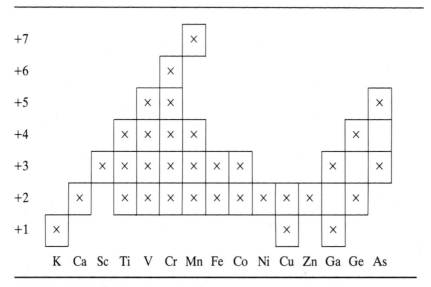

	K	Ca	Sc	Ti	V	Cr	Mn	Fe	Co	Ni	Cu	Zn	Ga	Ge	As
+7							×								
+6						×									
+5					×	×									×
+4				×	×	×	×							×	
+3			×	×	×	×	×	×	×				×		×
+2		×		×	×	×	×	×	×	×	×		×		
+1	×										×		×		

Note – for the 3d-metals, even wider ranges of oxidation states are attainable with suitable choice of ligands, e.g. manganese shows all states from −3 to +7 inclusive.

Consideration of the oxidation-state diagram shows that successive compounds, MX, MX$_2$, MX$_3$ etc. will be stable to disproportionation if the values of $\Delta H_f^0(MX)$, $\frac{1}{2}\Delta H_f^0(MX_2)$, $\frac{1}{3}\Delta H_f^0(MX_3)$ etc., become less negative along the series. These values are simply the slopes of the lines connecting the points for each compound to the origin. Thus, in a series of compounds, the lower members will all be stable to disproportionation only if the quantity **H**, defined below, is positive for all values of n.

$$\mathbf{H} = \frac{1}{n+1}\Delta H_f^0(MX_{n+1}) - \frac{1}{n}\Delta H_f^0(MX_n)$$

If **H** > 0 for all values of n, all the compounds MX_n will be stable to all the possible disproportionation reactions

$$(p+q)MX_n = qMX_{n-p} + pMX_{n+q}$$

Thus, lower members of the series owe their existence to factors which destabilise the higher members (see the discussion of copper in Appendix E).

The terms contributing to the ΔH_f^0-values are those given by the Born–Haber cycle:

$$\Delta H_f^0(MX_n) = \Delta H_f^0(M^{n+}) + n\Delta H_f^0(X^-) - U(MX_n) - (n+1)RT$$

$$\Delta H_f^0(MX_{n+1}) = \Delta H_f^0(M^{(n+1)+}) + (n+1)\Delta H_f^0(X^-) - U(MX_{n+1}) - (n+2)RT$$

where

$$\Delta H_f^0(M^{n+}) = \Delta H_{at}^0 + \sum_{i=1}^{n} I_i$$

Hence,

$$\mathbf{H} = \left[\frac{1}{n+1}\Delta H_f^0(M^{(n+1)+}) - \frac{1}{n}\Delta H_f^0(M^{n+})\right] -$$

$$- \left[\frac{1}{n+1}U(MX_{n+1}) - \frac{1}{n}U(MX_n)\right] -$$

$$- \left[\frac{n+2}{n+1}RT - \frac{n+1}{n}RT\right]$$

The last term may be ignored, since for T = 298 K, RT = 2·47 kJ mol^{-1}, and terms involving the formation of the anion have cancelled out. Since the quantities $\Delta H_f^0(M^{n+})$ and U are both positive, the criterion for stability to disproportionation, **H** > 0, requires that $(1/n)\Delta H_f^0(M^{n+})$ increase faster with increasing n more rapidly than $(1/n)U(MX_n)$. Of course, if the first of these increases too rapidly, $\Delta H_f^0(MX_{n+1})$ may become greater (less negative) than $\Delta H_f^0(MX_n)$, when MX_{n+1} becomes unstable to dissociation.

The operation of this criterion may be examined using data for metal oxides which should approximate closely to ionic compounds. If the change in radius of the cation is neglected, Kapustinskii's treatment $[U \propto \nu Z_1 Z_2]$ shows that $(1/n)U(MO_{n/2})$ (i.e. MX_n with $X = \frac{1}{2}O$) should increase in the ratio 1:1·35:1·67:2·00 for n = 1, 2, 3, 4. The ratios will increase slightly faster than this because the radius of the cation decreases with increasing oxidation state. The data of Table D-2 show that the 'experimental' lattice energies do increase at about this rate (1:1·4:1·8:2·3 at the beginning of the series and 1:1·25:1·6:2·1 at the end), and there is little difference between the d-block and p-block elements. [Strictly, it is the absolute difference between successive $(1/n)U(MX_n)$-values which are important; these are also fairly regular.]

Since there is little to distinguish the various types of metal in the lattice-energy trends, it is likely that the behavioural differences arise from $\Delta H_f^0(M^{n+})$. Table D-3 shows that $(1/n)\Delta H_f^0(M^{n+})$ increases with n, as expected, but that the p- and d-blocks show different trends in the rate of increase. In the d-block, the difference between successive values increases uniformly with

Table D.2 $(1/n)U(MO_{n/2})$-values (kJ mol^{-1})

n	K	Ca	Sc	Ti	V	Cr	Mn	Fe	Co	Ni	Cu	Zn	Ga	Ge
1	1 166			(1 340)	(1 380)	(1 420)	(1 440)	(1 440)	(1 430)	(1 420)	1 644	(1 380)	1 604	(1 420)
				614	*595*	*570*	*481*	*538*	*578*	*634*	*431*	*652*	*406*	*496*
2		1 749		1 954	1 975	1 990	1 921	1 978	2 008	2 054	2 075	2 032	(2 010)	1 916
				474	*509*	*551*	*643*	*533*					*793*	*914*
3			2 320	2 428	2 484	2 541	2 564	2 511					2 803	(2 830)
				599	*673*	*716*	*756*							*478*
4				3 027	3 157	3 257	3 300							3 208

Values in parentheses are estimates.
Values in italics are differences.
All U-values used refer to one mole of metal, e.g. for
n = 3, $\frac{1}{3}U(MO_{3/2}) = \frac{1}{6}U(M_2O_3)$.

Table D.3 $(1/n)\Delta H_f^0(M^{n+})$-values (kJ mol^{-1})

n	K	Ca	Sc	Ti	V	Cr	Mn	Fe	Co	Ni	Cu	Zn	Ga	Ge	As
1	509	767	957	1 129	1 165	1 049	998	1 185	1 183	1 166	1 084	1 031	951	1 132	947
		189	*139*	*90*	*125*	*271*	*256*	*95*	*231*	*293*	*437*	*351*	*514*	*202*	*425*
2		956	1 096	1 219	1 290	1 320	1 254	1 280	1 414	1 459	1 521	1 382	1 465	1 324	1 372
			539	*477*	*512*	*556*	*674*	*618*	*605*	*677*	*675*	*817*	*499*	*656*	*455*
3			1 527	1 696	1 802	1 876	1 928	1 898	2 019	2 136	2 196	2 199	1 964	1 990	1 827
				619	*700*	*756*	*767*	*901*	*771*	*815*	*871*	*946*	*1 076*	*605*	*751*
4				2 315	2 502	2 632	2 695	2 799	2 790	2 951	3 067	3 145	3 040	2 595	2 578

Values in italics are differences

Fig. D.1   Relative rates of increase of *p*-, *s*-, and *d*-electron ionisation energies

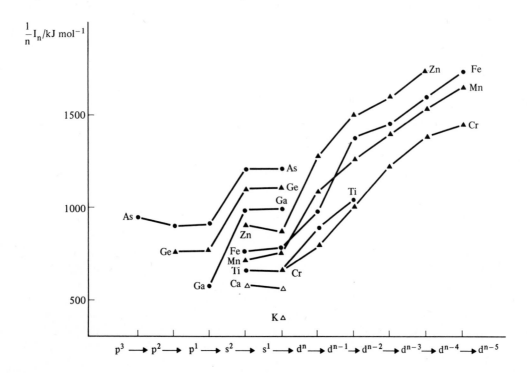

increasing n, whereas in the p-block the values increase much less regularly with the result that $\Delta H_f^0(M^{n+})$ increases with n more rapidly in the d-block than in the p-block; this difference is due entirely to the ionisation energies, as shown in Fig. D-1. The s- and p-block metals show the 'plateau' effect mentioned in Chapter 8, i.e. $(1/n)I_n$ remains roughly constant while electrons of the same subgroup are being removed. Hence, $(1/n)\Delta H_f^0(M^{n+})$ increases less rapidly than $(1/n)U(MX_n)$, so that intermediate oxidation states are unstable to disproportionation and the only attainable oxidation states are those corresponding to the removal of the whole subgroup of electrons, i.e. N or N–2 (where N is the Group number). In the d-block, on the other hand, ionisation energies rise more rapidly, outstripping the lattice energies and allowing the formation of the intermediate oxidation states, with the exception of the first which corresponds to the removal of an s-electron.

The difference in ionisation-energy trends is related to the different radial distributions of the s-, p- and d-electrons. The s- and p-electrons penetrate the atomic core and are influenced more directly by the nuclear charge than the d-electrons, which hardly penetrate the core at all. The binding energy (ionisation energy) of the d-electrons is therefore very dependent on the screening action of the outer electrons so that, as successive valence electrons are removed, the effective nuclear charge acting on the d-electrons increases much more rapidly than for s- and p-electrons.

It is interesting to note that the same difference in radial distribution and screening effects between the various types of electrons is also the basic reason for the interpolation of the d-block between the s- and p-blocks.

Notes
1. The interested student may like to consider the extension of this treatment to the $4f$-block.
2. The above treatment is given in terms of ionic solids, so that entropy terms may be neglected. Precisely similar conclusions follow from a treatment of the relative stabilities of ions in aqueous solution, using hydration enthalpies in place of lattice energies, except that it is less justifiable to ignore entropy terms. Also, for the aqueous case, $(1/n)\Delta H_f^0(M_{aq}^{n+})$-values must differ appreciably in order that one species shall exist (or be unstable) in the absence of neighbouring species. If the enthalpy (free energy) differences are small, the species will co-exist in equilibrium.
3. The treatment in terms of $(1/n)I_n$, on which the above arguments are based, is originally due to Phillips and Williams (cf. 'Inorganic Chemistry').

Comparison of nickel, copper and zinc

Of all the metals in the $3d$-block, only copper gives stable compounds in the +1 oxidation state. For the other metals this state is presumably unstable to disproportionation, and the lowest attainable oxidation state, in binary compounds, is +2. Despite the obvious covalency of many of the compounds in this region of the $3d$-series, a clue to the origin of this behaviour may be found in the ionic-model analysis. Some relevant data are given in Table E-1. Note the following points.

(a) Owing to a fortuitous balancing of trends, $\Delta H_f^0(M^{n+})$-values are similar for all three metals, but decrease slightly from nickel to zinc.

(b) Differences between $\Delta H_f^0(NiX_2)$ and $\Delta H_f^0(ZnX_2)$ are 100–150 kJ mol^{-1}, i.e. about the same as the difference in $\Delta H_f^0(M^{2+})$. This means that the lattice energies of corresponding compounds must be similar, and that it is reasonable to seek the origin of the behavioural differences in the $\Delta H_f^0(M^{n+})$-values. (There is also a small contribution from LFSE.)

If the lattice energies are also similar for the compounds MX, as may reasonably be assumed, then $\Delta H_f^0(MX)$ will be similar for the three metals, becoming more negative from nickel to zinc. On this basis, zinc(I) compounds should be more stable than copper(I) compounds, at least in an absolute thermodynamic sense. The differences between the metals must then lie in the relative stabilities (ΔH_f^0-values) of the compounds MX_2, which will govern whether MX will be stable to disproportionation. If $\Delta H_f^0(MX_2)$ is more than twice $\Delta H_f^0(MX)$, MX will be unstable to disproportionation. Everything thus depends on the value of the second ionisation energy. Nickel and zinc have very similar I_2-values, but that for copper is greater by about 200 kJ mol^{-1}, and this difference is sufficient to tip the balance of the stability to disproportionation. The increase in I_2 from nickel to copper is accounted for partly by the increase in nuclear charge and partly by a greater loss of exchange energy. For zinc, both electrons lost are $4s$-electrons.

Table E.1

	Ni	Cu	Zn
ΔH_{at}^0/kJ mol^{-1}	430	339	125
I_1/kJ mol^{-1}	736	1 084	906
I_2/kJ mol^{-1}	1 752	1 958	1 734
$\Delta H_f^0(M^+)$/kJ mol^{-1}	1 166	1 084	1 031
$\Delta H_f^0(M^{2+})$/kJ mol^{-1}	2 918	3 042	2 765
Electron config., M^0	d^8s^2	$d^{10}s^1$	$d^{10}s^2$
Electron config., M^+	d^9	d^{10}	$d^{10}s^1$
Electron config., M^{2+}	d^8	d^9	d^{10}
$\Delta H_f^0(MO)$/kJ mol^{-1}	−240	−157	−348
$\Delta H_f^0(MF_2)$/kJ mol^{-1}	−651	−543	−764

Appendix F
Ionic radii for six-coordination

from R.D. Shannon and R.D. Prewitt, *Acta Crystallographica*, **B26**, 1046 (1970) and **B25**, 925 (1969)

	r/pm		r/pm		r/pm		r/pm
s-block		Cr^{5+}	35†	Cd^{2+}	95	Tm^{3+}	88
Li^+	74	Cr^{4+}	55			Yb^{3+}	87
Na^+	102	Cr^{3+}	61·5			Lu^{3+}	86
K^+	138	Cr^{2+}	82	**5d-block**			
Rb^+	149	Mn^{7+}	26†	La^{3+}	104·5		
Cs^+	170	Mn^{6+}	27†	Hf^{4+}	71	**5f-block**	
Be^{2+}	27†	Mn^{4+}	54	Ta^{5+}	64	Th^{4+}	100
Mg^{2+}	72	Mn^{3+}	64·5	Ta^{4+}	66	Pa^{5+}	91‡
Ca^{2+}	100	Mn^{2+}	83	Ta^{3+}	67	Pa^{4+}	101‡
Sr^{2+}	113	Fe^{3+}	64·5	W^{6+}	60	U^{6+}	73
Ba^{2+}	136	Fe^{2+}	78	W^{4+}	65	U^{5+}	76
		Co^{3+}	61	Re^{7+}	57	U^{4+}	100‡
		Co^{2+}	74	Re^{6+}	52	U^{3+}	104
p-block		Ni^{3+}	60	Re^{4+}	63	Np^{4+}	98‡
Al^{3+}	53	Ni^{2+}	69	Os^{4+}	63	Np^{3+}	102
Ga^{3+}	62	Cu^{2+}	73	Ir^{4+}	63	Np^{2+}	110
In^{3+}	80	Cu^+	46	Ir^{3+}	73	Pu^{4+}	96‡
Tl^{3+}	88·5	Zn^{2+}	75	Pt^{4+}	63	Pu^{3+}	101
Tl^+	150			Pt^{2+}	60†	Am^{4+}	95‡
Ge^{4+}	54			Au^{3+}	70†	Am^{3+}	100
Sn^{4+}	69	**4d-block**		Hg^{2+}	102	Cm^{4+}	95‡
Sn^{2+}	122‡	Y^{3+}	90			Cm^{3+}	98
Pb^{4+}	77·5	Zr^{4+}	72			Bk^{4+}	93‡
Pb^{2+}	118	Nb^{5+}	64	**4f-block**		Bk^{3+}	96
Sb^{5+}	61	Nb^{4+}	69	Ce^{4+}	80	Cf^{3+}	95
Sb^{3+}	77†	Nb^{3+}	70	Ce^{3+}	101		
Bi^{3+}	102	Nb^{2+}	71	Pr^{4+}	78		
		Mo^{6+}	60	Pr^{3+}	100	**Anions**	
		Mo^{5+}	63	Nd^{3+}	98	O^{2-}	140
3d-block		Mo^{4+}	65	Pm^{3+}	97	F^-	133
Sc^{3+}	74·5	Mo^{3+}	67	Sm^{3+}	96	Cl^-	181
Ti^{4+}	60·5	Tc^{4+}	64	Eu^{3+}	95	Br^-	196
Ti^{3+}	67	Ru^{4+}	62	Eu^{2+}	117	I^-	220
Ti^{2+}	86	Ru^{3+}	68	Gd^{3+}	94		
V^{5+}	54	Rh^{4+}	61·5	Tb^{4+}	76		
V^{4+}	59	Rh^{3+}	66·5	Tb^{3+}	92		
V^{3+}	64	Pd^{4+}	62	Dy^{3+}	91		
V^{2+}	79	Pd^{2+}	64†	Ho^{3+}	90		
Cr^{6+}	30†	Ag^+	67§	Er^{3+}	89		

† 4-coordinate   ‡ 8-coordinate   § 2-coordinate

Index